AshDesign/Shutterstock.com

# 16 SIMPLE LINEAR REGRESSION AND CORRELATION

## CHAPTER OUTLINE



## Education and Income: How Are They Related?

DATA GSS2014*

You are probably a student in an undergraduate or graduate business or economics program. Your plan is to graduate, get a good job, and draw a high salary. You have probably assumed that more education equals better job equals higher income. Is this true? Fortunately, the General Social Survey recorded two variables that will help determine whether education and income are related and, if so, what the value of an additional year of education might be.

Jupiterimages/Comstock Images/Getty Images

**On page 660, we will provide our answer.**

# Introduction

**Regression analysis** is used to predict the value of one variable on the basis of other variables. This technique may be the most commonly used statistical procedure because, as you can easily appreciate, almost all companies and government institutions forecast variables such as product demand, interest rates, inflation rates, prices of raw materials, and labor costs.

The technique involves developing a mathematical equation or model that describes the relationship between the variable to be forecast, which is called the **dependent variable**, and variables that the statistics practitioner believes are related to the dependent variable. The dependent variable is denoted as $Y$, whereas the related variables are called **independent variables** and are denoted as $X_1, X_2, \ldots, X_k$ (where $k$ is the number of independent variables).

If we are interested only in determining whether a relationship exists, we employ correlation analysis, a technique that we have already introduced. In Chapter 3, we presented the graphical method to describe the association between two interval variables—the scatter diagram. We introduced the coefficient of correlation and covariance in Chapter 4.

Because regression analysis involves many new techniques and concepts, we divided the presentation into three chapters. In this chapter, we present techniques that allow us to determine the relationship between only two variables. In Chapter 17, we expand our discussion to more than two variables; in Chapter 18, we discuss how to build regression models.

Here are three illustrations of the use of regression analysis.

**Illustration 1** The product manager in charge of a particular brand of children's breakfast cereal would like to predict the demand for the cereal during the next year. To use regression analysis, she and her staff list the following variables as likely to affect sales:

Price of the product

Number of children 5 to 12 years of age (the target market)

Price of competitors' products

Effectiveness of advertising (as measured by advertising exposure)

Annual sales this year

Annual sales in previous years

**Illustration 2** A gold speculator is considering a major purchase of gold bullion. He would like to forecast the price of gold 2 years from now (his planning horizon), using regression analysis. In preparation, he produces the following list of independent variables:

Interest rates

Inflation rate

Price of oil

Demand for gold jewelry

Demand for industrial and commercial gold

Dow Jones Industrial Average

**Illustration 3** A real estate agent wants to predict the selling price of houses more accurately. She believes that the following variables affect the price of a house:

Size of the house (number of square feet)

Number of bedrooms

Frontage of the lot

Condition

Location

In each of these illustrations, the primary motive for using regression analysis is forecasting. Nonetheless, analyzing the relationship among variables can also be quite useful in managerial decision making. For instance, in the first application, the product manager may want to know how price is related to product demand so that a decision about a prospective change in pricing can be made.

Regardless of why regression analysis is performed, the next step in the technique is to develop a mathematical equation or model that accurately describes the nature of the relationship that exists between the dependent variable and the independent variables. This stage—which is only a small part of the total process—is described in the next section. In the ensuing sections of this chapter (and in Chapter 17), we will spend considerable time assessing and testing how well the model fits the actual data. Only when we're satisfied with the model do we use it to estimate and forecast.

## 16-1 Model

The job of developing a mathematical equation can be quite complex, because we need to have some idea about the nature of the relationship between each of the independent variables and the dependent variable. The number of different mathematical models that could be proposed is virtually infinite. Here is an example from Chapter 4.

$$\text{Profit} = (\text{Price per unit} - \text{variable cost per unit}) \times \text{Number of units sold} - \text{Fixed costs}$$

You may encounter the next example in a finance course:

$$F = P(1 + i)^n$$

where

$F$ = future value of an investment

$P$ = principle or present value

$i$ = interest rate per period

$n$ = number of periods

These are all examples of **deterministic models**, so named because such equations allow us to determine the value of the dependent variable (on the left side of the equation) from the values of the independent variables. In many practical applications of interest to us, deterministic models are unrealistic. For example, is it reasonable to believe that we can determine the selling price of a house solely on the basis of its size? Unquestionably, the size of a house affects its price, but many other variables (some of which may not be measurable) also influence price. What must be included in most practical models is a method to represent the randomness that is part of a real-life process. Such a model is called a **probabilistic model**.

To create a probabilistic model, we start with a deterministic model that approximates the relationship we want to model. We then add a term that measures the random error of the deterministic component.

Suppose that in illustration 3, the real estate agent knows that the cost of building a new house is about \$100 per square foot and that most lots sell for about \$100,000. The approximate selling price would be

$$y = 100{,}000 + 100x$$

where $y$ = selling price and $x$ = size of the house in square feet. A house of 2,000 square feet would therefore be estimated to sell for

$$y = 100{,}000 + 100(2{,}000) = 300{,}000$$

We know, however, that the selling price is not likely to be exactly \$300,000. Prices may actually range from \$200,000 to \$400,000. In other words, the deterministic model is not really suitable. To represent this situation properly, we should use the probabilistic model

$$y = 100{,}000 + 100x + \varepsilon$$

where $\varepsilon$ (the Greek letter epsilon) represents the **error variable**—the difference between the actual selling price and the estimated price based on the size of the house. The error thus accounts for all the variables, measurable and immeasurable, that are not part of the model. The value of $\varepsilon$ will vary from one sale to the next, even if $x$ remains constant. In other words, houses of exactly the same size will sell for different prices because of differences in location and number of bedrooms and bathrooms, as well as other variables.

In the three chapters devoted to regression analysis, we will present only probabilistic models. In this chapter, we describe only the straight-line model with one independent variable. This model is called the **first-order linear model**—sometimes called the **simple linear regression model**.*

**First-Order Linear Model**

$$y = \beta_0 + \beta_1 x + \varepsilon$$

where

$y$ = dependent variable

$x$ = independent variable

$\beta_0$ = $y$-intercept

$\beta_1$ = slope of the line (defined as rise/run)

$\varepsilon$ = error variable

The problem objective addressed by the model is to analyze the relationship between two variables, $x$ and $y$, both of which must be interval. To define the relationship between $x$ and $y$, we need to know the value of the coefficients $\beta_0$ and $\beta_1$. However, these coefficients are population parameters, which are almost always unknown. In the next section, we discuss how these parameters are estimated.

*We use the term *linear* in two ways. The "linear" in linear regression refers to the form of the model wherein the terms form a linear combination of the coefficients $\beta_0$ and $\beta_1$. Thus, for example, the model $y = \beta_0 + \beta_1 x^2 + \varepsilon$ is a linear combination whereas $y = \beta_0 + \beta_1^2 x + \varepsilon$ is not. The simple linear regression model $y = \beta_0 + \beta_1 x + \varepsilon$ describes a straight-line or linear relationship between the dependent variable and one independent variable. In this book, we use the linear regression technique only. Hence, when we use the word *linear* we will be referring to the straight-line relationship between the variables.

## 16-2 Estimating the Coefficients

We estimate the parameters $\beta_0$ and $\beta_1$ in a way similar to the methods used to estimate all the other parameters discussed in this book. We draw a random sample from the population of interest and calculate the sample statistics we need. However, because $\beta_0$ and $\beta_1$ represent the coefficients of a straight line, their estimators are based on drawing a straight line through the sample data. The straight line that we wish to use to estimate $\beta_0$ and $\beta_1$ is the "best" straight line—best in the sense that it comes closest to the sample data points. This best straight line, called the *least squares line*, is derived from calculus and is represented by the following equation:

$$\hat{y} = b_0 + b_1 x$$

Here $b_0$ is the $y$-intercept, $b_1$ is the slope, and $\hat{y}$ is the predicted or fitted value of $y$. In Chapter 4, we introduced the **least squares method**, which produces a straight line that minimizes the sum of the squared differences between the points and the line. The coefficients $b_0$ and $b_1$ are calculated so that the sum of squared deviations

$$\sum_{i=1}^{n} (y_i - \hat{y}_i)^2$$

is minimized. In other words, the values of $\hat{y}$ on average come closest to the observed values of $y$. The calculus derivation is available in the online appendix, Deriving the Normal Equations, which shows how the following formulas, first shown in Chapter 4, were produced.

**Least Squares Line Coefficients**

$$b_1 = \frac{s_{xy}}{s_x^2}$$

$$b_0 = \bar{y} - b_1 \bar{x}$$

where

$$s_{xy} = \frac{\sum_{i=1}^{n} (x_i - \bar{x})(y_i - \bar{y})}{n - 1}$$

$$s_x^2 = \frac{\sum_{i=1}^{n} (x_i - \bar{x})^2}{n - 1}$$

$$\bar{x} = \frac{\sum_{i=1}^{n} x_i}{n}$$

$$\bar{y} = \frac{\sum_{i=1}^{n} y_i}{n}$$

In Chapter 4, we provided shortcut formulas for the sample variance (page 98) and the sample covariance (page 110). Combining them provides a shortcut method to manually calculate the slope coefficient.

**Shortcut Formula for $b_1$**

$$b_1 = \frac{s_{xy}}{s_x^2}$$

$$s_{xy} = \frac{1}{n-1}\left[\sum_{i=1}^{n} x_i y_i - \frac{\sum_{i=1}^{n} x_i \sum_{i=1}^{n} y_i}{n}\right]$$

$$s_x^2 = \frac{1}{n-1}\left[\sum_{i=1}^{n} x_i^2 - \frac{\left(\sum_{i=1}^{n} x_i\right)^2}{n}\right]$$

Statisticians have shown that $b_0$ and $b_1$ are unbiased estimators of $\beta_0$ and $\beta_1$, respectively.

Although the calculations are straightforward, we would rarely compute the regression line manually because the work is time consuming. However, we illustrate the manual calculations for a very small sample.

EXAMPLE 16.1

DATA Xm16-01

## Annual Bonus and Years of Experience

The annual bonuses ($1,000s) of six employees with different years of experience were recorded as follows. We wish to determine the straight-line relationship between annual bonus and years of experience.

| Years of experience $x$ | 1 | 2 | 3 | 4 | 5 | 6 |
|---|---|---|---|---|---|---|
| Annual bonus $y$ | 6 | 1 | 9 | 5 | 17 | 12 |

SOLUTION:

To apply the shortcut formula, we need to compute four summations. Using a calculator, we find

$$\sum_{i=1}^{n} x_i = 21$$

$$\sum_{i=1}^{n} y_i = 50$$

$$\sum_{i=1}^{n} x_i y_i = 212$$

$$\sum_{i=1}^{n} x_i^2 = 91$$

The covariance and the variance of $x$ can now be computed:

$$s_{xy} = \frac{1}{n-1}\left[\sum_{i=1}^{n} x_i y_i - \frac{\sum_{i=1}^{n} x_i \sum_{i=1}^{n} y_i}{n}\right] = \frac{1}{6-1}\left[212 - \frac{(21)(50)}{6}\right] = 7.4$$

$$s_x^2 = \frac{1}{n-1}\left[\sum_{i=1}^{n} x_i^2 - \frac{\left(\sum_{i=1}^{n} x_i\right)^2}{n}\right] = \frac{1}{6-1}\left[91 - \frac{(21)^2}{6}\right] = 3.5$$

The sample slope coefficient is calculated next:

$$b_1 = \frac{s_{xy}}{s_x^2} = \frac{7.4}{3.5} = 2.114$$

The $y$-intercept is computed as follows:

$$\bar{x} = \frac{\sum x_i}{n} = \frac{21}{6} = 3.5$$

$$\bar{y} = \frac{\sum y_i}{n} = \frac{50}{6} = 8.333$$

$$b_0 = \bar{y} - b_1\bar{x} = 8.333 - (2.114)(3.5) = .934$$

Thus, the least squares line is

$$\hat{y} = .934 + 2.114x$$

Figure 16.1 depicts the least squares (or regression) line. As you can see, the line fits the data reasonably well. We can measure how well by computing the value of the minimized sum of squared deviations. The deviations between the actual data points and the line are called **residuals**, denoted $e_i$; that is,

$$e_i = y_i - \hat{y}_i$$

FIGURE **16.1** **Scatter Diagram with Regression Line for Example 16.1**

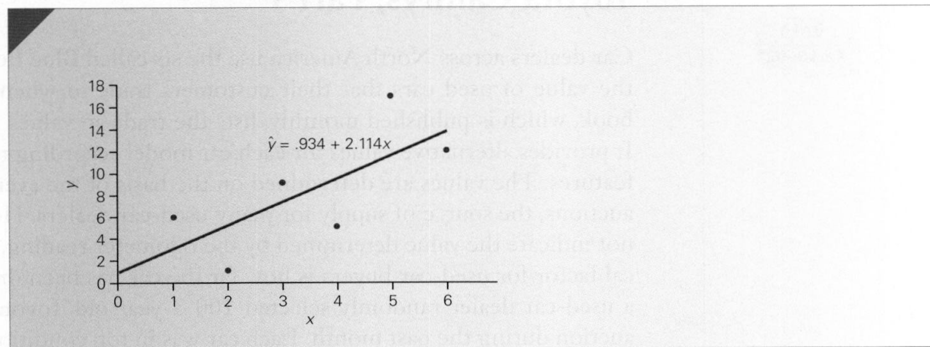


The residuals are observations of the error variable. Consequently, the minimized sum of squared deviations is called the **sum of squares for error**, denoted SSE.

The calculation of the residuals in this example is shown in Figure 16.2. Notice that we compute by $\hat{y}_i$ substituting $x_i$ into the formula of the regression line. The residuals are the differences between the observed values of $y_i$ and the fitted or predicted values of $\hat{y}_i$. Table 16.1 describes these calculations.

Thus, SSE = 81.104. No other straight line will produce a sum of squared deviations as small as 81.104. In that sense, the regression line fits the data best. The sum of squares for error is an important statistic because it is the basis for other statistics that assess how well the linear model fits the data. We will introduce these statistics in Section 16-4.

FIGURE **16.2** **Calculation of Residuals in Example 16.1**

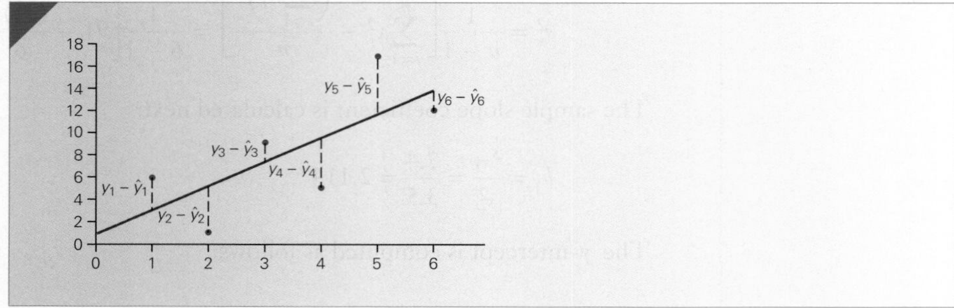


TABLE **16.1** **Calculation of Residuals in Example 16.1**

| $x_i$ | $y_i$ | $\hat{y}_i = .934 = 2.114x_i$ | $y_i - \hat{y}_i$ | $(y_i - \hat{y}_i)^2$ |
|---|---|---|---|---|
| 1 | 6 | 3.048 | 2.952 | 8.714 |
| 2 | 1 | 5.162 | −4.162 | 17.322 |
| 3 | 9 | 7.276 | 1.724 | 2.972 |
| 4 | 5 | 9.390 | −4.390 | 19.272 |
| 5 | 17 | 11.504 | 5.496 | 30.206 |
| 6 | 12 | 13.618 | −1.618 | 2.618 |
| | | | | $\sum(y_i - \hat{y}_i)^2 = 81.104$ |

**EXAMPLE 16.2**

DATA Xm16-02*

## Odometer Reading and Prices of Used Toyota Camrys, Part 1

Car dealers across North America use the so-called Blue Book to help them determine the value of used cars that their customers trade in when purchasing new cars. The book, which is published monthly, lists the trade-in values for all basic models of cars. It provides alternative values for each car model according to its condition and optional features. The values are determined on the basis of the average paid at recent used-car auctions, the source of supply for many used-car dealers. However, the Blue Book does not indicate the value determined by the odometer reading, despite the fact that a critical factor for used-car buyers is how far the car has been driven. To examine this issue, a used-car dealer randomly selected 100 3-year old Toyota Camrys that were sold at auction during the past month. Each car was in top condition and equipped with all the features that come standard with this car. The dealer recorded the price ($1,000) and the number of miles (thousands) on the odometer. Some of these data are listed here. The dealer wants to find the regression line.

| Car | Price ($1,000) | Odometer (1,000 mi) |
|---|---|---|
| 1 | 14.6 | 37.4 |
| 2 | 14.1 | 44.8 |
| 3 | 14.0 | 45.8 |
| ⋮ | ⋮ | ⋮ |
| 98 | 14.5 | 33.2 |
| 99 | 14.7 | 39.2 |
| 100 | 14.3 | 36.4 |

SOLUTION:

## IDENTIFY

Notice that the problem objective is to analyze the relationship between two interval variables. Because we believe that the odometer reading affects the selling price, we identify the former as the independent variable, which we label $x$, and the latter as the dependent variable, which we label $y$.

## COMPUTE

MANUALLY:

From the data set, we find

$$\sum_{i=1}^{n} x_i = 3{,}601.1$$

$$\sum_{i=1}^{n} y_i = 1{,}484.1$$

$$\sum_{i=1}^{n} x_i y_i = 53{,}155.93$$

$$\sum_{i=1}^{n} x_i^2 = 133{,}986.59$$

Next we calculate the covariance and the variance of the independent variable $x$:

$$s_{xy} = \frac{1}{n-1}\left[\sum_{i=1}^{n} x_i y_i - \frac{\sum_{i=1}^{n} x_i \sum_{i=1}^{n} y_i}{n}\right]$$

$$= \frac{1}{100-1}\left[53{,}155.93 - \frac{(3{,}601.1)(1{,}484.1)}{100}\right] = -2.909$$

$$s_x^2 = \frac{1}{n-1}\left[\sum_{i=1}^{n} x_i^2 - \frac{\left(\sum_{i=1}^{n} x_i\right)^2}{n}\right]$$

$$= \frac{1}{100-1}\left[133{,}986.59 - \frac{(3{,}601.1)^2}{100}\right] = 43.509$$

The sample slope coefficient is calculated next:

$$b_1 = \frac{s_{xy}}{s_x^2} = \frac{-2.909}{43.509} = -.0669$$

The $y$-intercept is computed as follows:

$$\bar{x} = \frac{\sum x_i}{n} = \frac{3{,}601.1}{100} = 36.011$$

$$\bar{y} = \frac{\sum y_i}{n} = \frac{1{,}484.1}{100} = 14.841$$

$$b_0 = \bar{y} - b_1\bar{x} = 14.841 - (-.0669)(36.011) = 17.250$$

The sample regression line is

$$\hat{y} = 17.250 - 0.0669x$$

## EXCEL Data Analysis

| | A | B | C | D | E | F | G |
|---|---|---|---|---|---|---|---|
| 1 | SUMMARY OUTPUT | | | | | | |
| 2 | | | | | | | |
| 3 | *Regression Statistics* | | | | | | |
| 4 | Multiple R | 0.8052 | | | | | |
| 5 | R Square | 0.6483 | | | | | |
| 6 | Adjusted R Square | 0.6447 | | | | | |
| 7 | Standard Error | 0.3265 | | | | | |
| 8 | Observations | 100 | | | | | |
| 9 | | | | | | | |
| 10 | ANOVA | | | | | | |
| 11 | | *df* | *SS* | *MS* | *F* | *Significance F* | |
| 12 | Regression | 1 | 19.26 | 19.26 | 180.64 | 5.75E-24 | |
| 13 | Residual | 98 | 10.45 | 0.11 | | | |
| 14 | Total | 99 | 29.70 | | | | |
| 15 | | | | | | | |
| 16 | | *Coefficients* | *Standard Error* | *t Stat* | *P-value* | *Lower 95%* | *Upper 95%* |
| 17 | Intercept | 17.25 | 0.182 | 94.73 | 3.57E-98 | 16.89 | 17.61 |
| 18 | Odometer | −0.0669 | 0.0050 | −13.44 | 5.75E-24 | −0.0767 | −0.0570 |

*INSTRUCTIONS*

1. Type or import data into two columns*, one storing the dependent variable and the other the independent variable. (Open Xm16-02.)
2. Click **Data**, **Data Analysis,** and **Regression.**
3. Specify the **Input** $Y$ **Range** (A1:A101) and the **Input** $X$ **Range** (B1:B101).

To draw the scatter diagram, follow the instructions provided in Chapter 3 on page 67.

## XLSTAT

| | A | B | C | D | E | F | G |
|---|---|---|---|---|---|---|---|
| 1 | **Regression of variable Price:** | | | | | | |
| 2 | | | | | | | |
| 3 | Goodness of fit statistics (Price): | | | | | | |
| 4 | Observations | 100 | | | | | |
| 5 | Sum of weights | 100 | | | | | |
| 6 | DF | 98 | | | | | |
| 7 | R² | 0.6483 | | | | | |
| 8 | Adjusted R² | 0.6447 | | | | | |
| 9 | MSE | 0.1066 | | | | | |
| 10 | RMSE | 0.3265 | | | | | |
| 11 | DW | | | | | | |
| 12 | | | | | | | |
| 13 | Analysis of variance (Price): | | | | | | |
| 14 | Source | DF | Sum of squares | Mean squares | F | Pr > F | |
| 15 | Model | 1 | 19.26 | 19.26 | 180.64 | **< 0.0001** | |
| 16 | Error | 98 | 10.45 | 0.11 | | | |
| 17 | Corrected Total | 99 | 29.70 | | | | |
| 18 | | | | | | | |
| 19 | Model parameters (Price): | | | | | | |
| 20 | Source | Value | Standard error | t | Pr > \|t\| | Lower bound (95%) | Upper bound (95%) |
| 21 | Intercept | 17.25 | 0.182 | 94.73 | **< 0.0001** | 16.89 | 17.61 |
| 22 | Odometer | −0.0669 | 0.0050 | −13.44 | **< 0.0001** | −0.0767 | −0.0570 |

*INSTRUCTIONS*

1. Type or import the data (Open Xm16-02).
2. Click **XLSTAT**, **Modeling data**, and **Linear regression**.
3. In the **Quantitative** box type the input range of Y (A1:A101). In the **X Explanatory variables Quantitative** box type the input range of X (B1:B101).
4. Click **Outputs** and check **Analysis of variance.** Click **OK.**

*If one or both columns contain an empty cell (representing missing data) the row must be removed.

The printouts include more statistics than we need right now. However, we will be discussing the rest of the printouts later.

## INTERPRET

The slope coefficient $b_1$ is $-0.0669$, which means that for each additional 1,000 miles on the odometer, the price decreases by an average of \$.0669 thousand. Expressed more simply, the slope tells us that for each additional mile on the odometer, the price decreases on average by \$.0669 or 6.69 cents.

The intercept is $b_0 = 17.250$. Technically, the intercept is the point at which the regression line and the $y$-axis intersect. This means that when $x = 0$ (i.e., the car was not driven at all) the selling price is \$17.250 thousand or \$17,250. We might be tempted to interpret this number as the price of cars that have not been driven. However, in this case, the intercept is probably meaningless. Because our sample did not include any cars with zero miles on the odometer, we have no basis for interpreting $b_0$. As a general rule, we cannot determine the value of $\hat{y}$ for a value of $x$ that is far outside the range of the sample values of $x$. In this example, the smallest and largest values of $x$ are 19.1 and 49.2, respectively. Because $x = 0$ is not in this interval, we cannot safely interpret the value of $\hat{y}$ when $x = 0$.

It is important to bear in mind that the interpretation of the coefficients pertains only to the sample, which consists of 100 observations. To infer information about the population, we need statistical inference techniques, which are described subsequently.

In the sections that follow, we will return to this problem and the computer output to introduce other statistics associated with regression analysis.

## EXERCISES

**16.1** The term *regression* was originally used in 1885 by Sir Francis Galton in his analysis of the relationship between the heights of children and parents. He formulated the "law of universal regression," which specifies that "each peculiarity in a man is shared by his kinsmen, but on average in a less degree." (Evidently, people spoke this way in 1885.) In 1903, two statisticians, K. Pearson and A. Lee, took a random sample of 1,078 father–son pairs to examine Galton's law ("On the Laws of Inheritance in Man, I. Inheritance of Physical Characteristics," *Biometrika* 2:457–462). Their sample regression line was

Son's height = 33.73 + .516 × Father's height

a. Interpret the coefficients.
b. What does the regression line tell you about the heights of sons of tall fathers?
c. What does the regression line tell you about the heights of sons of short fathers?

**16.2** Xr16-02 Attempting to analyze the relationship between advertising and sales, the owner of a furniture store recorded the monthly advertising budget (\$ thousands) and the sales (\$ millions) for a sample of 12 months. The data are listed here.

| **Advertising** | 23 | 46 | 60 | 54 | 28 | 33 |
|---|---|---|---|---|---|---|
| **Sales** | 9.6 | 11.3 | 12.8 | 9.8 | 8.9 | 12.5 |

| **Advertising** | 25 | 31 | 36 | 88 | 90 | 99 |
|---|---|---|---|---|---|---|
| **Sales** | 12.0 | 11.4 | 12.6 | 13.7 | 14.4 | 15.9 |

a. Draw a scatter diagram. Does it appear that advertising and sales are linearly related?
b. Calculate the least squares line and interpret the coefficients.

**16.3** Xr16-03 To determine how the number of housing starts is affected by mortgage rates an economist recorded the average mortgage rate and the number of housing starts in a large county for the past 10 years. These data are listed here.

| **Rate** | 8.5 | 7.8 | 7.6 | 7.5 | 8.0 |
|---|---|---|---|---|---|
| **Starts** | 115 | 111 | 185 | 201 | 206 |

| **Rate** | 8.4 | 8.8 | 8.9 | 8.5 | 8.0 |
|---|---|---|---|---|---|
| **Starts** | 167 | 155 | 117 | 133 | 150 |

a. Determine the regression line.
b. What do the coefficients of the regression line tell you about the relationship between mortgage rates and housing starts?

**16.4** Xr16-04 Critics of television often refer to the detrimental effects that all the violence shown on television has on children. However, there may be another problem. It may be that watching television also reduces the amount of physical exercise, causing weight gains. A sample of 15 10-year-old children was taken. The number of pounds each child was overweight was recorded (a negative number indicates the child is underweight). In addition, the number of hours of television viewing per week was also recorded. These data are listed here.

| **Television** | 42 | 34 | 25 | 35 | 37 | 38 | 31 | 33 |
|---|---|---|---|---|---|---|---|---|
| **Overweight** | 18 | 6 | 0 | −1 | 13 | 14 | 7 | 7 |

| **Television** | 19 | 29 | 38 | 28 | 29 | 36 | 18 |
|---|---|---|---|---|---|---|---|
| **Overweight** | −9 | 8 | 8 | 5 | 3 | 14 | −7 |

a. Draw the scatter diagram.
b. Calculate the sample regression line and describe what the coefficients tell you about the relationship between the two variables.

**16.5** Xr16-05 To help determine how many beers to stock the concession manager at Yankee Stadium wanted to know how the temperature affected beer sales. Accordingly, she took a sample of 10 games and recorded the number of beers sold and the temperature in the middle of the game.

| **Temperature** | 80 | 68 | 78 | 79 | 87 |
|---|---|---|---|---|---|
| **Number of beers** | 20,533 | 1,439 | 13,829 | 21,286 | 30,985 |

| **Temperature** | 74 | 86 | 92 | 77 | 84 |
|---|---|---|---|---|---|
| **Number of beers** | 17,187 | 30,240 | 37,596 | 9,610 | 28,742 |

a. Compute the coefficients of the regression line.
b. Interpret the coefficients.

*The exercises that follow were created to allow you to see how regression analysis is used to solve realistic problems. As a result, most feature a large number of observations. We anticipate that most students will solve these problems using a computer and statistical software. However, for students without these resources, we have computed the means, variances, and covariances that will permit them to complete the calculations manually. (See Appendix A.)*

**16.6** Xr16-06* In television's early years, most commercials were 60 seconds long. Now, however, commercials can be any length. The objective of commercials remains the same—to have as many viewers as possible remember the product in a favorable way and eventually buy it. In an experiment to determine how the length of a commercial is related to people's memory of it, 60 randomly selected people were asked to watch a 1-hour television program. In the middle of the show, a commercial advertising a brand of toothpaste appeared. Some viewers watched a commercial that lasted for 20 seconds, others watched one that lasted for 24 seconds, 28 seconds, . . . , 60 seconds. The essential content of the commercials was the same. After the show, each person was given a test to measure how much he or she remembered about the product. The commercial times and test scores (on a 30-point test) were recorded.

a. Draw a scatter diagram of the data to determine whether a linear model appears to be appropriate.
b. Determine the least squares line.
c. Interpret the coefficients.

**16.7** Xr16-07 Florida condominiums are popular winter retreats for many North Americans. In recent years, the prices have steadily increased. A real estate agent wanted to know why prices of similar-sized apartments in the same building vary. A possible answer lies in the floor. It may be that the higher the floor, the greater the sale price of the apartment. He recorded the price (in $1,000s) of 1,200 sq. ft. condominiums in several buildings in the same location that have sold recently and the floor number of the condominium.

a. Determine the regression line.
b. What do the coefficients tell you about the relationship between the two variables?

**16.8** Xr16-08 In 2010, the United States conducted a census of the entire country. The census is completed by mail. To help ensure that the questions are understood, a random sample of Americans take the questionnaire before it is sent out. As part of their analysis, they record the amount of time and ages of the sample. Use the least squares method to analyze the relationship between the amount of time taken to complete the questionnaire and the age of the individual answering the questions. What do the coefficients tell you about the relationship between the two variables?

## APPLICATIONS in HUMAN RESOURCES MANAGEMENT

Jack Hollingsworth/Brand X Pictures/Getty Images

### Retaining Workers

Human resource managers are responsible for a variety of tasks within organizations. As we pointed out in the introduction in Chapter 1, personnel or human resource managers are involved with recruiting new workers, determining which applicants are most suitable to hire, and helping with various aspects of monitoring the workforce, including absenteeism and worker turnover. For many firms, worker turnover is a costly problem. First, there is the cost of recruiting and attracting qualified workers. The firm must advertise vacant positions and make certain that applicants are judged properly. Second, the cost of training hirees can be high, particularly in technical areas. Third, new employees are often not as productive and efficient as experienced employees. Consequently, it is in the interests of the firm to attract and keep the best workers. Any information that the personnel manager can obtain is likely to be useful.

**16.9** Xr16-09 The human resource manager of a telemarketing firm is concerned about the rapid turnover of the firm's telemarketers. It appears that many telemarketers do not work very long before quitting. There may be a number of reasons, including relatively low pay, personal unsuitability for the work, and the low probability of advancement. Because of the high cost of hiring and training new workers, the manager decided to examine the factors that influence workers to quit. He reviewed the work history of a random sample of workers who have quit in the last year and recorded the number of weeks on the job before quitting and the age of each worker when originally hired.

a. Use regression analysis to describe how the work period and age are related.
b. Briefly discuss what the coefficients tell you.

**16.10** Xr16-10 Besides their known long-term effects, do cigarettes also cause short-term illnesses such as colds? To help answer this question, a sample of smokers was drawn. Each person was asked to report the average number of cigarettes smoked per day and the number of days absent from work due to colds last year.

a. Determine the regression line.
b. What do the coefficients tell you about the relationship between smoking cigarettes and sick days because of colds?

**16.11** Xr16-11 Fire damage in the United States amounts to billions of dollars, much of it insured. The time taken to arrive at the fire is critical. This raises the question, Should insurance companies lower premiums if the home to be insured is close to a fire station? To help make a decision, a study was undertaken wherein a number of fires were investigated. The distance to the nearest fire station (in miles) and the percentage of fire damage were recorded. Determine the least squares line and interpret the coefficients.

**16.12** Xr16-12* A real estate agent specializing in commercial real estate wanted a more precise method of judging the likely selling price (in $1,000s) of apartment buildings. As a first effort, she recorded the price of a number of apartment buildings sold recently and the number of square feet (in 1,000s) in the building.

a. Calculate the regression line.
b. What do the coefficients tell you about the relationship between price and square footage?

**16.13** Xr16-13 Millions of boats are registered in the United States. As is the case with automobiles, there is an active used-boat market. Many of the boats purchased require bank financing, and, as a result, it is important for financial institutions to be capable of accurately estimating the price of boats. One variable that affects the price is the number of hours the engine has been run. To determine the effect of the hours on the price, a financial analyst recorded the price (in $1,000s) of a sample of 2007 24-foot Sea Ray cruisers (one of the most popular boats) and the number of hours they had been run. Determine the least squares line and explain what the coefficients tell you.

**16.14** Xr03-62 (Exercise 3.62 revisited) In an attempt to determine the factors that affect the amount of energy used, 200 households were analyzed. In each, the number of occupants and the amount of electricity used were measured. Determine the regression line and interpret the results.

**16.15** Xr16-15 An economist for the federal government is attempting to produce a better measure of poverty than is currently in use. To help acquire information, she recorded the annual household income (in $1,000s) and the amount of money spent on food during one week for a random sample of households. Determine the regression line and interpret the coefficients.

**16.16** Xr16-16* An economist wanted to investigate the relationship between office rents (the dependent variable) and vacancy rates. Accordingly, he took a random sample of monthly office rents and the percentage of vacant office space in 30 different cities.

a. Determine the regression line.
b. Interpret the coefficients.

**16.17** Xr03-64 (Exercise 3.64 revisited) One general belief held by observers of the business world is that taller men earn more money than shorter men. In a University of Pittsburgh study, 250 MBA graduates, all about 30 years old, were polled and asked to report their height (in inches) and their annual income (to the nearest $1,000).

a. Determine the regression line.
b. What do the coefficients tell you?

## APPLICATIONS in HUMAN RESOURCES MANAGEMENT

Sergey Nivens/Shutterstock.com

### Testing Job Applicants

The recruitment process at many firms involves tests to determine the suitability of candidates. The tests may be written to determine whether the applicant has sufficient knowledge in his or her area of expertise to perform well on the job. There may be oral tests to determine whether the applicant's personality matches the needs of the job. Manual or technical skills can be tested through a variety of physical tests. The test results contribute to the decision to hire. In some cases, the test result is the only criterion to hire. Consequently, it is vital to ensure that the test is a reliable predictor of job performance. If the tests are poor predictors, they should be discontinued. Statistical analyses allow personnel managers to examine the link between the test results and job performance.

**16.18** Xr16-18 Although a large number of tasks in the computer industry are robotic, many operations require human workers. Some jobs require a great deal of dexterity to properly position components into place. A large North American computer maker routinely tests applicants for these jobs by giving a dexterity test that involves a number of intricate finger and hand movements. The tests are scored on a 100-point scale. Only those who have scored above 70 are hired. To determine whether the tests are valid predictors of job performance, the personnel manager drew a random sample of 45 workers who were hired 2 months ago. He recorded their test scores and the percentage of nondefective computers they produced in the last week. Determine the regression line and interpret the coefficients.

## 16-3 Error Variable: Required Conditions

In the previous section, we used the least squares method to estimate the coefficients of the linear regression model. A critical part of this model is the error variable $\varepsilon$. In the next section, we will present an inferential method that determines whether there is a relationship between the dependent and independent variables. Later we will show how we use the regression equation to estimate and predict. For these methods to be valid, however, four requirements involving the probability distribution of the error variable must be satisfied.

**Required Conditions for the Error Variable**

1. The probability distribution of $\varepsilon$ is normal.
2. The mean of the distribution is 0; that is, $E(\varepsilon) = 0$.
3. The standard deviation of $\varepsilon$ is $\sigma_\varepsilon$, which is a constant regardless of the value of $x$.
4. The value of $\varepsilon$ associated with any particular value of $y$ is independent of $\varepsilon$ associated with any other value of $y$.

Requirements 1, 2, and 3 can be interpreted in another way: For each value of $x$, $y$ is a normally distributed random variable whose mean is

$$E(y) = \beta_0 + \beta_1 x$$

and whose standard deviation is $\sigma_\varepsilon$. Notice that the mean depends on $x$. The standard deviation, however, is not influenced by $x$ because it is a constant over all values of $x$. Figure 16.3 depicts this interpretation. Notice that for each value of $x$, $E(y)$ changes, but the shape of the distribution of $y$ remains the same. In other words, for each $x$, $y$ is normally distributed with the same standard deviation.

FIGURE **16.3** **Distribution of *y* Given *x***

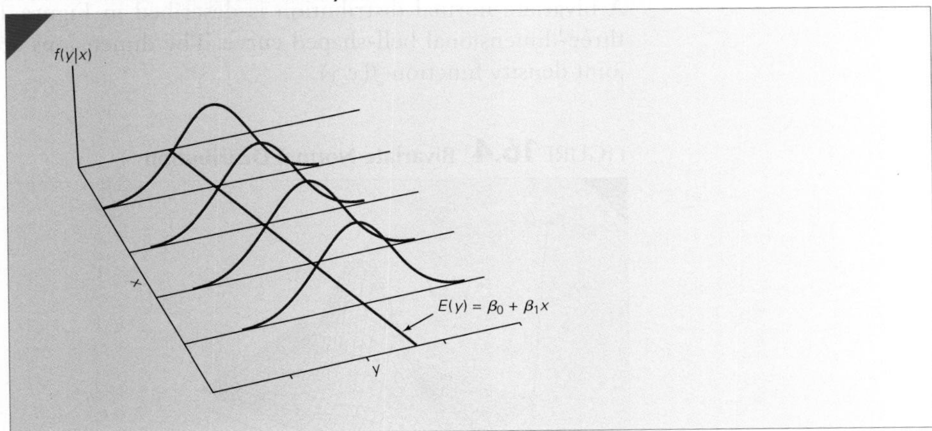


In Section 16-6, we will discuss how departures from these required conditions affect the regression analysis and how they are identified.

## 16-3a Observational and Experimental Data

In Chapter 5 and again in Chapter 13, we described the difference between observational and experimental data. We pointed out that statistics practitioners often design controlled experiments to enable them to interpret the results of their analyses more clearly than would be the case after conducting an observational study. Example 16.2 is an illustration of observational data. In that example, we merely observed the odometer reading and auction selling price of 100 randomly selected cars.

If you examine Exercise 16.6, you will see experimental data gathered through a controlled experiment. To determine the effect of the length of a television commercial on its viewers' memories of the product advertised, the statistics practitioner arranged for 60 television viewers to watch a commercial of differing lengths and then tested their memories of that commercial. Each viewer was randomly assigned a commercial length. The values of $x$ ranged from 20 to 60 and were set by the statistics practitioner as part of the experiment. For each value of $x$, the distribution of the memory test scores is assumed to be normally distributed with a constant variance.

We can summarize the difference between the experiment described in Example 16.2 and the one described in Exercise 16.6. In Example 16.2, both the odometer reading and the auction selling price are random variables. We hypothesize that for each possible odometer reading, there is a theoretical population of auction selling prices that are normally distributed with a mean that is a linear function of the odometer reading and a variance that is constant. In Exercise 16.6, the length of the commercial is not a random variable but a series of values selected by the statistics practitioner. For each commercial length, the memory test scores are required to be normally distributed with a constant variance.

Regression analysis can be applied to data generated from either observational or controlled experiments. In both cases, our objective is to determine how the independent variable is related to the dependent variable. However, observational data can be analyzed in another way. When the data are observational, both variables are random variables. We need not specify that one variable is independent and the other is dependent. We can simply determine *whether* the two variables are related. The equivalent of the required conditions described in the previous box is that the two variables are bivariate normally distributed. (Recall that in Section 7-2 we introduced the bivariate distribution, which describes the joint probability of two variables.) A bivariate normal distribution is described in Figure 16.4. As you can see, it is a three-dimensional bell-shaped curve. The dimensions are the variables $x, y$, and the joint density function $f(x, y)$.

FIGURE **16.4** **Bivariate Normal Distribution**

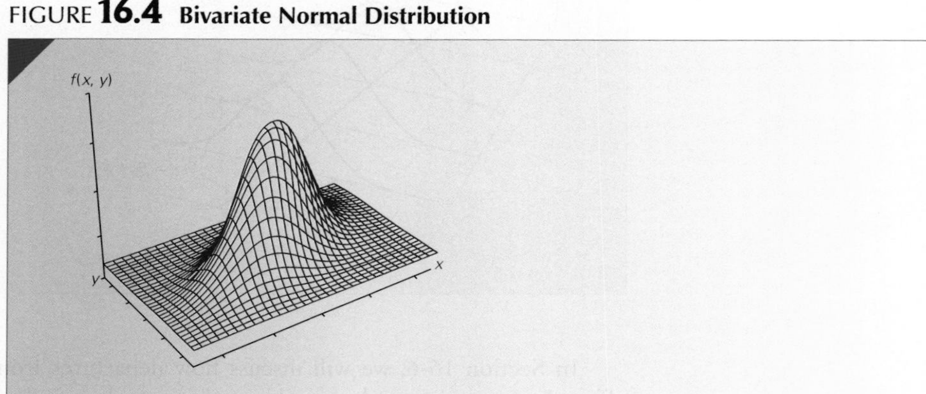

In Section 16-4, we will discuss the statistical technique that is used when both $x$ and $y$ are random variables and they are bivariate normally distributed. In Chapter 19, we will introduce a procedure applied when the normality requirement is not satisfied.

## EXERCISES

**16.19** Describe what the required conditions mean in Exercise 16.6. If the conditions are satisfied, what can you say about the distribution of memory test scores?

**16.20** What are the required conditions for Exercise 16.8? Do these seem reasonable?

**16.21** Assuming that the required conditions are satisfied in Exercise 16.13, what does this tell you about the distribution of used boat prices?

# 16-4 ASSESSING THE MODEL

The least squares method produces the best straight line. However, there may, in fact, be no relationship or perhaps a nonlinear relationship between the two variables. If so, a straight-line model is likely to be impractical. Consequently, it is important for us to assess how well the linear model fits the data. If the fit is poor, we should discard the linear model and seek another one.

Several methods are used to evaluate the model. In this section, we present two statistics and one test procedure to determine whether a linear model should be employed. They are the **standard error of estimate**, the $t$-test of the slope, and the coefficient of determination. All these methods are based on the sum of squares for error.

## 16-4a Sum of Squares for Error

The least squares method determines the coefficients that minimize the sum of squared deviations between the points and the line defined by the coefficients. Recall from Section 16-2 that the minimized sum of squared deviations is called the *sum of squares for error*, denoted SSE. In that section, we demonstrated the direct method of calculating SSE. For each value of $x$, we compute the value of $\hat{y}$. In other words, for $i = 1$ to $n$, we compute

$$\hat{y}_i = b_0 + b_1 x_i$$

For each point, we then compute the difference between the actual value of $y$ and the value calculated at the line, which is the residual. We square each residual and sum the squared values. Table 16.1 on page 638 shows these calculations for Example 16.1. To calculate SSE manually requires a great deal of arithmetic. Fortunately, there is a shortcut method available that uses the sample variances and the covariance.

**Shortcut Calculation of SSE**

$$\text{SSE} = \sum_{i=1}^{n}(y_i - \hat{y}_i)^2 = (n-1)\left(s_y^2 - \frac{s_{xy}^2}{s_x^2}\right)$$

where $s_y^2$ is the sample variance of the dependent variable.

## 16-4b Standard Error of Estimate

In Section 16-3, we pointed out that the error variable $\varepsilon$ is normally distributed with mean 0 and standard deviation $\sigma_\varepsilon$. If $\sigma_\varepsilon$ is large, some of the errors will be large, which implies that the model's fit is poor. If $\sigma_\varepsilon$ is small, the errors tend to be close to the mean (which is 0); as a result, the model fits well. Hence, we could use $\sigma_\varepsilon$ to measure the suitability of using a linear model. Unfortunately, $\sigma_\varepsilon$ is a population parameter and, like most other parameters, is unknown. We can, however, estimate $\sigma_\varepsilon$ from the data. The estimate is based on SSE. The unbiased estimator of the variance of the error variable $\sigma_\varepsilon^2$ is

$$s_\varepsilon^2 = \frac{\text{SSE}}{n-2}$$

The square root of $s_\varepsilon^2$ is called the *standard error of estimate*.

**Standard Error of Estimate**

$$s_\varepsilon = \sqrt{\frac{\text{SSE}}{n-2}}$$

EXAMPLE 16.3

## Odometer Reading and Prices of Used Toyota Camrys—Part 2

Find the standard error of estimate for Example 16.2 and describe what it tells you about the model's fit.

SOLUTION:

COMPUTE

MANUALLY:

To compute the standard error of estimate, we must compute SSE, which is calculated from the sample variances and the covariance. We have already determined the covariance and the variance of $x$: −2.909 and 43.509, respectively. The sample variance of $y$ (applying the shortcut method) is

$$s_y^2 = \frac{1}{n-1}\left[\sum_{i=1}^{n} y_i^2 - \frac{\left(\sum_{i=1}^{n} y_i\right)^2}{n}\right]$$

$$= \frac{1}{100-1}\left[22{,}055.23 - \frac{(1{,}484.1)^2}{100}\right]$$

$$= .300$$

$$\text{SSE} = (n-1)\left(s_y^2 - \frac{s_{xy}^2}{s_x^2}\right)$$
$$= (100-1)\left[.300 - \frac{(-2.909)^2}{43.509}\right]$$
$$= 10.445$$

The standard error of estimate follows:

$$s_\varepsilon = \sqrt{\frac{\text{SSE}}{n-2}} = \sqrt{\frac{10.445}{98}} = .3265$$

## EXCEL Data Analysis

| Standard Error | 0.3265 |
|---|---|

This part of the Excel printout was copied from the complete printout on page 640.

## XLSTAT

| RMSE | 0.3265 |
|---|---|

This part of the XLSTAT printout was copied from the complete printout on page 640.

## INTERPRET

The smallest value that $s_\varepsilon$ can assume is 0, which occurs when SSE = 0, that is, when all the points fall on the regression line. Thus, when $s_\varepsilon$ is small, the fit is excellent, and the linear model is likely to be an effective analytical and forecasting tool. If $s_\varepsilon$ is large, the model is a poor one, and the statistics practitioner should improve it or discard it.

We judge the value of $s_\varepsilon$ by comparing it to the values of the dependent variable $y$ or more specifically to the sample mean $\bar{y}$. In this example, because $s_\varepsilon = .3265$ and $\bar{y} = 14.841$, it does appear that the standard error of estimate is small. However, because there is no predefined upper limit on $s_\varepsilon$, it is often difficult to assess the model in this way. In general, the standard error of estimate cannot be used as an absolute measure of the model's utility.

Nonetheless, $s_\varepsilon$ is useful in comparing models. If the statistics practitioner has several models from which to choose, the one with the smallest value of $s_\varepsilon$ should generally be the one used. As you'll see, $s_\varepsilon$ is also an important statistic in other procedures associated with regression analysis.

## 16-4c Testing the Slope

To understand this method of assessing the linear model, consider the consequences of applying the regression technique to two variables that are not at all linearly related. If we could observe the entire population and draw the regression line, we would observe the scatter diagram shown in Figure 16.5. The line is horizontal, which means that no matter what value of $x$ is used, we would estimate the same value for $\hat{y}$; thus, $y$ is not linearly related to $x$. Recall that a horizontal straight line has a slope of 0, that is, $\beta_1 = 0$.

FIGURE **16.5** **Scatter Diagram of Entire Population with $\beta_1 = 0$**

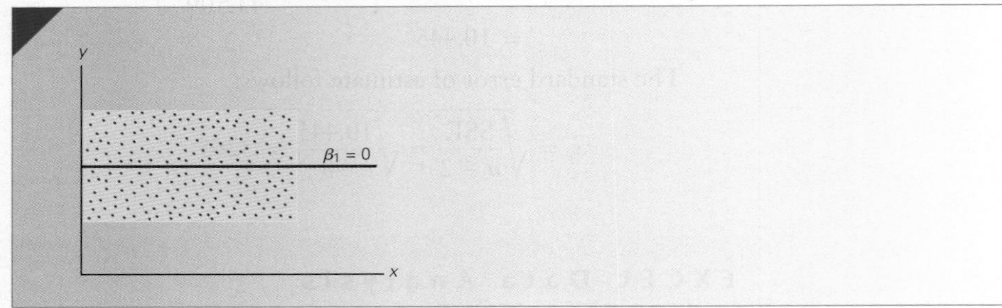


Because we rarely examine complete populations, the parameters are unknown. However, we can draw inferences about the population slope $\beta_1$ from the sample slope $b_1$.

The process of testing hypotheses about $\beta_1$ is identical to the process of testing any other parameter. We begin with the hypotheses. The null hypothesis specifies that there is no linear relationship, which means that the slope is 0. Thus, we specify

$$H_0: \quad \beta_1 = 0$$

It must be noted that if the null hypothesis is true, it does not necessarily mean that no relationship exists. For example, a quadratic relationship described in Figure 16.6 may exist where $\beta_1 = 0$.

FIGURE **16.6** **Quadratic Relationship**

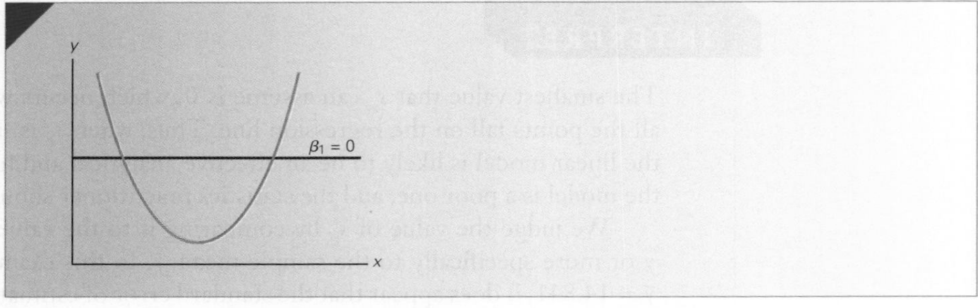


We can conduct one- or two-tail tests of $\beta_1$. Most often, we perform a two-tail test to determine whether there is sufficient evidence to infer that a linear relationship exists.*
We test the alternative hypothesis

$$H_1: \quad \beta_1 \neq 0$$

## 16-4d Estimator and Sampling Distribution

In Section 16-2, we pointed out that $b_1$ is an unbiased estimator of $\beta_1$; that is,

$$E(b_1) = \beta_1$$

*If the alternative hypothesis is true, it may be that a linear relationship exists or that a nonlinear relationship exists but that the relationship can be approximated by a straight line.

The estimated standard error of $b_1$ is

$$s_{b_1} = \frac{s_\varepsilon}{\sqrt{(n-1)s_x^2}}$$

where $s_\varepsilon$ is the standard error of estimate and $s_x^2$ is the sample variance of the independent variable. If the required conditions outlined in Section 16-3 are satisfied, the sampling distribution of the $t$-statistic

$$t = \frac{b_1 - \beta_1}{s_{b_1}}$$

is Student $t$ with degrees of freedom $\nu = n - 2$. Notice that the standard error of $b_1$ decreases when the sample size increases (which makes $b_1$ a consistent estimator of $\beta_1$) or the variance of the independent variable increases.

Thus, the test statistic and confidence interval estimator are as follows.

**Test Statistic for $\beta_1$**

$$t = \frac{b_1 - \beta_1}{s_{b_1}} \qquad \nu = n - 2$$

**Confidence Interval Estimator of $\beta_1$**

$$b_1 \pm t_{\alpha/2} s_{b_1} \qquad \nu = n - 2$$

EXAMPLE 16.4

## Are Odometer Reading and Price of Used Toyota Camrys Related?

Test to determine whether there is enough evidence in Example 16.2 to infer that there is a linear relationship between the auction price and the odometer reading for all 3-year-old Toyota Camrys. Use a 5% significance level.

SOLUTION:

We test the hypotheses

$$H_0: \beta_1 = 0$$

$$H_1: \beta_1 \neq 0$$

If the null hypothesis is true, no linear relationship exists. If the alternative hypothesis is true, some linear relationship exists.

COMPUTE

MANUALLY:

To compute the value of the test statistic, we need $b_1$ and $s_{b_1}$. In Example 16.2, we found

$$b_1 = -.0669$$

and

$$s_x^2 = 43.509$$

Thus,

$$s_{b_1} = \frac{s_\varepsilon}{\sqrt{(n-1)s_x^2}} = \frac{.3265}{\sqrt{(99)(43.509)}} = .00497$$

The value of the test statistic is

$$t = \frac{b_1 - \beta_1}{s_{b_1}} = \frac{-.0669 - 0}{.00497} = -13.46$$

The rejection region is

$$t < -t_{\alpha/2,\nu} = -t_{.025,98} \approx -1.984 \quad \text{or} \quad t > t_{\alpha/2,\nu} = t_{.025,98} \approx 1.984$$

## EXCEL Data Analysis

| | Coefficients | Standard Error | t Stat | P-value | Lower 95% | Upper 95% |
|---|---|---|---|---|---|---|
| Intercept | 17.25 | 0.182 | 94.73 | 3.57E-98 | 16.89 | 17.61 |
| Odometer | –0.0669 | 0.0050 | –13.44 | 5.75E-24 | –0.0767 | –0.0570 |

## XLSTAT

| Source | Value | Standard error | t | Pr > \|t\| | Lower bound (95%) | Upper bound (95%) |
|---|---|---|---|---|---|---|
| Intercept | 17.25 | 0.182 | 94.73 | < 0.0001 | 16.89 | 17.61 |
| Odometer | –0.0669 | 0.0050 | –13.44 | < 0.0001 | –0.0767 | –0.0570 |

## INTERPRET

The value of the test statistic is $t = -13.44$, with a $p$-value of 0. There is overwhelming evidence to infer that a linear relationship exists. What this means is that the odometer reading may affect the auction selling price of the cars. (See the subsection on cause-and-effect relationship on page 656.)

As was the case when we interpreted the $y$-intercept, the conclusion we draw here is valid only over the range of the values of the independent variable. We can infer that there is a relationship between odometer reading and auction price for the 3-year-old Toyota Camrys whose odometer readings lie between 19.1 (thousand) and 49.2 (thousand) miles (the minimum and maximum values of $x$ in the sample). Because we have no observations outside this range, we do not know how, or even whether, the two variables are related.

Notice that the printout includes a test for $\beta_0$. However, as we pointed out before, interpreting the value of the $y$-intercept can lead to erroneous, if not ridiculous, conclusions. Consequently, we generally ignore the test of $\beta_0$.

We can also acquire information about the relationship by estimating the slope coefficient. In this example, the 95% confidence interval estimate (approximating $t_{.025}$ with 98 degrees of freedom with $t_{.025}$ with 100 degrees of freedom) is

$$b_1 \pm t_{\alpha/2} s_{b_1} = -.0669 \pm 1.984(.00497) = -.0669 \pm .0099$$

We estimate that the slope coefficient lies between $-.0768$ and $-.0570$. Both Excel Data Analysis and XLSTAT print the interval estimate of the slope as well as the estimate of the intercept.

## 16-4e One-Tail Tests

If we wish to test for positive or negative linear relationships, we conduct one-tail tests. To illustrate, suppose that in Example 16.2 we wanted to know whether there is evidence of a negative linear relationship between odometer reading and auction selling price. We would specify the hypotheses as

$$H_0: \beta_1 = 0$$

$$H_1: \beta_1 < 0$$

The value of the test statistic would be exactly as computed previously (Example 16.4). However, in this case the $p$-value would be the two-tail $p$-value divided by 2; using Excel's $p$-value, this would be $(5.75 \times 10^{-24})/2 = 2.875 \times 10^{-24}$, which is still approximately 0.

## 16-4f Coefficient of Determination

The test of $\beta_1$ addresses only the question of whether there is enough evidence to infer that a linear relationship exists. In many cases, however, it is also useful to measure the strength of that linear relationship, particularly when we want to compare several different models. The statistic that performs this function is the **coefficient of determination**, which is denoted $R^2$. Statistics practitioners often refer to this statistic as the "$R$-square." Recall that we introduced the coefficient of determination in Chapter 4, where we pointed out that this statistic is a measure of the amount of variation in the dependent variable that is explained by the variation in the independent variable. However, we did not describe why we interpret the $R$-square in this way.

**Coefficient of Determination**

$$R^2 = \frac{s_{xy}^2}{s_x^2 s_y^2}$$

With a little algebra, statisticians can show that

$$R^2 = 1 - \frac{\text{SSE}}{\sum(y_i - \bar{y})^2}$$

We'll return to Example 16.1 to learn more about how to interpret the coefficient of determination. In Chapter 14, we partitioned the total sum of squares into two sources of variation. We do so here as well. We begin by adding and subtracting $\hat{y}_i$ from the deviation between $y_i$ from the mean $\bar{y}$; that is,

$$(y_i - \bar{y}) = (y_i - \bar{y}) + \hat{y}_i - \hat{y}_i$$

We observe that by rearranging the terms, the deviation between $y_i$ and $\bar{y}$ can be decomposed into two parts; that is,

$$(y_i - \bar{y}) = (y_i - \hat{y}_i) + (\hat{y}_i - \bar{y})$$

This equation is represented graphically (for $i = 5$) in Figure 16.7.

FIGURE **16.7** **Partitioning the Deviation for $i = 5$**

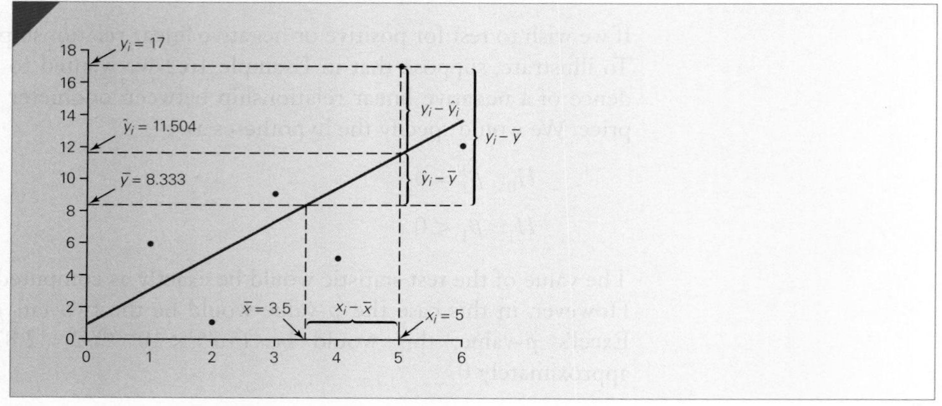


Now we ask why the values of $y$ are different from one another. From Figure 16.7, we see that part of the difference between $y_i$ and $\bar{y}$ is the difference between $\hat{y}_i$ and $\bar{y}$, which is accounted for by the difference between $x_i$ and $\bar{x}$. In other words, some of the variation in $y$ is explained by the changes to $x$. The other part of the difference between $y_i$ and $\bar{y}$, however, is accounted for by the difference between $y_i$ and $\hat{y}_i$. This difference is the residual, which represents variables not otherwise represented by the model. As a result, we say that this part of the difference is *unexplained* by the variation in $x$.

If we now square both sides of the equation, sum over all sample points, and perform some algebra, we produce

$$\sum(y_i - \bar{y})^2 = \sum(y_i - \hat{y}_i)^2 + \sum(\hat{y}_i - \bar{y})^2$$

The quantity on the left side of this equation is a measure of the variation in the dependent variable $y$. The first quantity on the right side of the equation is SSE, and the second term is denoted SSR, for sum of squares for regression. We can rewrite the equation as

$$\text{Variation in } y = \text{SSE} + \text{SSR}$$

As we did in the analysis of variance, we partition the variation of $y$ into two parts: SSE, which measures the amount of variation in $y$ that remains unexplained; and SSR, which measures the amount of variation in $y$ that is explained by the variation in the independent variable $x$. We can incorporate this analysis into the definition of $R^2$.

**Coefficient of Determination**

$$R^2 = 1 - \frac{\text{SSE}}{\sum(y_i - \bar{y})^2} = \frac{\sum(y_i - \bar{y})^2 - \text{SSE}}{\sum(y_i - \bar{y})^2} = \frac{\text{Explained variation}}{\text{Variation in } y}$$

It follows that $R^2$ measures the proportion of the variation in $y$ that can be explained by the variation in $x$.

EXAMPLE 16.5

## Measuring the Strength of the Linear Relationship between Odometer Reading and Price of Used Toyota Camrys

Find the coefficient of determination for Example 16.2 and describe what this statistic tells you about the regression model.

SOLUTION:

### COMPUTE

MANUALLY:

We have already calculated all the necessary components of this statistic. In Example 16.2 we found

$$s_{xy} = -2.909$$
$$s_x^2 = 43.509$$

and from Example 16.3

$$s_y^2 = .300$$

Thus,

$$R^2 = \frac{s_{xy}^2}{s_x^2 s_y^2} = \frac{(-2.909)^2}{(43.509)(.300)} = .6483$$

EXCEL Data Analysis

| R Square | 0.6483 |
|---|---|

XLSTAT

| R² | 0.6483 |
|---|---|

Both Excel and XLSTAT print a second $R^2$ statistic called the *coefficient of determination adjusted for degrees of freedom*. We will define and describe this statistic in Chapter 17.

### INTERPRET

We found that $R^2$ is equal to .6483. This statistic tells us that 64.83% of the variation in the auction selling prices is explained by the variation in the odometer readings. The remaining 35.17% is unexplained. Unlike the value of a test statistic, the coefficient of determination does not have a critical value that enables us to draw conclusions.

In general, the higher the value of $R^2$, the better the model fits the data. From the $t$-test of $\beta_1$ we already know that there is evidence of a linear relationship. The coefficient of determination merely supplies us with a measure of the strength of that relationship. As you will discover in the next chapter, when we improve the model, the value of $R^2$ increases.

## 16-4g Other Parts of the Computer Printout

The last part of the printout shown on page 640 relates to our discussion of the interpretation of the value of $R^2$, when its meaning is derived from the partitioning of the variation in $y$. The values of SSR and SSE are shown in an analysis of variance table similar to the tables introduced in Chapter 14. The general form of the table is shown in Table 16.2. The $F$-test performed in the ANOVA table will be explained in Chapter 17.

TABLE **16.2** **General Form of the ANOVA Table in the Simple Linear Regression Model**

| SOURCE | d.f. | SUMS OF SQUARES | MEAN SQUARES | *F*-STATISTIC |
|---|---|---|---|---|
| Regression | 1 | SSR | MSR = SSR/1 | $F$ = MSR/MSE |
| Error | $n - 2$ | SSE | MSE = SSE/($n$ − 2) | |
| Total | $n - 1$ | Variation in $y$ | | |

*Note:* Excel uses the word "Residual" to refer to the second source of variation, which we called "Error."

## 16-4h Developing an Understanding of Statistical Concepts

Once again, we encounter the concept of explained variation. We first discussed the concept in Chapter 13 when we introduced the matched pairs experiment, where the experiment was designed to reduce the variation among experimental units. This concept was extended in the analysis of variance, where we partitioned the total variation into two or more sources (depending on the experimental design). And now in regression analysis, we use the concept to measure how the dependent variable is related to the independent variable. We partition the variation of the dependent variable into the sources: the variation explained by the variation in the independent variable and the unexplained variation. The greater the explained variation, the better the model is. We often refer to the coefficient of determination as a measure of the explanatory power of the model.

## 16-4i Cause-and-Effect Relationship

A common mistake is made by many students when they attempt to interpret the results of a regression analysis when there is evidence of a linear relationship. They imply that changes in the independent variable cause changes in the dependent variable. It must be emphasized that we cannot infer a causal relationship from statistics alone. Any inference about the cause of the changes in the dependent variable must be justified by a reasonable theoretical relationship. For example, statistical tests established that the more one smoked, the greater the probability of developing lung cancer. However, this analysis did not prove that smoking causes lung cancer. It only demonstrated that smoking and lung cancer were somehow related. Only when medical investigations established the connection were scientists able to confidently declare that smoking causes lung cancer.

As another illustration, consider Example 16.2 where we showed that the odometer reading is linearly related to the auction price. Although it seems reasonable to conclude that decreasing the odometer reading would cause the auction price to rise, the conclusion may not be entirely true. It is theoretically possible that the price is determined by the overall condition of the car and that the condition generally worsens when the car is driven longer. Another analysis would be needed to establish the veracity of this conclusion.

Be cautious about the use of the terms *explained variation* and *explanatory power of the model*. Do not interpret the word *explained* to mean *caused*. We say that the coefficient of determination measures the amount of variation in $y$ that is explained (not caused) by the variation in $x$. Thus, regression analysis can only show that a statistical relationship exists. We cannot infer that one variable causes another.

Recall that we first pointed this out in Chapter 3 using the following sentence:

Correlation is not causation.

## 16-4j Testing the Coefficient of Correlation

When we introduced the coefficient of correlation (also called the **Pearson coefficient of correlation**) in Chapter 4, we observed that it is used to measure the strength of association between two variables. However, the coefficient of correlation can be useful in another way. We can use it to test for a linear relationship between two variables.

When we are interested in determining *how* the independent variable is related to the dependent variable, we estimate and test the linear regression model. The $t$-test of the slope presented previously allows us to determine whether a linear relationship actually exists. As we pointed out in Section 16-3, the statistical test requires that for each value of $x$, there exists a population of values of $y$ that are normally distributed with a constant variance. This condition is required whether the data are experimental or observational.

In many circumstances, we're interested in determining only *whether* a linear relationship exists and not the form of the relationship. When the data are observational and the two variables are bivariate normally distributed (See Section 16-3.) we can calculate the coefficient of correlation and use it to test for linear association.

As we noted in Chapter 4, the population coefficient of correlation is denoted $\rho$ (the Greek letter *rho*). Because $\rho$ is a population parameter (which is almost always unknown), we must estimate its value from the sample data. Recall that the sample coefficient of correlation is defined as follows.

**Sample Coefficient of Correlation**

$$r = \frac{s_{xy}}{s_x s_y}$$

When there is no linear relationship between the two variables, $\rho = 0$. To determine whether we can infer that $\rho$ is 0, we test the hypotheses

$$H_0: \ \rho = 0$$

$$H_1: \ \rho \neq 0$$

The test statistic is defined in the following way.

**Test Statistic for Testing $\rho = 0$**

$$t = r\sqrt{\frac{n-2}{1-r^2}}$$

**which is Student $t$ distributed with $v = n - 2$ degrees of freedom provided that the variables are bivariate normally distributed.**

EXAMPLE 16.6

## Are Odometer Reading and Price of Used Toyota Camrys Linearly Related? Testing the Coefficient of Correlation

Conduct the $t$-test of the coefficient of correlation to determine whether odometer reading and auction selling price are linearly related in Example 16.2. Assume that the two variables are bivariate normally distributed.

SOLUTION:

COMPUTE

MANUALLY:

The hypotheses to be tested are

$$H_0: \rho = 0$$
$$H_1: \rho \neq 0$$

In Example 16.2, we found $s_{xy} = -2.909$ and $s_x^2 = 43.509$. In Example 16.5, we determined that $s_y^2 = .300$. Thus,

$$s_x = \sqrt{43.509} = 6.596$$
$$s_y = \sqrt{.300} = .5477$$

The coefficient of correlation is

$$r = \frac{s_{xy}}{s_x s_y} = \frac{-2.909}{(6.596)(.5477)} = -.8052$$

The value of the test statistic is

$$t = r\sqrt{\frac{n-2}{1-r^2}} = -.8052\sqrt{\frac{100-2}{1-(-.8052)^2}} = -13.44$$

Notice that this is the same value we produced in the $t$-test of the slope in Example 16.4. Because both sampling distributions are Student $t$ with 98 degrees of freedom, the $p$-value and conclusion are also identical.

## EXCEL Workbook

| | A | B | C | D |
|---|---|---|---|---|
| 1 | t-Test of Correlation Coefficient | | | |
| 2 | | | | |
| 3 | Sample correlation | 0.8052 | t Stat | 13.44 |
| 4 | Sample size | 100 | P(T<=t) one-tail | 2.85E-24 |
| 5 | Alpha | 0.05 | t Critical one-tail | 1.6604 |
| 6 | | | P(T<=t) two-tail | 5.71E-24 |
| 7 | | | t Critical two-tail | 1.9842 |

*INSTRUCTIONS*

1. Calculate the coefficient of correlation. (See page 119 for instructions.)
2. Open the **Test Statistics Workbook** and click the **t-Test_Correlation** tab.
3. Input the coefficient of correlation, the sample size and the value of $\alpha$.

## XLSTAT

| | A | B | C |
|---|---|---|---|
| 8 | Correlation matrix (Pearson): | | |
| 9 | | | |
| 10 | Variables | Price | Odometer |
| 11 | Price | 1 | -0.8052 |
| 12 | Odometer | -0.8052 | 1 |
| 13 | | | |
| 14 | | | |
| 15 | p-values: | | |
| 16 | | | |
| 17 | Variables | Price | Odometer |
| 18 | Price | 0 | 0.000 |
| 19 | Odometer | < 0.0001 | 0 |

*INSTRUCTIONS*

1. Type or import the data (Open Xm16-02).
2. Click **XLSTAT**, **Correlation/Association test**, and **Correlation tests.**
3. In the **Observations/variables table** box type the input range of (A1:B101). Specify Type of correlation: **Pearson.**
4. Click **Outputs** and check **Correlations** and **p-values.** Click **OK.**

Notice that the $t$-test of $\rho$ and the $t$-test of $\beta_1$ in Example 16.4 produced identical results. This should not be surprising because both tests are conducted to determine whether there is evidence of a linear relationship. The decision about which test to use is based on the type of experiment and the information we seek from the statistical analysis. If we're interested in discovering the relationship between two variables, or if we've conducted an experiment where we controlled the values of the independent variable (as in Exercise 16.6), the $t$-test of $\beta_1$ should be applied. If we're interested only in determining *whether* two random variables that are bivariate normally distributed are linearly related, the $t$-test of $\rho$ should be applied.

As is the case with the $t$-test of the slope, we can also conduct one-tail tests. We can test for a positive or a negative linear relationship.

# General Social Survey: Education and Income—How Are They Related? Solution

Jupiterimages/Comstock Images/Getty Images

## IDENTIFY

The problem objective is to analyze the relationship between two interval variables. Because we want to know how education affects income, the independent variable is education (EDUC) and the dependent variable is income (RINCOME).

## COMPUTE

### EXCEL Data Analysis

| | A | B | C | D | E | F | G |
|---|---|---|---|---|---|---|---|
| 1 | SUMMARY OUTPUT | | | | | | |
| 2 | | | | | | | |
| 3 | *Regression Statistics* | | | | | | |
| 4 | Multiple R | 0.3666 | | | | | |
| 5 | R Square | 0.1344 | | | | | |
| 6 | Adjusted R Square | 0.1338 | | | | | |
| 7 | Standard Error | 37,121 | | | | | |
| 8 | Observations | 1523 | | | | | |
| 9 | | | | | | | |
| 10 | ANOVA | | | | | | |
| 11 | | *df* | *SS* | *MS* | *F* | *Significance F* | |
| 12 | Regression | 1 | 325,326,669,319 | 325,326,669,319 | 236.10 | 1.22E-49 | |
| 13 | Residual | 1521 | 2,095,847,445,175 | 1,377,940,464 | | | |
| 14 | Total | 1522 | 2,421,174,114,494 | | | | |
| 15 | | | | | | | |
| 16 | | *Coefficients* | *Standard Error* | *t Stat* | *P-value* | *Lower 95%* | *Upper 95%* |
| 17 | Intercept | -23,982 | 4,605 | -5.21 | 2.17E-07 | -33,015 | -14,950 |
| 18 | EDUC | 4,898 | 319 | 15.37 | 1.22E-49 | 4,273 | 5,523 |

## INTERPRET

The regression equation is $\hat{y} = -23{,}982 + 4898x$. The slope coefficient tells us that on average for each additional year of education income increases by $4,898. The intercept is clearly meaningless. We test to determine whether there is evidence of a linear relationship.

$H_0$: $\beta_1 = 0$

$H_1$: $\beta_1 \neq 0$

The test statistic is $t = 15.37$ and the $p$-value is $1.22 \times 10^{-49}$, which is virtually 0. The coefficient of determination is $R^2 = .1344$, which means that 13.44% of the variation in income is explained by the variation in education, and the remaining 86.56% is not explained.

### 16-4k Violation of the Required Condition

When the normality requirement is unsatisfied, we can use a nonparametric technique—the Spearman rank correlation coefficient (Chapter 19*) to replace the $t$-test of $\rho$.

## EXERCISES

***Use a 5% significance level for all tests of hypotheses.***

**16.22** You have been given the following data:

| $x$ | 1 | 3 | 4 | 6 | 9 | 8 | 10 |
|---|---|---|---|---|---|---|---|
| $y$ | 1 | 8 | 15 | 33 | 75 | 70 | 95 |

a. Draw the scatter diagram. Does it appear that $x$ and $y$ are related? If so, how?
b. Test to determine whether there is evidence of a linear relationship.

**16.23** Suppose that you have the following data:

| $x$ | 3 | 5 | 2 | 6 | 1 | 4 |
|---|---|---|---|---|---|---|
| $y$ | 25 | 110 | 9 | 250 | 3 | 71 |

a. Draw the scatter diagram. Does it appear that $x$ and $y$ are related? If so, how?
b. Test to determine whether there is evidence of a linear relationship.

**16.24** Refer to Exercise 16.2.
a. Determine the standard error of estimate.
b. Is there evidence of a linear relationship between advertising and sales?
c. Estimate $\beta_1$ with 95% confidence.
d. Compute the coefficient of determination and interpret this value.
e. Briefly summarize what you have learned in parts (a) through (d).

**16.25** Calculate the coefficient of determination and conduct a test to determine whether a linear relationship exists between housing starts and mortgage interest in Exercise 16.3.

**16.26** Is there evidence of a linear relationship between the number of hours of television viewing and how overweight the child is in Exercise 16.4?

**16.27** Determine whether there is evidence of a negative linear relationship between temperature and the number of beers sold at Yankee Stadium in Exercise 16.5.

*Exercises 16.28–16.44 require the use of a computer and software. The answers may be calculated manually. See Appendix A for the sample statistics.*

**16.28** Refer to Exercise 16.6.
a. What is the standard error of estimate? Interpret its value.
b. Describe how well the memory test scores and length of television commercial are linearly related.
c. Are the memory test scores and length of commercial linearly related? Test using a 5% significance level.
d. Estimate the slope coefficient with 90% confidence.

**16.29** Refer to Exercise 16.7. Apply the three methods of assessing the model to determine how well the linear model fits.

**16.30** Is there enough evidence to infer that age and the amount of time needed to complete the questionnaire are linearly related in Exercise 16.8?

**16.31** Refer to Exercise 16.9. Use two statistics to measure the strength of the linear association. What do these statistics tell you?

**16.32** Is there evidence of a linear relationship between number of cigarettes smoked and number of sick days in Exercise 16.10?

**16.33** Refer to Exercise 16.11.
a. Test to determine whether there is evidence of a linear relationship between distance to the nearest fire station and percentage of damage.
b. Estimate the slope coefficient with 95% confidence.
c. Determine the coefficient of determination. What does this statistic tell you about the relationship?

**16.34** Refer to Exercise 16.12.
a. Determine the standard error of estimate, and describe what this statistic tells you about the regression line.
b. Can we conclude that the size and price of the apartment building are linearly related?
c. Determine the coefficient of determination and discuss what its value tells you about the two variables.

*Instructors who wish to teach the use of the Spearman rank correlation coefficient here can use the online appendix Spearman Rank Correlation Coefficient and Test.

**16.35** Is there enough evidence to infer that as the number of hours of engine use increases, the price decreases in Exercise 16.13?

**16.36** Assess fit of the regression line in Exercise 16.14.

**16.37** Refer to Exercise 16.15.

a. Determine the coefficient of determination and describe what it tells you.
b. Conduct a test to determine whether there is evidence of a linear relationship between household income and food budget.

**16.38** Can we infer that office rents and vacancy rates are linearly related in Exercise 16.16?

**16.39** Are height and income in Exercise 16.17 positively linearly related?

**16.40** Refer to Exercise 16.18.

a. Compute the coefficient of determination and describe what it tells you.
b. Can we infer that aptitude test scores and percentages of nondefectives are linearly related?

**16.41** Repeat Exercise 16.13 using the $t$-test of the coefficient of correlation to determine whether there is a negative linear relationship between the number of hours of engine use and the selling price of the used boats.

**16.42** Repeat Exercise 16.6 using the $t$-test of the coefficient of correlation. Is this result identical to the one you produced in Exercise 16.6?

**16.43** Are food budget and household income in Exercise 16.15 linearly related? Employ the $t$-test of the coefficient of correlation to answer the question.

**16.44** Refer to Exercise 16.10. Use the $t$-test of the coefficient of correlation to determine whether there is evidence of a positive linear relationship between number of cigarettes smoked and the number of sick days.

**16.45** Xr16-45 Do more educated people spend more time watching or news on the Internet? To help answer the question, a statistics practitioner undertook a survey that asked a random sample of people how many years of education they had and the amount of time they spend in a typical day watching or reading news on the Internet?

a. Determine whether there is enough evidence to infer that a linear relationship exists between the two variables.
b. If there is a linear relationship estimate with 95% confidence the marginal increase in the time watching or reading news on the Internet for each additional year of education.

**16.46** Xr03-70 Refer to Exercise 3.70 where we looked at the relationship between the grade of a particular coin (Canadian 1925 nickel) and its auction selling price.

a. Is there sufficient evidence to conclude that the two variables are linearly related?
b. Compute the coefficient of determination and briefly explain what it tells you.

**16.47** Xr16-47 National news on television features commercials describing pharmaceutical drugs that treat ailments that plague older people. Apparently, the major networks believe that older people tend to watch national newscasts. The marketing manager of a drug company conducted a survey that took a random sample of people older than 60 years of age and recorded their age and the number of days they watched national on television in a typical week.

a. Test to determine whether there is enough evidence to conclude that there is a linear relationship between age and number of days watching national news.
b. Calculate the coefficient of determination and briefly describe what it tells you.

**16.48** Xr16-48 In most presidential elections in the United States, the voter turnout is quite low, often in the neighborhood of 50%. Political workers would like to be able to predict who is likely to vote. Thus, it is important to know which variables are related to intention to vote. A political pollster took a random sample of registered voters 3 months before an election. Each respondent was asked the following question, "How definite is your intention to vote or not?" The results were recorded as 1 = Definitely will not vote; 2, 3, 4, 5, 6, 7, 8, 9, 10 = Definitely will vote. Also recorded was the age of the respondent. Is there sufficient evidence to infer that age (AGE) and intention to vote (DEFINITE) are linearly related?

**16.49** Xr03-71 Refer to Exercise 3.71 wherein we looked at the relationship between temperature and distance that golf balls travel.

a. Conduct a regression analysis to determine whether there is enough evidence of a positive linear relationship
b. Interpret the slope coefficient.
c. Determine the coefficient of determination and describe the information it provides.

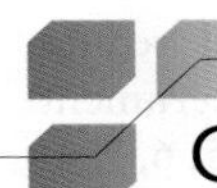

## GENERAL SOCIAL SURVEY EXERCISES

*Excel users: You must delete rows containing empty cells.* ***Use a 5% significance level for all tests.***

**16.50** GSS2014* Does one's income (RINCOME) affect his or her position on the question, Should the government reduce income differences between rich and poor (EQWLTH: 1 = Government should reduce income differences; 2, 3, 4, 5, 6, 7 = No government action)? Answer the question by testing the relationship between the two variables.

**16.51** GSS2014* Conduct an analysis of the relationship between income (RINCOME) and age (AGE). Estimate with 95% confidence the average increase in income for each additional year of age.

**16.52** GSS2014* Does television appeal to the lowest common denominator? If so, we would expect more educated people to watch less television. Is there sufficient evidence to conclude that more educated people (EDUC) watch less television (TVHOURS)?

**16.53** GSS2014* It seems rather obvious that the longer one works the more one earns. The question is how much more one earns annually for each additional hour of work. Conduct an analysis of annual income (INCOME) and number of hours per week of work (HRS1).

a. Test to determine whether there is a positive linear relationship.
b. Estimate with 95% confidence the increase in annual income for each additional hour of work per week.

**16.54** GSS2014* Is there a linear relationship between age (AGE) and how many hours per week one works (HRS1)? Conduct a test to answer the question.

**16.55** GSS2014* Television advertisers always want to know who is watching their televised advertising. Do older people watch more television than do younger people? Do the data provide sufficient evidence to infer that there is a positive linear relationship between age (AGE) and television watched (TVHOURS)?

**16.56** GSS2014* How does having more family members earning income (EARNRS) affect total family income (INCOME)? Conduct an analysis to determine whether there is a positive linear relationship between the two variables, and, if so, estimate with 95% confidence the average increase in total family income for each additional of earners.

**16.57** GSS2014* Are more educated (EDUC) people more likely to support government action to reduce income differences across the country differences (EQWLTH: 1 = Government should reduce income differences; 2, 3, 4, 5, 6, 7 = No government action)? Conduct a test to answer the question.

**16.58** GSS2014* Do more educated people tend to marry individuals with similar educational experience? Test to determine whether a married person's years of education (EDUC) are positively linearly related to his or her spouse's level of education (SPEDUC).

**16.59** GSS2014* An economic theory suggests that as people become richer they tend to have more children. Analyze the relationship between income (INCOME) and number of children (CHILDS) to test the theory.

**16.60** GSS2014* If one spouse works longer hours does this mean that the other spouse also works longer hours? Test the relationship between HRS1 and SPHRS1 to answer the question.

**16.61** GSS2014* Does staying in university longer mean that postpone having children? If so, we would expect a positive linear relationship between years of education (EDUC) and the age when one has his or her first child (AGEKDBORN). Test to determine whether there is sufficient statistical evidence of this relationship.

**16.62** GSS2014* Refer to Exercise 16.61. We would expect that more educated people would have fewer children. Analyze the relationship between education (EDUC) and number of children (CHILDS).

**16.63** GSS2014* Does the amount of education that one completes influence the amount of education his son or daughter completes? Test the relationship between a person's education (EDUC) and his or her father's education (PAEDUC).

**16.64** GSS2014* Refer to Exercise 16.63. Is there sufficient evidence of a positive linear relationship between the years of education (EDUC) and the years of education of one's mother (MAEDUC)?

**16.65** GSS2014* Are harder-working Americans more likely to urge to want government to reduce income differences? Test to determine whether there is sufficient evidence of a positive linear relationship between hours of work per week (HRS1) and position on whether government should reduce income differences (EQWLTH: 1 = Government should reduce income differences; 2, 3, 4, 5, 6, 7 = No government action).

## Survey of Consumer Finances Exercises

**16.66** SCF2013:\MC* We who educate would like to believe that people who have more education are more likely to do well professionally and financially. Fortunately, we have a number of surveys with real data to confirm our beliefs. Analyze the relationship between years of education (EDUC) of the head of middle-class households and income (INCOME).

a. Is there enough evidence to conclude that more education is related to more income?

b. Estimate the marginal change in income for each additional year of education.

**16.67** SCF2013:\MC* How does education (EDUC) affect financial success among the heads of middle-class households? Conduct a regression analysis and determine the following.

a. Is there evidence of a positive linear relationship between education and total financial assets (FIN)?

b. Estimate with 95% confidence the marginal increase in total financial assets for each additional year of education.

c. Find the coefficient of determination and describe its value.

**16.68** SCF2013:\MC* Do you need more years of education to get further into debt? This question can be answered by determining the relationship between number of years of education (EDUC) and household debt (DEBT). Undertake a regression analysis to determine the following.

a. Is there sufficient evidence to infer a linear relationship between the two variables?

b. Interpret the slope coefficient.

c. Calculate the coefficient of determination and describe what this statistic tells you about the linear relationship.

**16.69** SCF2013:\MC* An increasing number of people are attending colleges and universities. The effect of this trend is that younger people will be more educated than older people. Conduct a test to determine whether age (AGE) and years of education (EDUC) are negatively linearly related among the heads of middle-class households. Report the *p*-value of the test.

**16.70** SCF2013:\MC* It seems obvious that for people who take out student loans more years of education lead to larger student debt.

a. Conduct a test to determine whether there is a positive linear relationship between years of education (EDUC) and total value of student loans (EDN_INST).

b. Estimate the marginal increase in student debt for each additional year of education.

**16.71** SCF2013:\MC* Are younger middle-class people more likely to eat out at restaurants than older people? Conduct a test to determine whether there is sufficient evidence to infer that age (AGE) and amount spent on food away from home (FOODAWAY) are negatively related?

**16.72** SCF2013:\MC* Another way to interpret the results of Exercise 16.71 is that older people spend less on all food because their families are smaller (children have left home) or that they eat less expensive meals. If so, then we would expect that age (AGE) and amount spent on food at home FOODHOME) are also negatively related. Conduct a test to determine whether this is true. What is the *p*-value of the test?

**16.73** SCF2013:\MC* It takes many years to build up capital gains. Use a statistical analysis to determine whether there is enough evidence to conclude that as one grows older one increases unrealized capital gains (AGE, KGTOTAL). What is the *p*-value of the test?

**16.74** SCF2013:\MC* How much more do households have to spend on food when there are children living at home?

a. Conduct a test to determine whether there is evidence of a positive linear relationship between total annual amount spent on food at home (FOODHOME) and number of children in the household (KIDS).

b. Estimate the amount spent for each additional child.

**16.75** SCF2013:\MC* Repeat Exercise 16.74 for amount spent on food away from home (FOODAWAY).

## 16-5 Using the Regression Equation

Using the techniques in Section 16-4, we can assess how well the linear model fits the data. If the model fits satisfactorily, we can use it to forecast and estimate values of the dependent variable. To illustrate, suppose that in Example 16.2, the used-car dealer wanted to predict the selling price of a 3-year-old Toyota Camry with 40 (thousand) miles on the odometer. Using the regression equation, with $x = 40$, we get

$$\hat{y} = 17.250 - .0669x = 17.250 - 0.0669(40) = 14.574$$

We call this value the **point prediction**, and $\hat{y}$ is the point estimate or predicted value for $y$ when $x = 40$. Thus, the dealer would predict that the car would sell for $14,574.

By itself, however, the point prediction does not provide any information about how closely the value will match the true selling price. To discover that information, we must use an interval. In fact, we can use one of two intervals: the prediction interval of a particular value of $y$ or the confidence interval estimator of the expected value of $y$.

### 16-5a Predicting the Particular Value of y for a Given x

The first confidence interval we present is used whenever we want to predict a one-time occurrence for a particular value of the dependent variable when the independent variable is a given value $x_g$. This interval, often called the **prediction interval**, is calculated in the usual way (point estimator ± bound on the error of estimation). Here the point estimate for $y$ is $\hat{y}$, and the bound on the error of estimation is shown below.

**Prediction Interval**

$$\hat{y} \pm t_{\alpha/2,n-2} s_\varepsilon \sqrt{1 + \frac{1}{n} + \frac{(x_g - \bar{x})^2}{(n-1)s_x^2}}$$

where $x_g$ is the given value of $x$ and $\hat{y} = b_0 + b_1 x_g$

### 16-5b Estimating the Expected Value of y for a Given x

The conditions described in Section 16-3 imply that, for a given value of $x$, there is a population of values of $y$ whose mean is

$$E(y) = \beta_0 + \beta_1 x$$

To estimate the mean of $y$ or long-run average value of $y$, we would use the following interval referred to simply as the confidence interval. Again, the point estimator is $\hat{y}$, but the bound on the error of estimation is different from the prediction interval shown below.

**Confidence Interval Estimator of the Expected Value of y**

$$\hat{y} \pm t_{\alpha/2,n-2} s_\varepsilon \sqrt{\frac{1}{n} + \frac{(x_g - \bar{x})^2}{(n-1)s_x^2}}$$

Unlike the formula for the prediction interval, this formula does not include the 1 under the square-root sign. As a result, the **confidence interval estimate of the expected value of $y$** will be narrower than the prediction interval for the same given value of $x$ and confidence level. This is because there is less error in estimating a mean value as opposed to predicting an individual value.

## EXAMPLE 16.7 Predicting the Price and Estimating the Mean Price of Used Toyota Camrys

a. A used-car dealer is about to bid on a 3-year-old Toyota Camry equipped with all the standard features and with 40,000 ($x_g = 40$) miles on the odometer. To help him decide how much to bid, he needs to predict the selling price.

b. The used-car dealer mentioned in part (a) has an opportunity to bid on a lot of cars offered by a rental company. The rental company has 250 Toyota Camrys all equipped with standard features. All the cars in this lot have about 40,000 ($x_g = 40$) miles on their odometers. The dealer would like an estimate of the selling price of all the cars in the lot.

SOLUTION:

### IDENTIFY

a. The dealer would like to predict the selling price of a single car. Thus, he must employ the prediction interval

$$\hat{y} \pm t_{\alpha/2,n-2}s_\varepsilon\sqrt{1 + \frac{1}{n} + \frac{(x_g - \bar{x})^2}{(n-1)s_x^2}}$$

b. The dealer wants to determine the mean price of a large lot of cars, so he needs to calculate the confidence interval estimator of the expected value:

$$\hat{y} \pm t_{\alpha/2,n-2}s_\varepsilon\sqrt{\frac{1}{n} + \frac{(x_g - \bar{x})^2}{(n-1)s_x^2}}$$

Technically, this formula is used for infinitely large populations. However, we can interpret our problem as attempting to determine the average selling price of all Toyota Camrys equipped as described above, all with 40,000 miles on the odometer. The crucial factor in part (b) is the need to estimate the mean price of a number of cars. We arbitrarily select a 95% confidence level.

### COMPUTE

MANUALLY:

From previous calculations, we have the following:

$$\hat{y} = 17.250 - .0669(40) = 14.574$$

$$s_\varepsilon = .3265$$

$s_x^2 = 43.509$

$\bar{x} = 36.011$

From Table 4 in Appendix B, we find

$$t_{\alpha/2} = t_{.025,98} \approx t_{.025,100} = 1.984$$

a. The 95% prediction interval is

$$\hat{y} \pm t_{\alpha/2,n-2} s_\varepsilon \sqrt{1 + \frac{1}{n} + \frac{(x_g - \bar{x})^2}{(n-1)s_x^2}}$$

$$= 14.574 \pm 1.984 \times .3265 \sqrt{1 + \frac{1}{100} + \frac{(40 - 36.011)^2}{(100-1)(43.509)}}$$

$$= 14.574 \pm .652$$

The lower and upper limits of the prediction interval are $13,922 and $15,226, respectively.

b. The 95% confidence interval estimator of the mean price is

$$\hat{y} \pm t_{\alpha/2,n-2} s_\varepsilon \sqrt{\frac{1}{n} + \frac{(x_g - \bar{x})^2}{(n-1)s_x^2}}$$

$$= 14.574 \pm 1.984 \times .3265 \sqrt{\frac{1}{100} + \frac{(40 - 36.011)^2}{(100-1)(43.509)}}$$

$$= 14.574 \pm .076$$

The lower and upper limits of the confidence interval estimate of the expected value are $14,498 and 14,650, respectively.

## EXCEL Workbook

| | A | B | C | D | E |
|---|---|---|---|---|---|
| 1 | Predict & Estimate of y | | | | |
| 2 | | | | | |
| 3 | Sample mean of x | 36.011 | Confidence Interval Estimate | | |
| 4 | Sample variance of x | 43.509 | 14.57 | ± | 0.076 |
| 5 | Sample size | 100 | Lower confidence limit | | 14.498 |
| 6 | Regression coefficients | | Upper confidence limit | | 14.650 |
| 7 | Intercept | 17.25 | | | |
| 8 | Slope | -0.0669 | Prediction Interval | | |
| 9 | SSE | 10.45 | 14.57 | ± | 0.652 |
| 10 | Confidence level | 0.95 | Lower prediction limit | | 13.922 |
| 11 | Given value of x | 40 | Upper prediction limit | | 15.226 |

*INSTRUCTIONS*

1. Calculate the mean and variance of the independent variable x.
2. Conduct a regression analysis.
3. Open the **Estimators Workbook** and click the **Prediction** tab.
4. Input the sample mean and variance of $X$, the sample size, the regression coefficients a and b, SSE, the confidence level and the given value of $X$.

**XLSTAT**

| | A | B | C | D | E | F |
|---|---|---|---|---|---|---|
| 56 | Odometer | Pred(Price) | Lower bound 95% (Mean) | Upper bound 95% (Mean) | Lower bound 95% | Upper bound 95% |
| 57 | 40.000 | 14.574 | 14.498 | 14.650 | 13.922 | 15.227 |

*INSTRUCTIONS*

1. Conduct a regression analysis. Type the given value of $x$ in any empty cell.
2. Click **Options** and specify the **Confidence interval(%)** (95)
3. Click **Prediction**. In the **X/Explanatory variables** box check **Quantitative** and type the cell containing the given value of $x$. Click **OK.**

**INTERPRET**

We predict that one car will sell for between $13,925 and $15,226. The average selling price of the population of 3-year-old Toyota Camrys is estimated to lie between $14,498 and $14,650. Because predicting the selling price of one car is more difficult than estimating the mean selling price of all similar cars, the prediction interval is wider than the interval estimate of the expected value.

## 16-5c Effect of the Given Value of x on the Intervals

Calculating the two intervals for various values of $x$ results in the graph in Figure 16.8. Notice that both intervals are represented by curved lines. This is because the farther the given value of $x$ is from $\bar{x}$, the greater the estimated error becomes. This part of the estimated error is measured by

$$\frac{(x_g - \bar{x})^2}{(n - 1)s_x^2}$$

which appears in both the prediction interval and the interval estimate of the expected value.

FIGURE **16.8** **Interval Estimate and Prediction Interval**

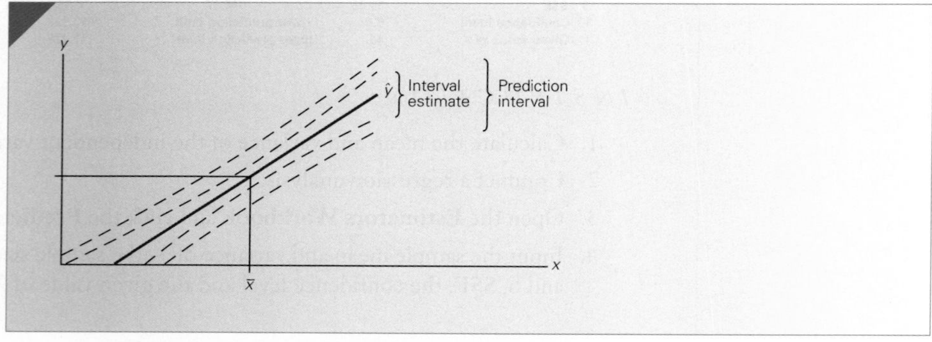

## EXERCISES

**16.76** Briefly describe the difference between predicting a value of $y$ and estimating the expected value of $y$.

**16.77** Will the prediction interval always be wider than the estimation interval for the same value of the independent variable? Briefly explain.

**16.78** Use the regression equation in Exercise 16.2 to predict with 90% confidence the sales when the advertising budget is $80,000.

**16.79** Estimate with 90% confidence the mean monthly number of housing starts when the mortgage interest rate is 7% in Exercise 16.3.

**16.80** Refer to Exercise 16.4.
a. Predict with 90% confidence the number of pounds overweight for a child who watches 35 hours of television per week.
b. Estimate with 90% confidence the mean number of pounds overweight for children who watch 35 hours of television per week.

**16.81** Refer to Exercise 16.5. Predict with 90% confidence the number of beers to be sold when the temperature is 75 degrees.

*Exercises 16.82–16.94 require the use of a computer and software. The answers may be calculated manually. See Appendix A for the sample statistics.*

**16.82** Refer to Exercise 16.6.
a. Predict with 95% confidence the memory test score of a viewer who watches a 30-second commercial.
b. Estimate with 95% confidence the mean memory test score of people who watch 30-second commercials.

**16.83** Refer to Exercise 16.7.
a. Predict with 95% confidence the selling price of a 1,200 sq.ft. condominium on the 20 th floor.
b. Estimate with 99% confidence the average selling price of a 1,200 sq.ft. condominium on the 15th floor.

**16.84** Refer to Exercise 16.8. Estimate with 90% confidence the mean amount of time for 40-year-old Americans to complete the census.

**16.85** Refer to Exercise 16.9. The company has just hired a 22-year-old telemarketer. Predict with 95% confidence how long he will stay with the company.

**16.86** Refer to Exercise 16.10. Predict with 95% confidence the number of sick days for individuals who smoke on average 40 cigarettes per day.

**16.87** Refer to Exercise 16.11.
a. Predict with 95% confidence the percentage loss due to fire for a house that is 8 miles away from the nearest fire station.
b. Estimate with 95% confidence the average percentage loss due to fire for houses that are 5 miles away from the nearest fire station.

**16.88** Refer to Exercise 16.12. Estimate with 95% confidence the mean price of 60,000 sq.ft. apartment buildings.

**16.89** Refer to Exercise 16.13. Predict with 99% confidence the price of a 1999 24-ft. Sea Ray cruiser with 400 hours of engine use.

**16.90** Refer to Exercise 16.14. Estimate with 90% confidence the mean electricity consumption for households with four occupants.

**16.91** Refer to Exercise 16.15. Predict the food budget of a family whose household income is $60,000. Use a 90% confidence level.

**16.92** Refer to Exercise 16.16. Predict with 95% confidence the monthly office rent in a city when the vacancy rate is 8%.

**16.93** Refer to Exercise 16.17.
a. Estimate with 95% confidence the mean annual income of 6'2" (74 inches)-tall men.
b. Suppose that an individual is 5'8" (68 inches). Predict with 95% confidence his annual income.

**16.94** Refer to Exercise 16.18. Estimate with 95% confidence the mean percentage of defectives for workers who score 80 on the dexterity test.

**16.95** Xr16-45 Refer to Exercise 16.45. Estimate with 95% confidence the mean time spent watching or reading news on the Internet for the population of people who have completed 12 years of education.

**16.96** Xr03-70 Refer to Exercise 16.46. Use a prediction interval with 90% confidence to predict the auction selling price of one Canada 1925 nickel with a grade of 40.

**16.97** Xr16-47 Refer to Exercise 16.47. Estimate with 90% confidence the mean number of days watching the national news on television for the population of 70-year-olds.

**16.98** Xr16-48 Refer to Exercise 16.48. Predict with 90% confidence how definite is the intention to vote for one 50-year-old.

**16.99** Xr03-71 Refer to Exercise 16.49. The temperature is 80 degrees. Predict with 95% confidence how far the golfer's next drive will travel.

**16.100** Pick any one of the previous five exercises and briefly describe why the intervals are so wide.

## General Social Survey Exercises

*For Exercises 16.101 to 16.111, construct a prediction interval and a confidence interval estimate of the expected value of the dependent variable for the given value of the independent variable.* ***Use a 95% confidence level.***

**16.101** GSS2014* Refer to Exercise 16.51. Annual income of someone who is 45 years old.

**16.102** GSS2014* Refer to Exercise 16.52. Number of hours of television watching per day for people with 12 years of education.

**16.103** GSS2014* Refer to Exercise 16.53. Income of someone who works 40 hours per week.

**16.104** GSS2014* Refer to Exercise 16.54. Number of hours of *t* work per week for some who is 60 years old.

**16.105** GSS2014* Refer to Exercise 16.55. Number of hours of television per day of a 65-year-old.

**16.106** GSS2014* Refer to Exercise 16.56. Total family income of a family with four earners.

**16.107** GSS2014* Refer to Exercise 16.59. Income of someone with one child.

**16.108** GSS2014* Refer to Exercise 16.62. Number of children of a person with 11 years of education.

**16.109** GSS2014* Refer to Exercise 16.63. Number of years of education of a person whose father had 15 years of education.

**16.110** GSS2014* Refer to Exercise 16.64. Number of years of education of a person whose mother had 20 years of education.

**16.111** GSS2014* Refer to Exercise 16.65. Position on the issue of whether government should reduce income differences of someone who works 50 hours per week.

**16.112** Pick any 1 (or more) of the 11 exercises above and briefly describe why the prediction interval is so wide.

# 16-6 / Regression Diagnostics—I

In Section 16-3, we described the required conditions for the validity of regression analysis. Simply put, the error variable must be normally distributed with a constant variance, and the errors must be independent of each other. In this section, we show how to diagnose violations. In addition, we discuss how to deal with observations that are unusually large or small. Such observations must be investigated to determine whether an error was made in recording them.

## 16-6a Residual Analysis

Most departures from required conditions can be diagnosed by examining the residuals, which we discussed in Section 16-4. Most computer packages allow you to output the values of the residuals and apply various graphical and statistical techniques to this variable.

We can also compute the standardized residuals. We standardize residuals in the same way we standardize all variables, by subtracting the mean and dividing by the standard deviation. The mean of the residuals is 0, and because the standard deviation

$\sigma_\varepsilon$ is unknown, we must estimate its value. The simplest estimate is the standard error of estimate $s_\varepsilon$. Thus,

$$\text{Standardized residuals for point } i = \frac{e_i}{s_\varepsilon}$$

## EXCEL Data Analysis

Excel calculates the standardized residuals by dividing the residuals by the standard deviation of the residuals. (The difference between the standard error of estimate and the standard deviation of the residuals is that in the formula of the former the denominator is $n - 2$, whereas in the formula for the latter, the denominator is $n - 1$.)

Part of the printout (we show only the first five and last five values) for Example 16.2 follows.

| | A | B | C | D |
|---|---|---|---|---|
| 1 | RESIDUAL OUTPUT | | | |
| 2 | | | | |
| 3 | *Observation* | *Predicted Price* | *Residuals* | *Standard Residuals* |
| 4 | 1 | 14.748 | −0.148 | −0.456 |
| 5 | 2 | 14.253 | −0.153 | −0.472 |
| 6 | 3 | 14.186 | −0.186 | −0.574 |
| 7 | 4 | 15.183 | 0.417 | 1.285 |
| 8 | 5 | 15.129 | 0.471 | 1.449 |
| 9 | | | | |
| 10 | | | | |
| 11 | | | | |
| 12 | | | | |
| 13 | 96 | 14.828 | −0.028 | −0.087 |
| 14 | 97 | 14.962 | −0.362 | −1.115 |
| 15 | 98 | 15.029 | −0.529 | −1.628 |
| 16 | 99 | 14.628 | 0.072 | 0.222 |
| 17 | 100 | 14.815 | −0.515 | −1.585 |

### *INSTRUCTIONS*

Proceed with the three steps of regression analysis described on page 640. Before clicking **OK**, select **Residuals** and **Standardized Residuals**. The predicted values, residuals, and standardized residuals will be printed.

## XLSTAT

| | A | B | C | D | E | F |
|---|---|---|---|---|---|---|
| 1 | Predictions and residuals (Price): | | | | | |
| 2 | Observation | Odometer | Price | Pred(Price) | Residual | Std. residual |
| 3 | Obs1 | 37.400 | 14.600 | 14.748 | -0.148 | -0.454 |
| 4 | Obs2 | 44.800 | 14.100 | 14.253 | -0.153 | -0.470 |
| 5 | Obs3 | 45.800 | 14.000 | 14.186 | -0.186 | -0.571 |
| 6 | Obs4 | 30.900 | 15.600 | 15.183 | 0.417 | 1.278 |
| 7 | Obs5 | 31.700 | 15.600 | 15.129 | 0.471 | 1.442 |
| 98 | | | | | | |
| 99 | | | | | | |
| 100 | Obs96 | 36.200 | 14.800 | 14.828 | -0.028 | -0.087 |
| 101 | Obs97 | 34.200 | 14.600 | 14.962 | -0.362 | -1.109 |
| 102 | Obs98 | 33.200 | 14.500 | 15.029 | -0.529 | -1.620 |
| 103 | Obs99 | 39.200 | 14.700 | 14.628 | 0.072 | 0.221 |
| 104 | Obs100 | 36.400 | 14.300 | 14.815 | -0.515 | -1.577 |

### *INSTRUCTIONS*

1. Conduct a regression analysis.
2. Click **Outputs** and check **Predictions and residuals.** Click **OK.**

An analysis of the residuals will allow us to determine whether the error variable is nonnormal, whether the error variance is constant, and whether the errors are independent. We begin with nonnormality.

## 16-6b Nonnormality

As we've done throughout this book, we check for normality by drawing the histogram of the residuals. Figure 16.9 is Excel's version (XLSTAT's is similar). As you can see, the histogram is bell shaped, leading us to believe that the error is normally distributed.

FIGURE **16.9** **Histogram of Residuals for Example 16.2**

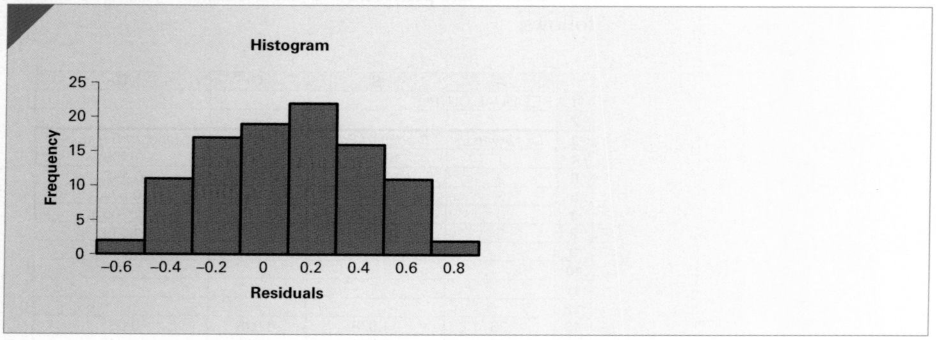

## 16-6c Heteroscedasticity

The variance of the error variable $\sigma_\varepsilon^2$ is required to be constant. When this requirement is violated, the condition is called **heteroscedasticity**. (You can impress friends and relatives by using this term. If you can't pronounce it, try **homoscedasticity**, which refers to the condition where the requirement is satisfied.) One method of diagnosing heteroscedasticity is to plot the residuals against the predicted values of $y$. We then look for a change in the spread of the plotted points.* Figure 16.10 describes such a situation. Notice that in this illustration, $\sigma_\varepsilon^2$ appears to be small when $\hat{y}$ is small and large when $\hat{y}$ is large. Of course, many other patterns could be used to depict this problem.

FIGURE **16.10** **Plot of Residuals Depicting Heteroscedasticity**

*The online appendix Szroeter's Test describes a test for heteroscedasticity.

Figure 16.11 illustrates a case in which $\sigma_\varepsilon^2$ is constant. As a result, there is no apparent change in the variation of the residuals.

FIGURE **16.11** **Plot of Residuals Depicting Homoscedasticity**

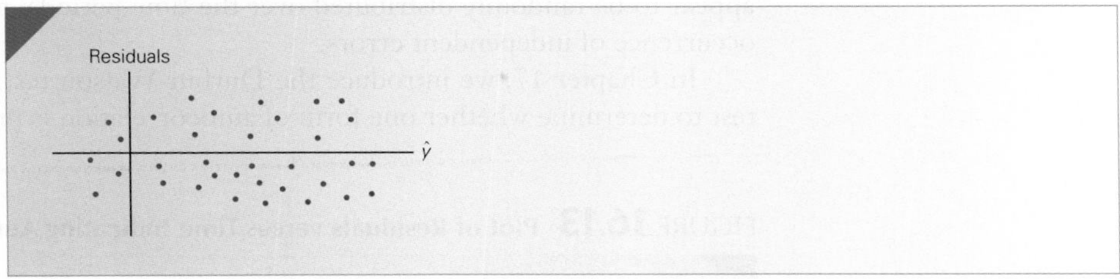


Excel's plot of the residuals versus the predicted values of $y$ for Example 16.2 is shown in Figure 16.12. There is no sign of heteroscedasticity.

FIGURE **16.12** **Plot of Predicted Values versus Residuals for Example 16.2**

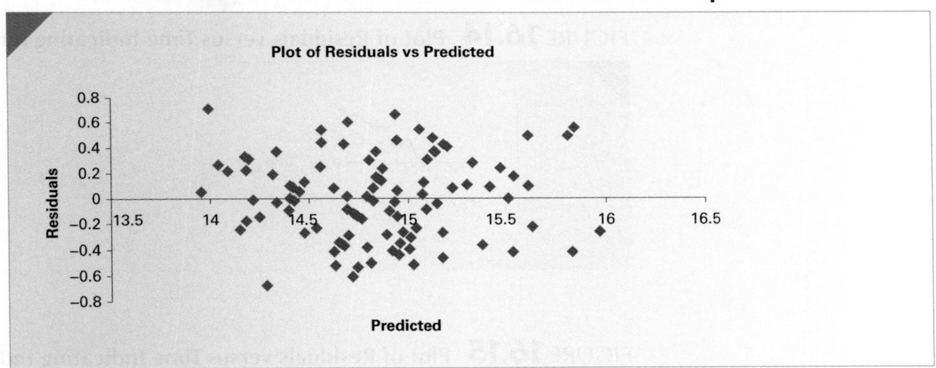


## 16-6d Nonindependence of the Error Variable

In Chapter 3, we briefly described the difference between cross-sectional and time-series data. Cross-sectional data are observations made at approximately the same time, whereas a time series is a set of observations taken at successive points of time. The data in Example 16.2 are cross-sectional because all of the prices and odometer readings were taken at about the same time. If we were to observe the auction price of cars every week for, say, a year, that would constitute a time series.

Condition 4 states that the values of the error variable are independent. When the data are time series, the errors often are correlated. Error terms that are correlated over time are said to be **autocorrelated** or **serially correlated**. For example, suppose that, in an analysis of the relationship between annual gross profits and some independent variable, we observe the gross profits for the years 1991 to 2010. The observed values of $y$ are denoted $y_1, y_2, \ldots y_{20}$, where $y_1$ is the gross profit for 1991, $y_2$ is the gross profit for 1992, and so on. If we label the residuals $e_1, e_2, \ldots, e_{20}$, then—if the independence requirement is satisfied—there should be no relationship among the residuals. However, if the residuals are related, it is likely that autocorrelation exists.

We can often detect autocorrelation by graphing the residuals against the time periods. If a pattern emerges, it is likely that the independence requirement is violated. Figures 16.13 (alternating positive and negative residuals) and 16.14 (increasing residuals) exhibit patterns indicating autocorrelation. (Notice that we joined the points to make it easier to see the patterns.) Figure 16.15 shows no pattern (the residuals appear to be randomly distributed over the time periods) and thus likely represent the occurrence of independent errors.

In Chapter 17, we introduce the Durbin-Watson test, which is another statistical test to determine whether one form of autocorrelation is present.

FIGURE **16.13** **Plot of Residuals versus Time Indicating Autocorrelation (Alternating)**

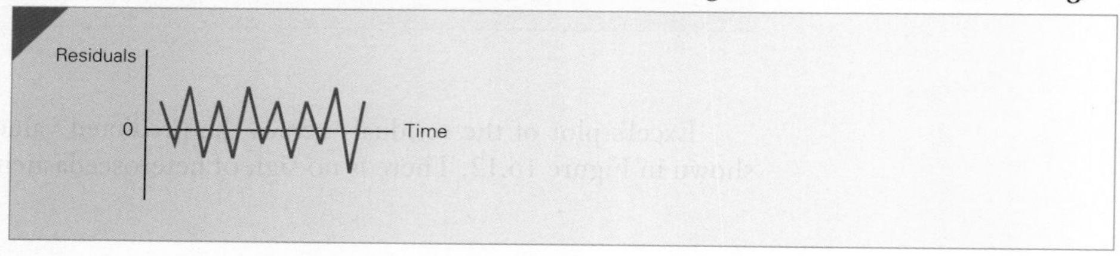


FIGURE **16.14** **Plot of Residuals versus Time Indicating Autocorrelation (Increasing)**

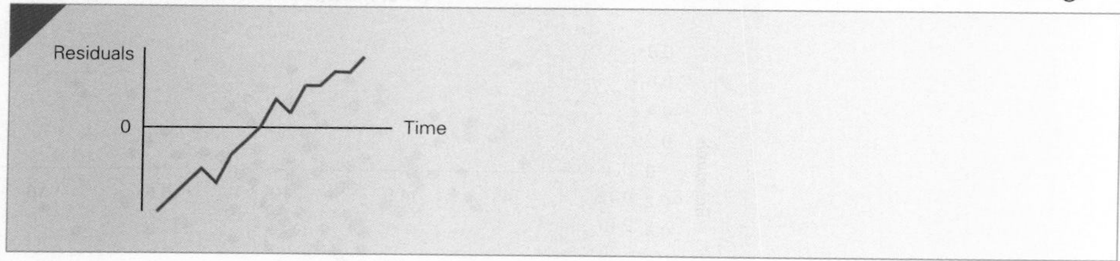


FIGURE **16.15** **Plot of Residuals versus Time Indicating Independence**

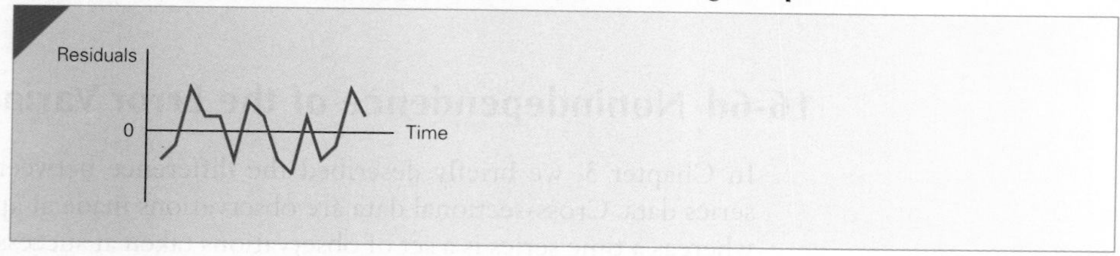


## 16-6e Outliers

An **outlier** is an observation that is unusually small or unusually large. To illustrate, consider Example 16.2, where the range of odometer readings was 19.1 to 49.2 thousand miles. If we had observed a value of 5,000 miles, we would identify that point as an outlier. We need to investigate several possibilities.

1. There was an error in recording the value. To detect an error, we would check the point or points in question. In Example 16.2, we could check the car's odometer to determine whether a mistake was made. If so, we would correct it before proceeding with the regression analysis.

2. The point should not have been included in the sample. Occasionally, measurements are taken from experimental units that do not belong with the sample. We can check to ensure that the car with the 5,000-mile odometer reading was actually 3 years old. We should also investigate the possibility that the odometer was rolled back. In either case, the outlier should be discarded.

3. The observation was simply an unusually large or small value that belongs to the sample and that was recorded properly. In this case, we would do nothing to the outlier. It would be judged to be valid.

Outliers can be identified from the scatter diagram. Figure 16.16 depicts a scatter diagram with one outlier. The statistics practitioner should check to determine whether the measurement was recorded accurately and whether the experimental unit should be included in the sample.

FIGURE **16.16** **Scatter Diagram with One Outlier**

The standardized residuals also can be helpful in identifying outliers. Large absolute values of the standardized residuals should be investigated.

## 16-6f Influential Observations

Occasionally, in a regression analysis, one or more observations have a large influence on the statistics. Figure 16.17 describes such an observation and the resulting least squares line. If the point had not been included, the least squares line in Figure 16.18 would have been produced. Obviously, one point has had an enormous influence on the results. Influential points can be identified by the scatter diagram. The point may be an outlier and as such must be checked.

FIGURE **16.17** **Scatter Diagram with One Influential Observation**

FIGURE **16.18** **Scatter Diagram without the Influential Observation**

### 16-6g Procedure for Regression Diagnostics

The order of the material presented in this chapter is dictated by pedagogical requirements. Consequently, we presented the least squares method of assessing the model's fit, predicting and estimating using the regression equation, coefficient of correlation, and finally, the regression diagnostics. In a practical application, the regression diagnostics would be conducted earlier in the process. It is appropriate to investigate violations of the required conditions when the model is assessed and before using the regression equation to predict and estimate. The following steps describe the entire process. (In Chapter 18, we will discuss model building, for which the following steps represent only a part of the entire procedure.)

1. Develop a model that has a theoretical basis; that is, for the dependent variable in question, find an independent variable that you believe is linearly related to it.
2. Gather data for the two variables. Ideally, conduct a controlled experiment. If that is not possible, collect observational data.
3. Draw the scatter diagram to determine whether a linear model appears to be appropriate. Identify possible outliers.
4. Determine the regression equation.
5. Calculate the residuals and check the required conditions:
   Is the error variable nonnormal?
   Is the variance constant?
   Are the errors independent?
   Check the outliers and influential observations.
6. Assess the model's fit.
   Compute the standard error of estimate.
   Test to determine whether there is a linear relationship. (Test $\beta_1$ or $\rho$.)
   Compute the coefficient of determination.
7. If the model fits the data, use the regression equation to predict a particular value of the dependent variable or estimate its mean (or both).

## EXERCISES

**16.113** You are given the following six points:

| $x$ | −5 | −2 | 0 | 3 | 4 | 7 |
|---|---|---|---|---|---|---|
| $y$ | 15 | 9 | 7 | 6 | 4 | 1 |

a. Determine the regression equation.
b. Use the regression equation to determine the predicted values of $y$.
c. Use the predicted and actual values of $y$ to calculate the residuals.
d. Compute the standardized residuals.
e. Identify possible outliers.

**16.114** Refer to Exercise 16.2. Calculate the residuals and the predicted values of $y$.

**16.115** Calculate the residuals and predicted values of $y$ in Exercise 16.3.

**16.116** Refer to Exercise 16.4.
a. Calculate the residuals.
b. Calculate the predicted values of $y$.
c. Plot the residuals (on the vertical axis) and the predicted values of $y$.

**16.117** Calculate and plot the residuals and predicted values of $y$ for Exercise 16.5.

*The following exercises require the use of a computer and software.*

**16.118** Refer to Exercise 16.6.

a. Determine the residuals and the standardized residuals.
b. Draw the histogram of the residuals. Does it appear that the errors are normally distributed? Explain.
c. Identify possible outliers.
d. Plot the residuals versus the predicted values of $y$. Does it appear that heteroscedasticity is a problem? Explain.

**16.119** Refer to Exercise 16.7.

a. Does it appear that the errors are normally distributed? Explain.
b. Does it appear that heteroscedasticity is a problem? Explain.

**16.120** Are the required conditions satisfied in Exercise 16.8?

**16.121** Refer to Exercise 16.9.

a. Determine the residuals and the standardized residuals.
b. Draw the histogram of the residuals. Does it appear that the errors are normally distributed? Explain.
c. Identify possible outliers.
d. Plot the residuals versus the predicted values of $y$. Does it appear that heteroscedasticity is a problem? Explain.

**16.122** Refer to Exercise 16.10. Are the required conditions satisfied?

**16.123** Refer to Exercise 16.11.

a. Determine the residuals and the standardized residuals.
b. Draw the histogram of the residuals. Does it appear that the errors are normally distributed? Explain.
c. Identify possible outliers.
d. Plot the residuals versus the predicted values of $y$. Does it appear that heteroscedasticity is a problem? Explain.

**16.124** Check the required conditions for Exercise 16.12.

**16.125** Refer to Exercise 16.13. Are the required conditions satisfied?

**16.126** Refer to Exercise 16.14.

a. Determine the residuals and the standardized residuals.
b. Draw the histogram of the residuals. Does it appear that the errors are normally distributed? Explain.
c. Identify possible outliers.
d. Plot the residuals versus the predicted values of $y$. Does it appear that heteroscedasticity is a problem? Explain.

**16.127** Are the required conditions satisfied for Exercise 16.15?

**16.128** Check to ensure that the required conditions for Exercise 16.16 are satisfied.

**16.129** Are the required conditions satisfied for Exercise 16.17?

**16.130** Perform a complete diagnostic analysis for Exercise 16.18 to determine whether the required conditions are satisfied.

## CHAPTER SUMMARY

Simple linear regression and correlation are techniques for analyzing the relationship between two interval variables. Regression analysis assumes that the two variables are linearly related. The least squares method produces estimates of the intercept and the slope of the regression line. Considerable effort is expended in assessing how well the linear model fits the data. We calculate the standard error of estimate, which is an estimate of the standard deviation of the error variable. We test the slope to determine whether there is sufficient evidence of a linear relationship. The strength of the linear association is measured by the coefficient of determination. When the model provides a good fit, we can use it to predict the particular value and to estimate the expected value of the dependent variable. We can also use the Pearson correlation coefficient to measure and test the relationship between two bivariate normally distributed variables. We completed this chapter with a discussion of how to diagnose violations of the required conditions.

## IMPORTANT TERMS:

Regression analysis 632
Dependent variable 632
Independent variable 632
Deterministic model 633
Probabilistic model 633
Error variable 634
First-order linear model 634
Simple linear regression model 634
Least squares method 635
Residuals 637
Sum of squares for error 637
Standard error of estimate 647
Coefficient of determination 653
Pearson coefficient of correlation 657
Point prediction 665
Prediction interval 665
Confidence interval estimate of the expected value of $y$ 666
Heteroscedasticity 672
Homoscedasticity 672
Autocorrelation 673
Serial correlation 673

## SYMBOLS:

| Symbol | Pronounced | Represents |
|---|---|---|
| $\beta_0$ | Beta sub zero or beta zero | $y$-intercept |
| $\beta_1$ | Beta sub one or beta one | Slope coefficient |
| $\varepsilon$ | Epsilon | Error variable |
| $\hat{y}$ | $y$ hat | Fitted or calculated value of $y$ |
| $b_0$ | $b$ sub zero or $b$ zero | Sample $y$-intercept coefficient |
| $b_1$ | $b$ sub one or $b$ one | Sample slope coefficient |
| $\sigma_\varepsilon$ | Sigma sub epsilon or sigma epsilon | Standard deviation of error variable |
| $s_\varepsilon$ | $s$ sub epsilon or $s$ epsilon | Standard error of estimate |
| $s_{b_1}$ | $s$ sub $b$ sub one or $s$ $b$ one | Standard error of $b_1$ |
| $R^2$ | $R$ squared | Coefficient of determination |
| $x_g$ | $x$ sub $g$ or $x$ $g$ | Given value of $x$ |
| $\rho$ | Rho | Pearson coefficient of correlation |
| $r$ | | Sample coefficient of correlation |
| $e_i$ | $e$ sub $i$ or $e$ $i$ | Residual of $i$th point |

## FORMULAS:

Sample slope

$$b_1 = \frac{s_{xy}}{s_x^2}$$

Sample $y$-intercept

$$b_0 = \bar{y} - b_1\bar{x}$$

Sum of squares for error

$$\text{SSE} = \sum_{i=1}^{n}(y_i - \hat{y}_i)^2$$

Standard error of estimate

$$s_\varepsilon = \sqrt{\frac{\text{SSE}}{n-2}}$$

Test statistic for the slope

$$t = \frac{b_1 - \beta_1}{s_{b_1}}$$

Standard error of $b_1$

$$s_{b_1} = \frac{s_\varepsilon}{\sqrt{(n-1)s_x^2}}$$

Coefficient of determination

$$R^2 = \frac{s_{xy}^2}{s_x^2 s_y^2} = 1 - \frac{\text{SSE}}{\sum(y_i - \bar{y})^2}$$

Prediction interval

$$\hat{y} \pm t_{\alpha/2,n-2} s_\varepsilon \sqrt{1 + \frac{1}{n} + \frac{(x_g - \bar{x})^2}{(n-1)s_x^2}}$$

Confidence interval estimator of the expected value of $y$

$$\hat{y} \pm t_{\alpha/2,n-2} s_\varepsilon \sqrt{\frac{1}{n} + \frac{(x_g - \bar{x})^2}{(n-1)s_x^2}}$$

Sample coefficient of correlation

$$r = \frac{s_{xy}}{s_x s_y}$$

Test statistic for testing $\rho = 0$

$$t = r\sqrt{\frac{n-2}{1-r^2}}$$

## COMPUTER OUTPUT AND INSTRUCTIONS:

| Technique | Excel |
|---|---|
| Regression | 640 |
| Correlation | 659 |
| Prediction interval | 667 |
| Regression diagnostics | 671 |

# CHAPTER EXERCISES

*The following exercises require the use of a computer and software. The answers to some of the questions may be calculated manually. See Appendix A for the sample statistics.* ***Conduct all tests of hypotheses at the 5% significance level.***

**16.131** Xr16-131 The manager of Colonial Furniture has been reviewing weekly advertising expenditures. During the past 6 months, all advertisements for the store have appeared in the local newspaper. The number of ads per week has varied from one to seven. The store's sales staff has been tracking the number of customers who enter the store each week. The number of ads and the number of customers per week for the past 26 weeks were recorded.

a. Determine the sample regression line.
b. Interpret the coefficients.
c. Can the manager infer that the larger the number of ads, the larger the number of customers?
d. Find and interpret the coefficient of determination.
e. In your opinion, is it a worthwhile exercise to use the regression equation to predict the number of customers who will enter the store, given that Colonial intends to advertise five times in the newspaper? If so, find a 95% prediction interval. If not, explain why not.

**16.132** Xr16-132 The president of a company that manufactures car seats has been concerned about the number and cost of machine breakdowns. The problem is that the machines are old and becoming quite unreliable. However, the cost of replacing them is quite high, and the president is not certain that the cost can be made up in today's slow economy. To help make a decision about replacement, he gathered data about last month's costs for repairs and the ages (in months) of the plant's 20 welding machines.

a. Find the sample regression line.
b. Interpret the coefficients.
c. Determine the coefficient of determination, and discuss what this statistic tells you.
d. Conduct a test to determine whether the age of a machine and its monthly cost of repair are linearly related.
e. Is the fit of the simple linear model good enough to allow the president to predict the monthly repair cost of a welding machine that is 120 months old? If so, find a 95% prediction interval. If not, explain why not.

**16.133** Xr16-133 An agronomist wanted to investigate the factors that determine crop yield. Accordingly, she undertook an experiment wherein a farm was divided into 30 one-acre plots. The amount of fertilizer applied to each plot was varied. Corn was then planted, and the amount of corn harvested at the end of the season was recorded.

a. Find the sample regression line, and interpret the coefficients.

b. Can the agronomist conclude that there is a linear relationship between the amount of fertilizer and the crop yield?
c. Find the coefficient of determination, and interpret its value.
d. Does the simple linear model appear to be a useful tool in predicting crop yield from the amount of fertilizer applied? If so, produce a 95% prediction interval of the crop yield when 300 pounds of fertilizer are applied. If not, explain why not.

**16.134** Xr16-134 Every year, the U.S. Federal Trade Commission rates cigarette brands according to their levels of tar and nicotine, substances that are hazardous to smokers' health. Additionally, the commission includes the amount of carbon monoxide, which is a by-product of burning tobacco that seriously affects the heart. A random sample of 25 brands was taken.

a. Are the levels of tar and nicotine linearly related?
b. Are the levels of nicotine and carbon monoxide linearly related?

**16.135** Xr16-135 Some critics of television complain that the amount of violence shown on television contributes to violence in our society. Others point out that television also contributes to the high level of obesity among children. We may have to add financial problems to the list. A sociologist theorized that people who watch television frequently are exposed to many commercials, which in turn leads them to buy more, finally resulting in increasing debt. To test this belief, a sample of 430 families was drawn. For each, the total debt and the number of hours the television is turned on per week were recorded. Perform a statistical procedure to help test the theory.

**16.136** Xr16-136 The analysis that the human resources manager performed in Exercise 16.18 indicated that the dexterity test is not a predictor of job performance. However, before discontinuing the test, he decided that the problem is that the statistical analysis was flawed because it examined the relationship between test score and job performance only for those who scored well in the test. (Recall that only those who scored above 70 were hired; applicants who achieved scores below 70 were not hired.) The manager decided to perform another statistical analysis. A sample of 50 job applicants who scored above 50 were hired, and as before the workers' performance was measured. The test scores and percentages of nondefective computers produced were recorded. On the basis of these data, should the manager discontinue the dexterity tests?

**16.137** Xr16-137 Mutual funds minimize risks by diversifying the investments they make. There are mutual funds that specialize in particular types of investments. For example, the TD Precious Metal Mutual Fund buys shares in gold mining companies. The value of this mutual fund depends on a number of factors related to the companies in which the fund invests as well as on the price of gold. To investigate the relationship between the value of the fund and the price of gold, an MBA student gathered the daily fund price and the daily price of gold for a 28-day period. Can we infer from these data that there is a positive linear relationship between the value of the fund and the price of gold? (The authors are grateful to Jim Wheat for writing this exercise.)

**16.138** Xr03-67 (Exercise 3.67 revisited) A very large contribution to profits for a movie theater is the sale of popcorn, soft drinks, and candy. A movie theater manager speculated that the longer the time between showings of a movie, the greater the sales of concessions. To acquire more information the manager conducted an experiment. For a month he varied the amount of time between movie showings and calculated the sales. Can the manager conclude that when the times between movies increase so do sales?

**16.139** Xr16-139* A computer dating service typically asks for various pieces of information such as height, weight, income, and so on. One such service requested the length of index fingers. The only plausible reason for this request is to act as a proxy on height. Women have often complained that men lie about their heights. If there is a strong relationship between heights and index fingers, the information can be used to "correct" false claims about heights. To test the relationship between the two variables researchers gathered the heights and lengths of index fingers (in centimeters) of 121 students.

a. Graph the relationship between the two variables.
b. Is there sufficient evidence to infer that height and length of index fingers are linearly related?
c. Predict with 95% confidence the height of someone whose index finger is 6.5 cm long. Is this prediction likely to be useful? Explain. (The authors would like to thank Howard Waner for supplying the problem and data.)

*The following exercises employ data files associated with two previous exercises.*

**16.140** Xr12-31* In addition to the data recorded for Exercises 12.31 and 13.227, we recorded the grade point average of the students who held down part-time jobs. Determine whether there is evidence of a linear relationship between the hours spent at part-time jobs and the grade point averages.

**16.141** Xr13-19* Exercise 13.19 described a survey that asked people between 18 and 34 years of age and 35 to 50 years of age how much time they spent listening to FM radio each day. Also recorded were the amounts spent on music throughout the year. Can we infer that a linear relationship exists between listening times and amounts spent on music?

## General Social Survey Exercises

*If we interpret the responses to POLVIEWS (1 = Extremely liberal, 2 = Liberal, 3 = Slightly liberal, 4 = Moderate, 5 = Slightly conservative, 6 = Conservative, 7 = Extremely conservative) as an interval variable we can acquire useful information about where people stand on the liberal–conservative spectrum.*

**16.142** Discuss what assumption(s) is necessary to make the POLVIEWS spectrum responses an interval variable.

**16.143** GSS2014* As people grow older do they become more conservative? If so, there should be a positive linear relationship between age (AGE) and political philosophy (POLVIEWS). Use an appropriate statistical procedure to determine whether there is enough evidence to infer that as people grow older they become more conservative. Report the $p$-value of the test.

**16.144** GSS2014* Is there sufficient evidence to conclude that as income (RINCOME) rises people grow more conservative (POLVIEWS)? What is the $p$-value?

**16.145** GSS2014* Do more educated individuals lean to the liberal end of the political philosophy spectrum? Conduct a test to determine whether there is enough evidence to conclude that as education (EDUC) increases the political philosophy score (POLVIEWS) decreases. Briefly describe what the $p$-value of the test tells you.

*Exercises 16.146–16.149 address the question of what should governments do and not do. For each question determine whether there is enough evidence to infer that individuals on the liberal end of the political philosophy (POLVIEWS) would choose government action and those on the conservative end would choose no government action. Report the p-value of each test and the coefficient of determination. Briefly describe what the p-value of the coefficient of determination tells you about the linear relationship.*

**16.146** GSS2014* EQWLTH: Should government reduce income differences between rich and poor? (1 = Government should reduce differences; 2, 3, 4, 5, 6, 7 = No government action.)

**16.147** GSS2014* HELPPOOR: Should government improve standard of living of poor people? (1 = Government act; 2, 3, 4, 5 = People should help themselves.)

**16.148** GSS2014* HELPNOT: Should government do more or less to solve country's problems? (1 = Government should do more; 2, 3, 4, 5 = Government does too much.)

**16.149** GSS2014* HELPSICK: Is it government's responsibility to help pay for doctor and hospital bills? (1 = Government should help, 2, 3, 4, 5 = People should help themselves.)

**16.150** Summarize what you have discovered about the relationship between political philosophy and preference for government action in Exercises 16.146–16.149. In particular, discuss the coefficients of determination.

## CASE 16.1 Insurance Compensation for Lost Revenues*

Kobby Dagan/Shutterstock.com

In July 1990, a rock-and-roll museum opened in Atlanta, Georgia. The museum was located in a large city block containing a variety of stores. In late July 1992, a fire that started in one of these stores burned the entire block, including the museum. Fortunately, the museum had taken out insurance to cover the cost of rebuilding as well as lost revenue. As a general rule, insurance companies base their payment on how well the company performed in the past. However, the owners of the museum argued that the revenues were increasing, and hence they were entitled to more money under their insurance plan. The argument was based on the revenues and attendance figures of an amusement park, featuring rides and other similar attractions that had opened nearby. The amusement park opened in December 1991. The two entertainment facilities were operating jointly during the last 4 weeks of 1991 and the first 28 weeks of 1992 (the point at which the fire destroyed the museum). In April 1995, the museum reopened with considerably more features than the original one.

The attendance figures for both facilities for December 1991 to October 1995 are listed in columns 1 (museum) and 2 (amusement park). During the period when the museum was closed, the data show zero attendance.

The owners of the museum argued that the weekly attendance from the 29th week of 1992 to the 16th week of 1995 should be estimated using the most current data (17th to 42nd week of 1995). The insurance company argued that the estimates should be based on the 4 weeks of 1991 and the 28 weeks of 1992, when both facilities were operating and before the museum reopened with more features than the original museum.

a. Estimate the coefficients of the simple regression model based on the insurance company's argument. In other words, use the attendance figures for the last 4 weeks in 1991 and the next 28 weeks in 1992 to estimate the coefficients. Then use the model to calculate point predictions for the museum's weekly attendance figures when the museum was closed. Calculate the predicted total attendance.

b. Repeat part (a) using the museum's argument—that is, use the attendance figures after the reopening in 1995 to estimate the regression coefficients and use the equation to predict the weekly attendance when the museum was closed. Calculate the total attendance that was lost because of the fire.

c. Write a report to the insurance company discussing this analysis and include your recommendation about how much the insurance company should award the museum?

*The case and the data are real. The names have been changed to preserve anonymity. The author wishes to thank Dr. Kevin Leonard for supplying the problem and the data.

## CASE 16.2 Predicting University Grades from High School Grades*

DATA C16-02

Andresr/Shutterstock.com

Ontario high school students must complete a minimum of six Ontario Academic Credits (OACs) to gain admission to a university in the province. Most students take more than six OACs because universities take the average of the best six in deciding which students to admit. Most programs at universities require high school students to select certain courses. For example, science programs require two of chemistry, biology, and physics. Students applying to engineering must complete at least two mathematics OACs as well as physics. In recent years, one business program began an examination of all aspects of its program, including the criteria used to admit students. Students are required to take English and calculus OACs, and the minimum high school average is about 85%. Strangely enough, even though students are required to complete English and calculus, the marks in these subjects are not included in the average unless they are in the top six courses in a student's transcript. To examine the issue, the registrar took a random sample of students who recently graduated with the BBA (bachelor of business administration degree). He recorded the university GPA (range 0 to 12), the high school average based on the best six courses, and the high school average using English and calculus and the four next best marks.

a. Is there a relationship between university grades and high school average using the best six OACs?
b. Is there a relationship between university grades and high school average using the best four OACs plus calculus and English?
c. Write a report to the university's academic vice president describing your statistical analysis and your recommendations.

*The author is grateful to Leslie Grauer for her help in gathering the data for this case.

# APPENDIX 16 / REVIEW OF CHAPTERS 12 TO 16

We have now presented two dozen inferential techniques. Undoubtedly, the task of choosing the appropriate technique is growing more difficult. Table A16.1 lists all the statistical inference methods covered since Chapter 12. Figure A16.1 is a flowchart to help you choose the correct technique.

**TABLE A16.1 Summary of Statistical Techniques in Chapters 12 to 16**

| |
|---|
| $t$-test of $\mu$ |
| Estimator of $\mu$ (including estimator of $N\mu$) |
| $\chi^2$-test of $\sigma^2$ |
| Estimator of $\sigma^2$ |
| $z$-test of $p$ |
| Estimator of $p$ (including estimator of $Np$) |
| Equal-variances $t$-test of $\mu_1 - \mu_2$ |
| Equal-variances estimator of $\mu_1 - \mu_2$ |
| Unequal-variances $t$-test of $\mu_1 - \mu_2$ |
| Unequal-variances estimator of $\mu_1 - \mu_2$ |
| $t$-test of $\mu_D$ |
| Estimator of $\mu_D$ |
| $F$-test of $\sigma_1^2/\sigma_2^2$ |
| Estimator of $\sigma_1^2/\sigma_2^2$ |
| $z$-test of $p_1 - p_2$ (Case 1) |
| $z$-test of $p_1 - p_2$ (Case 2) |
| Estimator of $p_1 - p_2$ |
| One-way analysis of variance (including multiple comparisons) |
| Two-way (randomized blocks) analysis of variance |
| Two-factor analysis of variance |
| $\chi^2$-goodness-of-fit test |
| $\chi^2$-test of a contingency table |
| Simple linear regression and correlation (including $t$-tests of $\beta_1$ and $\rho$, and prediction and confidence intervals) |

FIGURE **A16.1** **Flowchart of Techniques in Chapters 12 to 16**

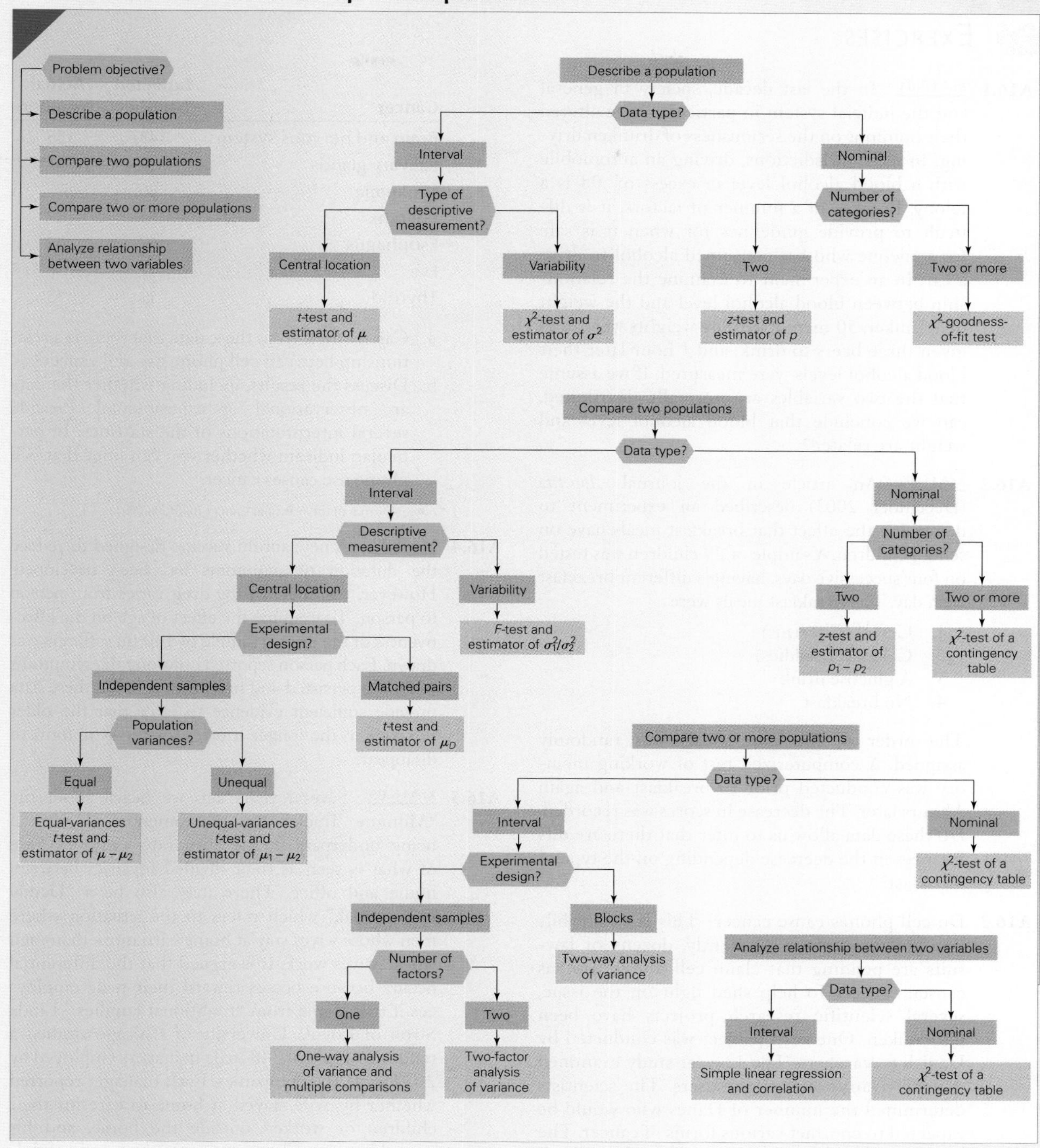

# EXERCISES

**A16.1** XrA16-01 In the last decade, society in general and the judicial system in particular have altered their opinions on the seriousness of drunken driving. In most jurisdictions, driving an automobile with a blood alcohol level in excess of .08 is a felony. Because of a number of factors, it is difficult to provide guidelines for when it is safe for someone who has consumed alcohol to drive a car. In an experiment to examine the relationship between blood alcohol level and the weight of a drinker, 50 men of varying weights were each given three beers to drink, and 1 hour later their blood alcohol levels were measured. If we assume that the two variables are normally distributed, can we conclude that blood alcohol level and weight are related?

**A16.2** XrA16-02 An article in the journal *Appetite* (December 2003) described an experiment to determine the effect that breakfast meals have on school children. A sample of 29 children was tested on four successive days, having a different breakfast each day. The breakfast meals were

1. Cereal (Cheerios)
2. Cereal (Shreddies)
3. A glucose drink
4. No breakfast

The order of breakfast meals was randomly assigned. A computerized test of working memory was conducted prior to breakfast and again 2 hours later. The decrease in scores was recorded. Do these data allow us to infer that there are differences in the decrease depending on the type of breakfast?

**A16.3** Do cell phones cause cancer? This is a multibillion-dollar question. Currently, dozens of lawsuits are pending that claim cell phone use has caused cancer. To help shed light on the issue, several scientific research projects have been undertaken. One such project was conducted by Danish researchers The 13-year study examined 420,000 Danish cell phone users. The scientists determined the number of Danes who would be expected to contract various forms of cancer. The expected number and the actual number of cell phone users who developed each type of cancer are listed here.

| Cancer | Expected Number | Actual Number |
|---|---|---|
| Brain and nervous system | 143 | 135 |
| Salivary glands | 9 | 7 |
| Leukemia | 80 | 77 |
| Pharynx | 52 | 32 |
| Esophagus | 57 | 42 |
| Eye | 12 | 8 |
| Thyroid | 13 | 13 |

a. Can we infer from these data that there is a relationship between cell phone use and cancer?
b. Discuss the results, including whether the data are observational or experimental. Provide several interpretations of the statistics. In particular, indicate whether you can infer that cell phone use causes cancer.

*Source:* Journal of the National Cancer Institute, 2001.

**A16.4** XrA16-04 A new antiflu vaccine designed to reduce the duration of symptoms has been developed. However, the effect of the drug varies from person to person. To examine the effect of age on the effectiveness of the drug, a sample of 140 flu sufferers was drawn. Each person reported how long the symptoms of the flu persisted and his or her age. Do these data provide sufficient evidence to infer that the older the patient, the longer it takes for the symptoms to disappear?

**A16.5** XrA16-05 Several years ago we heard about the "Mommy Track," the phenomenon of women being underpaid in the corporate world because of what is seen as their divided loyalties between home and office. There may also be a "Daddy Differential," which refers to the situation where men whose wives stay at home earn more than men whose wives work. It is argued that the differential occurs because bosses reward their male employees if they come from "traditional families." Linda Stroh of Loyola University of Chicago studied a random sample of 348 male managers employed by 20 *Fortune 500* companies. Each manager reported whether his wife stayed at home to care for their children or worked outside the home, and his annual income. The incomes (in thousands of dollars) were recorded. The incomes of the managers whose wives stay at home are stored in column 1.

Column 2 contains the incomes of managers whose wives work outside the home.

a. Can we conclude that men whose wives stay at home earn more than men whose wives work outside the home?
b. If your answer in part (a) is affirmative, does this establish a case for discrimination? Can you think of another cause-and-effect scenario? Explain.

**A16.6** XrA16-06 There are enormous differences between health-care systems in the United States and Canada. In a study to examine one dimension of these differences, 300 heart attack victims in each country were randomly selected. (Results of the study conducted by Dr. Daniel Mark of Duke University Medical Center, Dr. David Naylor of Sunnybrook Hospital in Toronto, and Dr. Paul Armstrong of the University of Alberta were published in the *Toronto Sun*, October 27, 1994.) Each patient was asked the following questions regarding the effect of his or her treatment:

1. How many days did it take you to return to work?
2. Do you still have chest pain? (This question was asked 1 month, 6 months, and 12 months after the patients' heart attacks.)

The responses were recorded in the following way:

Column 1: Code representing nationality: 1 = U.S.; 2 = Canada
Column 2: Responses to question 1
Column 3: Responses to question 2–1 month after heart attack: 2 = yes; 1 = no
Column 4: Responses to question 2–6 months after heart attack: 2 = yes; 1 = no
Column 5: Responses to question 2–12 months after heart attack: 2 = yes; 1 = no

Can we conclude that recovery is faster in the United States?

**A16.7** XrA16-07 Betting on the results of National Football League games is a popular North American activity. In some states and provinces, it is legal to do so provided that wagers are made through a government-authorized betting organization. In the province of Ontario, Pro-Line serves that function. Bettors can choose any team on which to wager, and Pro-Line sets the odds, which determine the winning payoffs. It is also possible to bet that in any game a tie will be the result. (A tie is defined as a game in which the winning margin is 3 or fewer points. A win occurs when the winning margin is greater than 3.) To assist bettors, Pro-Line lists the favorite for each game and predicts the point spread between the two teams. To judge how well Pro-Line predicts outcomes, the Creative Statistics Company tracked the results of a recent season. It recorded whether a team was favored by (1) 3 or fewer points, (2) 3.5 to 7 points, (3) 7.5 to 11 points, or (4) 11.5 or more points. It also recorded whether the favored team (1) won, (2) lost, or (3) tied. These data are recorded in columns 1 (Pro-Line's predictions) and 2 (game results). Can we conclude that Pro-Line's forecasts are useful for bettors?

**A16.8** XrA16-08 As all baseball fans know, first base is the only base that the base runner may overrun. At both second and third base, the runner may be tagged out if he runs past the base. Consequently, on close plays at second and third base, the runner will slide, enabling him to stop at the base. In recent years, however, several players have chosen to slide headfirst when approaching first base, claiming that this is faster than simply running over the base. In an experiment to test this claim, 25 players on one National League team were recruited. Each player ran to first base with and without sliding, and the times to reach the base were recorded. Can we conclude that sliding is slower than not sliding?

**A16.9** XrA16-09 How does mental outlook affect a person's health? The answer to this question may allow physicians to care more effectively for their patients. In an experiment to examine the relationship between attitude and physical health, Dr. Daniel Mark, a heart specialist at Duke University, studied 1,719 men and women who had recently undergone a heart catheterization, a procedure that checks for clogged arteries. Patients undergo this procedure when heart disease results in chest pain. All of the patients in the experiment were in about the same condition. In interviews, 14% of the patients doubted that they would recover sufficiently to resume their daily routines. Dr. Mark identified these individuals as pessimists; the others were (by default) optimists. After one year, Dr. Mark recorded how many patients were still alive. The data are stored in columns 1 (1 = optimist, 2 = pessimist) and 2 (2 = alive, 1 = dead). Do these data allow us to infer that pessimists are less likely to survive than optimists with similar physical ailments?

**A16.10** XrA16-10 Physicians have been recommending more exercise for their patients, particularly those who are overweight. One benefit of regular exercise appears to be a reduction in cholesterol, a substance associated with heart disease. To study the relationship more carefully, a physician took a random sample of 50 patients who do not exercise and measured their cholesterol levels. He then started them on regular exercise programs. After

4 months, he asked each patient how many minutes per week (on average) he or she exercised; he also measured their cholesterol levels. Column 1 = weekly exercise in minutes, column 2 = cholesterol level before exercise program, and column 3 = cholesterol level after exercise program.

a. Do these data allow us to infer that the amount of exercise and the reduction in cholesterol levels are related?
b. Produce a 95% interval of the amount of cholesterol reduction for someone who exercises for 100 minutes per week.
c. Produce a 95% interval for the average cholesterol reduction for people who exercise for 120 minutes per week.

**A16.11** XrA16-11 An economist working for a state university wanted to acquire information about salaries in publicly funded and private colleges and universities. She conducted a survey of 623 public-university faculty members and 592 private-university faculty members asking each to report his or her rank (instructor = 1, assistant professor = 2, associate professor = 3, and professor = 4) and current salary ($1,000).

a. Conduct a test to determine whether public colleges and universities and private colleges and universities pay different salaries when all ranks are combined.
b. For each rank, determine whether there is enough evidence to infer that the private college and university salaries differ from that of publicly funded colleges and universities.
c. If the answers to parts (a) and (b) differ, suggest a cause.
d. Conduct a test to determine whether your suggested cause is valid.

*Source:* Adapted from the American Association of University Professors, *AAUP Annual Report on the Economic Status of the Profession.*

**A16.12** XrA16-12 Millions of people suffer from migraine headaches. The costs in work days lost, medication, and treatment are measured in the billions of dollars. A study reported in the *Journal of the American Medical Association* (2005, 203: 2118–2125) described an experiment that examined whether acupuncture is an effective procedure in treating migraines. A random sample of 302 migraine patients was selected and divided into three groups. Group 1 was treated with acupuncture; group 2 was treated with sham acupuncture (patients believed that they were being treated with acupuncture but were not); and group 3 was not treated at all. The number of headache days per month was recorded for each patient before the treatments began. The number of headache days per month after treatment was also measured.

a. Conduct a test to determine whether there are differences in the number of headache days before treatment between the three groups of patients.
b. Test to determine whether differences exist after treatment. If so, what are the differences?
c. Why was the test in part (a) conducted?

**A16.13** XrA16-13 The battle between customers and car dealerships is often intense. Customers want the lowest price, and dealers want to extract as much money as possible. One source of conflict is the trade-in car. Most dealers will offer a relatively low trade-in in anticipation of negotiating the final package. In an effort to determine how dealers operate, a consumer organization undertook an experiment. Seventy-two individuals were recruited. Each solicited an offer on his or her 5-year-old Toyota Camry. The exact same car was used throughout the experiment. The only variables were the age and gender of the "owner." The ages were categorized as (1) young, (2) middle, and (3) senior. The cash offers are stored in columns 1 and 2. Column 1 stores the data for female owners, and column 2 contains the offers made to male owners. The first 12 rows in both columns represent the offers made to young people, the next 12 rows represent the middle group, and the last 12 rows represent the elderly owners.

a. Can we infer that differences exist between the six groups?
b. If differences exist, determine whether the differences are due to gender, age, or some interaction.

**A16.14** XrA16-14 In the presidential elections of 2000 and 2004, the vote in the state of Florida was crucial. It is important for the political parties to track party affiliation. Surveys in Broward and Miami-Dade counties were conducted in 1990, 1996, 2000, and 2004. The numbers of Democrats, Republicans, and other voters were recorded for both counties and for all four years. Test each of the following.

a. Party affiliation changed over the four surveys in Broward.
b. Party affiliation changed over the four surveys in Miami-Dade.
c. There were differences between Broward and Miami-Dade in 2004.

**A16.15** XrA16-15 Auto manufacturers are required to test their vehicles for a variety of pollutants in the exhaust. The amount of pollutant varies even among identical vehicles so that several vehicles must be tested. The engineer in charge of testing has collected data (in grams per kilometer driven) on the amounts of two pollutants—carbon monoxide and nitrous oxide—for 50 identical vehicles.

The engineer believes the company can save money by testing for only one of the pollutants because the two pollutants are closely linked; that is, if a car is emitting a large amount of carbon monoxide, it will also emit a large amount of nitrous oxide. Do the data support the engineer's belief?

**A16.16** XrA16-16 In 2003, there were 129,142,000 workers in the United States The general manager for a public transportation company wanted to learn more about how workers commute to work and how long it takes them. A random sample of workers was interviewed. Each reported how he or she typically get to work and how long it takes. Estimate with 95% confidence the total amount of time spent commuting.

*Source:* U.S. Census Bureau. (Data for this exercise were adapted from the *Statistical Abstract of the United States, 2006,* Table 1083.)

## General Social Survey Exercises

***Conduct all tests at the 5% significance level. Use a 95% confidence level for estimates.***

In 2012, there were 221,963,000 Americans aged 21 years or more.

**A16.17** GSS2012* Does the amount of education affect respondents' beliefs about the role of government in the following question? "Should government do more or less to solve country's problems?" The responses are HELPNOT: 1 = Government should do more; 2, 3, 4, 5 = Government does too much. Is there enough evidence to conclude that there are differences in the responses among the five categories of educational attainment (DEGREE: 0 = Left high school, 1 = High school, 2 = Junior college, 3 = Bachelor's degree, 4 = Graduate)?

**A16.18** GSS2012* The survey asked respondents the following question: "Generally speaking, do you think of yourself as a Republican Democrat, Independent, or what?" Estimate the number of Americans who consider themselves Republicans (PARTYID: 5 = Not strong Republican, 6 = Strong Republican).

**A16.19** GSS2012* Are Republicans more financially successful than either Democrats or Independents? Are there differences in total family income (INCOME) between the three political categories (PARTYID3: 1 = Democrat, 2 = Independent, 3 = Republican)? Conduct a test to answer the question.

**A16.20** GSS2012* The survey asked respondents the following question, "Should government reduce income differences between rich and poor?" How does the educational attainment affect responses to the question? Use an appropriate technique to determine whether education (EDUC) and support for government action to reduce income differences between rich and poor (EQWLTH: 1 = Government act; 2, 3, 4, 5, 6, 7 = No government action) are linearly related.

**A16.21** GSS2012* The survey asked respondents the following question, "Should government improve standard of living of poor people?" The responses are HELPPOOR: 1 = Government act; 2, 3, 4, 5 = People should help themselves. Is there enough evidence to infer that there are differences between Democrats, Independents, and Republicans (PARTYID3) in their answers to the question?

**A16.22** GSS2012* Estimate the number of Americans who were born outside the United States (BORN: 1 = United States, 2 = Not in the United States).

**A16.23** GSS2012* The survey asked the following question. A doctor tells a couple that there is one chance in four that their child will have an inherited disease. Does this mean that each of the couple's children will have the same risk of suffering the illness? (ODDS2: 1 = Yes, 2 = No, 8 = Don't know, 9 = No answer) Estimate the number of Americans who know the correct answer.

**A16.24** GSS2012* As societies age the demands on the health-care system grow. It becomes more important for individuals to ensure that they are taking steps to become and maintain good health. The survey asked respondents to judge their own health. Is there enough evidence to conclude that majority of the population believes that their health is excellent or good (HEALTH: 1 = Excellent, 2 = Good)?

**A16.25** GSS2012* The world economy took a hit during the 2007–2009 financial crisis. Have American families recovered? Estimate with 95% confidence to mean family income (INCOME).

**A16.26** GSS2012* Do individuals who want the government to help people improve their standard of living also believe that government should do more to solve the country's problems? Conduct a test to determine whether there is a positive linear relationship between these variables (HELPPOOR: Should government improve standard of living of poor people? 1 = Government act; 2, 3, 4,

5 = People should help themselves; HELPNOT: Should government do more or less to solve country's problems? 1 = Government should do more; 2, 3, 4, 5 = Government does too much).

**A16.27** GSS2012* Do people who work for themselves (WRKSLF: 1 = Self-employed, 2 = Someone else) make more income (RINCOME) than people who work for someone else? Conduct a test to answer the question.

**A16.28** GSS2012* Do native-born Americans work harder than Americans born outside the United States (BORN: 1 = United States, 2 = Not in the United States)? Is there enough statistical evidence to conclude that those born in the United States work longer hours (HRS1) than non-natives?

**A16.29** GSS2012* One measure of the health of the economy is how many workers believe that it is easy to find a job with another employer with approximately the same income and fringe benefits as they have now. Estimate the number of people who believe that it is very easy (JOBFIND: 1 = Very easy).

**A16.30** GSS2012* Is there enough evidence to conclude that Republicans get the correct answer to the following question correct more often than do Democrats (PARTYID3: 1 = Democrat, 3 = Republican): "The center of the earth is very hot." (1 = True, 2 = False, 8 = Don't know, 9 = No answer)? The correct answer: True.

**A16.31** GSS2012* Do people tend to marry similarly educated individuals? To answer the question, perform a statistical analysis to determine whether there is enough evidence to infer that one's educational attainment (EDUC) and spouse's educational attainment (SPEDUC) are positively linearly related.

## Survey of Consumer Finances

***Conduct all tests at the 5% significance level. Use a 95% confidence level for estimates.***

According to the U.S. Census, there were 220,958,853 adults in the United States in 2010.

**A16.32** SCF2010:\All* Is there enough evidence to conclude that there are differences between the three working categories (OCCAT2: 1 = Managerial/professional, 2= Technical/sales/services, 3 = Other) in terms of whether the household declared bankruptcy in the previous 5 years (BNKRUPLAST5: 1 = Yes)?

**A16.33** SCF2010:\MC* Do middle-class households headed by women (HHSEX: 1 = Male, 2 = Female) spend more money on food at home than their male counterparts (FOODHOME)? Conduct a test to answer the question.

**A16.34** SCF2010:\All* Are female and male heads of households equally likely to carry a balance on their credit cards? Conduct a test to determine whether there is a difference between the sexes (HHSEX: 1 = Male, 2 = Female) with respect to carrying a balance on credit cards (NOCCBAL: 0 = Carry a balance, 1 = Do not carry a balance).

**A16.35** SCF2010:\All* Females are now attending colleges and universities in greater numbers than men. In the past men were more likely than women to have graduate degrees. Conduct a test to determine whether there is enough evidence to infer that males (HHSEX: 1 = Male, 2 = Female) continue to be more likely than females to have a graduate degree (EDUC 17 = Graduate degree).

**A16.36** SCF2010:\All* In 2010, the American economy was still faltering because of the housing meltdown during 2007–2009. One sign of the difficulty is people struggling to pay their living expenses. Estimate the number of people who said that their overall household expenses were unusually high (EXPENSHILO: 1).

**A16.37** SCF2010:\All* Is there sufficient evidence to conclude that there are differences in income (INCOME) between the four categories of educational attainment (EDCL: 1 = No high school diploma, 2 = High school diploma, 3 = Some college, 4 = College degree)?

**A16.38** SCF2010:\UC The upper class in the 2010 survey had household net worth between $1,345,975 and $7,402,095. Money kept in checking accounts earns no interest but are kept to pay bills. Estimate the mean amount held in checking accounts by households in the upper class (CHECKING).

**A16.39** SCF2010:\UC* Do upper-class households get a great deal of the income from interest and dividends? To answer the question, estimate the mean interest and dividend income for upper-class households (INTDIVINC).

**A16.40** SCF2010:\All* One way to examine the issue of family structure is to determine the number of households with no spouse or partner. Estimate the proportion of households whose head is neither married nor living with partner (MARRIED: 2).

**A16.41** SCF2010:\MC* Do middle-class heads of households who have a high school diploma only have more assets (ASSET) than those who did not finish high school (EDCL: 1 = No high school diploma, 2 = High school diploma)? Use an appropriate statistical technique to answer the question.

## CASE A16.1 Nutrition Education Programs*

DATA CA16-01

Nutrition education programs, which teach clients how to lose weight or reduce cholesterol levels through better eating patterns, have been growing in popularity. The nurse in charge of one such program at a local hospital wanted to know whether the programs actually work. A random sample was drawn of 33 clients who attended a nutrition education program for those with elevated cholesterol levels. The study recorded the weight, cholesterol levels, total dietary fat intake per average day, total dietary cholesterol intake per average day, and percent of daily calories from fat. These data were gathered both before and 3 months after the program. The researchers also determined the clients' genders, ages, and heights. The data are stored in the following way:

Column 1: Gender (1 = female, 2 = male)
Column 2: Age
Column 3: Height (in meters)
Columns 4 and 5: Weight, before and after (in kilograms)
Columns 6 and 7: Cholesterol level, before and after
Columns 8 and 9: Total dietary fat intake per average day, before and after (in grams)
Columns 10 and 11: Dietary cholesterol intake per average day, before and after (in milligrams)
Columns 12 and 13: Percent daily calories from fat, before and after

The nurse would require the following information:

a. In terms of each of weight, cholesterol level, fat intake, cholesterol intake, and calories from fat, is the program a success?
b. Does gender affect the amount of reduction in each of weight, cholesterol level, fat intake, cholesterol intake, and calories from fat?
c. Does age affect the amount of reduction in weight, cholesterol level, fat intake, cholesterol intake, and calories from fat cholesterol?

*The author would like to thank Karen Cavrag for writing this case.

# 17

Comstock Images/Getty Images

# MULTIPLE REGRESSION

## CHAPTER OUTLINE



## General Social Survey

### Variables That Affect Income

DATA
GSS2014*

In the Chapter 16 opening example, we showed using the General Social Survey that income and education are linearly related. This raises the question, What other variables affect one's income? To answer this question, we need to expand the simple linear regression technique used in the previous chapter to allow for more than one independent variable.

Here is a list of all the interval variables the General Social Survey created:

Age (AGE)

Years of education of respondent, spouse, father, and mother (EDUC, SPEDUC, PAEDUC, MAEDUC)

Mundoview/Shutterstock.com

**Our answer appears on page 695.**

Hours of work per week of respondent and of spouse (HRS1 and SPHRS1)
Number of family members earning money (EARNRS)
Number of children (CHILDS)
Age when first child was born (AGEKDBRN)
Number of hours of television viewing per day (TVHOURS)
Score on question, Should government reduce income differences between rich and poor? (EQWLTH)
Score on question, Should government improve standard of living of poor people? (HELPPOOR)
Score on question, Should government do more or less to solve country's problems? (HELPNOT)
Score on question, Is it government's responsibility to help pay for doctor and hospital bills? (HELPSICK)

The goal is create a regression analysis that includes all variables that you believe affect income (RINCOME).

## Introduction

In the previous chapter, we employed the simple linear regression model to analyze how one variable (the dependent variable $y$) is related to another interval variable (the independent variable $x$). The restriction of using only one independent variable was motivated by the need to simplify the introduction to regression analysis. Although there are a number of applications where we purposely develop a model with only one independent variable (see Section 4-6, for example), in general we prefer to include as many independent variables as are believed to affect the dependent variable. Arbitrarily limiting the number of independent variables also limits the usefulness of the model.

In this chapter, we allow for any number of independent variables. In so doing, we expect to develop models that fit the data better than would a simple linear regression model. We begin by describing the multiple regression model and listing the required conditions. We let the computer produce the required statistics and use them to assess the model's fit and diagnose violations of the required conditions. We use the model by interpreting the coefficients, predicting the particular value of the dependent variable, and estimating its expected value.

## 17-1 Model and Required Conditions

We now assume that $k$ independent variables are potentially related to the dependent variable. Thus, the model is represented by the following equation:

$$y = \beta_0 + \beta_1 x_1 + \beta_2 x_2 + \cdots + \beta_k x_k + \varepsilon$$

where $y$ is the dependent variable, $x_1, x_2, \ldots, x_k$ are the independent variables, $\beta_0, \beta_1, \ldots, \beta_k$ are the coefficients, and $\varepsilon$ is the error variable. The independent variables may actually be functions of other variables. For example, we might define some of the independent variables as follows:

$$x_2 = x_1^2$$
$$x_5 = x_3 x_4$$
$$x_7 = \log(x_6)$$

In Chapter 18, we will discuss how and under what circumstances such functions can be used in regression analysis.

The error variable is retained because, even though we have included additional independent variables, deviations between predicted values of $y$ and actual values of $y$ will still occur. Incidentally, when there is more than one independent variable in the regression model, we refer to the graphical depiction of the equation as a **response surface** rather than as a straight line. Figure 17.1 depicts a scatter diagram of a response surface with $k = 2$. (When $k = 2$, the regression equation creates a plane.) Of course, whenever $k$ is greater than 2, we can only imagine the response surface; we cannot draw it.

**FIGURE 17.1 Scatter Diagram and Response Surface with $k = 2$**

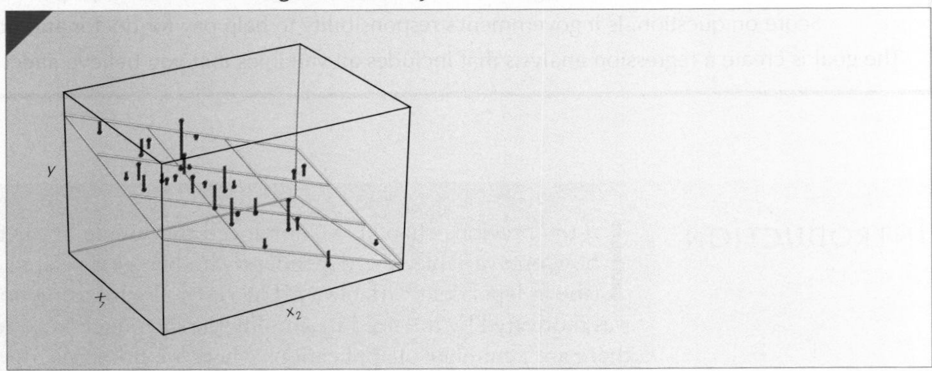


An important part of the regression analysis comprises several statistical techniques that evaluate how well the model fits the data. These techniques require the following conditions, which we introduced in the previous chapter.

**Required Conditions for Error Variable**

1. The probability distribution of the error variable $\varepsilon$ is normal.
2. The mean of the error variable is 0.
3. The standard deviation of $\varepsilon$ is $\sigma_\varepsilon$, which is a constant.
4. The errors are independent.

In Section 16-6, we discussed how to recognize when the requirements are unsatisfied. Those same procedures can be used to detect violations of required conditions in the multiple regression model.

We now proceed as we did in Chapter 16. We discuss how the model's coefficients are estimated and how we assess the model's fit. However, there is one major difference between Chapters 16 and 17. In Chapter 16, we allowed for the possibility that some students will perform the calculations manually. The multiple regression model involves so many computations that it is virtually impossible to conduct the analysis without a computer. All analyses in this chapter will be performed by Excel and XLSTAT. Your job will be to interpret the output.

## 17-2 Estimating the Coefficients and Assessing the Model

The multiple regression equation is expressed similarly to the simple regression equation. The general form is

$$\hat{y} = b_0 + b_1x_1 + b_2x_2 + \cdots + b_kx_k$$

where $k$ is the number of independent variables.

The procedures introduced in Chapter 16 are extended to the multiple regression model. However, in Chapter 16, we first discussed how to interpret the coefficients and then discussed how to assess the model's fit. In practice, we reverse the process. That is, the first step is to determine how well the model fits. If the model's fit is poor, there is no point in a further analysis of the coefficients of that model. A much higher priority is assigned to the task of improving the model. We will discuss the art and science of model building in Chapter 18. In this chapter, we show how a regression analysis is performed.

We'll illustrate the procedure with the chapter-opening example.

### 17-2a Step 1: Select the Independent Variables That You Believe May Be Related to the Dependent Variable

Here are the available variables from the General Social Survey of 2014 and the reason why we have selected each one:

Age (AGE): For most people, income increases with age.

Years of education (EDUC): We've already shown (Chapter 16 opening example) that education is linearly related to income.

Hours of work per week (HRS1): Obviously, more hours of work should produce more income.

Spouse's hours of work (SPHRS1): It is possible that, if one's spouse works more and earns more, the other spouse may choose to work less and thus earn less.

Number of family members earning money (EARNRS): As is the case with SPHRS1, if more family members earn income there may be less pressure on the respondent to work harder.

Number of children (CHILDS): Children are expensive, which may encourage their parents to work harder and thus earn more.

You may be wondering why we don't simply include all the interval variables that are available to us. There are three reasons. First, the objective is to determine whether our hypothesized model is valid and whether the independent variables in the model are linearly related to the dependent variable. That is, we should screen the independent variables and include only those that in theory affect the dependent variable.

Second, by including large numbers of independent variables we increase the probability of Type I errors. For example, if we include 100 independent variables, none of which are related to the dependent variable, we're likely to conclude that five of them are linearly related to the dependent variable. This is a problem that we discussed in Chapter 14.

Third, because of a problem called multicollinearity (described in Section 17-3), we may conclude that none of the independent variables are linearly related to the dependent variable when in fact one or more are.

## 17-2b Step 2: Use a Computer to Compute All the Coefficients and Other Statistics

### EXCEL Data Analysis

| | A | B | C | D | E | F | G |
|---|---|---|---|---|---|---|---|
| 1 | SUMMARY OUTPUT | | | | | | |
| 2 | *Regression Statistics* | | | | | | |
| 3 | Multiple R | 0.5879 | | | | | |
| 4 | R Square | 0.3456 | | | | | |
| 5 | Adjusted R Square | 0.3366 | | | | | |
| 6 | Standard Error | 35,841 | | | | | |
| 7 | Observations | 446 | | | | | |
| 8 | | | | | | | |
| 9 | ANOVA | | | | | | |
| 10 | | *df* | *SS* | *MS* | *F* | *Significance F* | |
| 11 | Regression | 6 | 297,785,757,583 | 49,630,959,597 | 38.64 | 1.13E-37 | |
| 12 | Residual | 439 | 563,941,027,310 | 1,284,603,707 | | | |
| 13 | Total | 445 | 861,726,784,894 | | | | |
| 14 | | | | | | | |
| 15 | | *Coefficients* | *Standard Error* | *t Stat* | *P-value* | *Lower 95%* | *Upper 95%* |
| 16 | Intercept | −108,240 | 14,854 | −7.29 | 1.48E-12 | −137,433 | −79,046 |
| 17 | AGE | 974.0 | 155.2 | 6.28 | 8.27E-10 | 669.06 | 1279 |
| 18 | EDUC | 5680 | 607.4 | 9.35 | 4.45E-19 | 4486 | 6874 |
| 19 | HRS1 | 1091 | 117.1 | 9.32 | 5.55E-19 | 861.37 | 1322 |
| 20 | SPHRS1 | −250.9 | 127.4 | −1.97 | 0.0496 | −501.34 | −0.460 |
| 21 | EARNRS | 958.5 | 3045 | 0.31 | 0.7531 | −5026 | 6943 |
| 22 | CHILDS | −1765 | 1384 | −1.28 | 0.2029 | −4486 | 955.5 |

*INSTRUCTIONS*

1. Type or import the data (Open GSS2014). Arrange the columns so that the independent variables are in adjacent columns. Delete rows that have blanks in any of the columns (see Xm17-00).
2. Click **Data**, **Data Analysis**, and **Regression**.
3. Specify the **Input *Y* Range** (B1:B447), the Input ***X* Range** (C1:H447), and a value for $\alpha$ (.05).

### XLSTAT

| | B | C | D | E | F | G | H |
|---|---|---|---|---|---|---|---|
| 10 | **Regression of variable RINCOME:** | | | | | | |
| 11 | Goodness of fit statistics (RINCOME): | | | | | | |
| 13 | Observations | 446 | | | | | |
| 14 | Sum of weights | 446 | | | | | |
| 15 | DF | 439 | | | | | |
| 16 | R² | 0.3456 | | | | | |
| 17 | Adjusted R² | 0.3366 | | | | | |
| 18 | MSE | 1,284,603,707 | | | | | |
| 19 | RMSE | 35,841 | | | | | |
| 20 | DW | 1.762 | | | | | |
| 21 | Analysis of variance (RINCOME): | | | | | | |
| 22 | Source | DF | Sum of squares | Mean squares | F | Pr > F | |
| 23 | Model | 6 | 297,785,757,583 | 49,630,959,597 | 38.64 | < 0.0001 | |
| 24 | Error | 439 | 563,941,027,310 | 1,284,603,707 | | | |
| 25 | Corrected Total | 445 | 861,726,784,893 | | | | |
| 29 | Model parameters (RINCOME): | | | | | | |
| 30 | Source | Value | Standard error | t | Pr > \|t\| | Lower bound (95%) | Upper bound (95%) |
| 31 | Intercept | −108,240 | 14,854 | −7.29 | < 0.0001 | −137,433 | −79,046 |
| 32 | AGE | 974.0 | 155.2 | 6.28 | < 0.0001 | 669.1 | 1279 |
| 33 | EDUC | 5680 | 607.4 | 9.35 | < 0.0001 | 4486 | 6874 |
| 34 | HRS1 | 1091 | 117.1 | 9.32 | < 0.0001 | 861.4 | 1322 |
| 35 | SPHRS1 | −250.9 | 127.4 | −1.97 | 0.0496 | −501.3 | −0.460 |
| 36 | EARNRS | 958.5 | 3045 | 0.31 | 0.7531 | −5026 | 6943 |
| 37 | CHILDS | −1765 | 1384 | −1.28 | 0.2029 | −4486 | 955.5 |

*INSTRUCTIONS*

1. Type or import the data (Open GSS2014). Copy the relevant variables into a new spreadsheet. Arrange the columns so that the independent variables are in adjacent columns. See Xm17-00X.
2. Click **XLSTAT**, **Modeling data**, and **Linear regression**. In the **Quantitative** box type the input range of Y (B1:B2539). In the **X Explanatory variables** and **Quantitative** box type the input range of X (C1:H2539).
3. Click **Outputs** and check **Analysis of variance**.
4. Click **Missing data** and select **Remove the observations** and **Across all Ys**. Click **OK**.

**INTERPRET**

The regression model is estimated by:

$$\hat{y}\text{ (INCOME)} = -108{,}240 + 974.0\text{ AGE} + 5680\text{ EDUC} + 1091\text{ HRS1} - 250.9\text{ SPHRS} + 958.5\text{ EARNRS} - 1765\text{ CHILDS}$$

## 17-2c Step 3: Assess the Model

We assess the model in three ways: the standard error of estimate, the coefficient of determination (both introduced in Chapter 16), and the $F$-test of the analysis of variance (presented subsequently).

## 17-2d Standard Error of Estimate

Recall that $\sigma_\varepsilon$ is the standard deviation of the error variable $\varepsilon$ and that, because $\sigma_\varepsilon$ is a population parameter, it is necessary to estimate its value by using $s_\varepsilon$. In multiple regression, the standard error of estimate is defined as follows:

**Standard Error of Estimate**

$$s_\varepsilon = \sqrt{\frac{\text{SSE}}{n - k - 1}}$$

where $n$ is the sample size and $k$ is the number of independent variables in the model.

As we noted in Chapter 16, each of our software packages reports the standard error of estimate in a different way.

**EXCEL Data Analysis**

| 7 | Standard Error | 35,841 |
|---|---|---|

**XLSTAT**

| 9 | RMSE | 35,841 |
|---|---|---|

**INTERPRET**

Recall that we judge the magnitude of the standard error of estimate relative to the values of the dependent variable, and particularly to the mean of $y$. In this example, $\bar{y} = 55{,}768$ (not shown in printouts). It appears that the standard error of estimate is quite large.

## 17-2e Coefficient of Determination

Recall from Chapter 16 that the coefficient of determination is defined as:

$$R^2 = 1 - \frac{\text{SSE}}{\sum(y_i - \bar{y})^2}$$

**EXCEL Data Analysis**

| 5 | R Square | 0.3456 |
|---|---|---|

**XLSTAT**

| 6 | R² | 0.3456 |
|---|---|---|

**INTERPRET**

This means that 34.56% of the total variation in income is explained by the variation in the six independent variables, whereas 65.44% remains unexplained.

Notice that Excel and XLSTAT print a second $R^2$ statistic, called the **coefficient of determination adjusted for degrees of freedom**, which has been adjusted to take into account the sample size and the number of independent variables. The rationale for this statistic is that, if the number of independent variables $k$ is large relative to the sample size $n$, the unadjusted $R^2$ value may be unrealistically high. To understand this point, consider what would happen if the sample size is 2 in a simple linear regression model. The line would fit the data perfectly resulting in $R^2 = 1$ when, in fact, there may be no linear relationship. To avoid creating a false impression, the adjusted $R^2$ is often calculated. Its formula is as follows:

**Coefficient of Determination Adjusted for Degrees of Freedom**

$$\text{Adjusted } R^2 = 1 - \frac{\text{SSE}/(n-k-1)}{\sum(y_i - \bar{y})^2/(n-1)} = 1 - \frac{\text{MSE}}{s_y^2}$$

If $n$ is considerably larger than $k$, the unadjusted and adjusted $R^2$ values will be similar. But if SSE is quite different from 0 and $k$ is large compared to $n$, the unadjusted and adjusted values of $R^2$ will differ substantially. If such differences exist, the analyst should be alerted to a potential problem in interpreting the coefficient of determination. In this example, the adjusted coefficient of determination is .3366, indicating that, no matter how we measure the coefficient of determination, the model's fit is not very good.

## 17-2f Testing the Validity of the Model

In the simple linear regression model, we tested the slope coefficient to determine whether sufficient evidence existed to allow us to conclude that there was a linear relationship between the independent variable and the dependent variable. However, because there is only one independent variable in that model, that same $t$-test also tested to determine whether that model is valid. When there is more than one independent variable, we need another method to test the overall validity of the model. The technique is a version of the analysis of variance, which we introduced in Chapter 14.

To test the validity of the regression model, we specify the following hypotheses:

$H_0$: $\beta_1 = \beta_2 = \cdots = \beta_k = 0$

$H_1$: At least one $\beta_i$ is not equal to 0.

If the null hypothesis is true, none of the independent variables $x_1, x_2, \ldots, x_k$ is linearly related to $y$, and therefore the model is invalid. If at least one $\beta_i$ is not equal to 0, the model does have some validity.

When we discussed the coefficient of determination in Chapter 16, we noted that the total variation in the dependent variable [measured by $\sum(y_i - \bar{y})^2$] can be decomposed into two parts: the explained variation (measured by SSR) and the unexplained variation (measured by SSE). That is:

Total variation in $y$ = SSR + SSE

Furthermore, we established that, if SSR is large relative to SSE, the coefficient of determination will be high—signifying a good model. On the other hand, if SSE is large, most of the variation will be unexplained, which indicates that the model provides a poor fit and consequently has little validity.

The test statistic is the same one we encountered in Section 14-1, where we tested for the equivalence of two or more population means. To judge whether SSR is large enough relative to SSE to allow us to infer that at least one coefficient is not equal to 0, we compute the ratio of the two mean squares. (Recall that the mean square is the sum of squares divided by its degrees of freedom; recall, too, that the ratio of two mean squares is $F$ distributed as long as the underlying population is normal—a required condition for this application.) The calculation of the test statistic is summarized in an analysis of variance (ANOVA) table, whose general form appears in Table 17.1. The Excel and XLSTAT ANOVA tables are shown next.

TABLE **17.1** **Analysis of Variance Table for Regression Analysis**

| SOURCE OF VARIATION | DEGREES OF FREEDOM | SUMS OF SQUARES | MEAN SQUARES | F-STATISTIC |
|---|---|---|---|---|
| Regression | $k$ | SSR | MSR = SSR/$k$ | $F$ = MSR/MSE |
| Residual | $n - k - 1$ | SSE | MSE = SSE/$(n - k - 1)$ | |
| Total | $n - 1$ | $\sum(y_i - \bar{y})^2$ | | |

**EXCEL Data Analysis**

| | | | | | | |
|---|---|---|---|---|---|---|
| 10 | ANOVA | | | | | |
| 11 | | *df* | *SS* | *MS* | *F* | *Significance F* |
| 12 | Regression | 6 | 297,785,757,583 | 49,630,959,597 | 38.64 | 1.13E-37 |
| 13 | Residual | 439 | 563,941,027,310 | 1,284,603,707 | | |
| 14 | Total | 445 | 861,726,784,894 | | | |

**XLSTAT**

| | | | | | | |
|---|---|---|---|---|---|---|
| 12 | Analysis of variance (RINCOME): | | | | | |
| 13 | Source | DF | Sum of squares | Mean squares | F | Pr > F |
| 14 | Model | 6 | 297,785,757,583 | 49,630,959,597 | 38.64 | **< 0.0001** |
| 15 | Error | 439 | 563,941,027,310 | 1,284,603,707 | | |
| 16 | Corrected Total | 445 | 861,726,784,893 | | | |

A large value of $F$ indicates that most of the variation in $y$ is explained by the regression equation and that the model is valid. A small value of $F$ indicates that most of the variation in $y$ is unexplained. The rejection region allows us to determine whether $F$ is large enough to justify rejecting the null hypothesis. For this test, the rejection region is:

$$F > F_{\alpha,k,n-k-1}$$

In Example 17.1, the rejection region (assuming $\alpha = .05$) is:

$$F > F_{\alpha,k,n-k-1} = F_{.05,6,439} \approx 2.10$$

As you can see from the printout, $F = 38.64$. The printout also includes the $p$-value of the test, which is 0. Obviously, there is a great deal of evidence to infer that the model is valid.

Although each assessment measurement offers a different perspective, all agree in their assessment of how well the model fits the data, because all are based on the sum of squares for error, SSE. The standard error of estimate is:

$$s_\varepsilon = \sqrt{\frac{\text{SSE}}{n-k-1}}$$

and the coefficient of determination is:

$$R^2 = 1 - \frac{\text{SSE}}{\sum(y_i - \bar{y})^2}$$

When the response surface hits every single point, SSE = 0. Hence, $s_\varepsilon = 0$ and $R^2 = 1$.

If the model provides a poor fit, we know that SSE will be large [its maximum value is $\sum(y_i - \bar{y})^2$], $s_\varepsilon$ will be large, and [since SSE is close to $\sum(y_i - \bar{y})^2$] $R^2$ will be close to 0.

The $F$-statistic also depends on SSE. Specifically,

$$F = \frac{\text{MSR}}{\text{MSE}} = \frac{\left(\sum(y_i - \bar{y})^2 - \text{SSE}\right)/k}{\text{SSE}/(n-k-1)}$$

When SSE = 0:

$$F = \frac{\sum (y_i - \bar{y})^2/k}{0/(n-k-1)}$$

which is infinitely large. When SSE is large, SSE is close to $\sum (y_i - \bar{y})^2$ and $F$ is quite small.

The relationship among $s_\varepsilon$, $R^2$, and $F$ is summarized in Table 17.2.

TABLE **17.2** **Relationship Among SSE, $s_\varepsilon$, $R^2$, and $F$**

| SSE | $s_\varepsilon$ | $R^2$ | $F$ | ASSESSMENT OF MODEL |
|---|---|---|---|---|
| 0 | 0 | 1 | $\infty$ | Perfect |
| Small | Small | Close to 1 | Large | Good |
| Large | Large | Close to 0 | Small | Poor |
| $\sum(y_i - \bar{y})^2$ | $\sqrt{\frac{\sum(y_i - \bar{y})^2}{n-k-1}}$* | 0 | 0 | Invalid |

*When $n$ is large and $k$ is small, this quantity is approximately equal to the standard deviation of $y$.

## 17-2g Interpreting the Coefficients

The coefficients $b_0, b_1, \ldots, b_k$ describe the relationship between each of the independent variables and the dependent variable in the sample. We need to use inferential methods (described below) to draw conclusions about the population. In our example, the sample consists of the 446 observations. The population is composed of all American adults.

**Intercept** The intercept is $b_0 = -108,240$. This is the average income when all the independent variables are zero. As we observed in Chapter 16, it is often misleading to try to interpret this value, particularly if 0 is outside the range of the values of the independent variables (as is the case here).

**Age** The relationship between income and age is described by $b_1 = 974.0$. From this number, we learn that in this model, for each additional year of age, income increases on average by \$974, assuming that the other independent variables in this model are held constant.

**Education** The coefficient $b_2 = 5680$ specifies that in this sample for each additional year of education the income increases on average by \$5680, assuming the constancy of the other independent variables.

**Hours of Work** The relationship between hours of work per week is expressed by $b_3 = 1091$. We interpret this number as the average increase in annual income for each additional hour of work per week keeping the other independent variables fixed in this sample.

**Spouse's Hours of Work** The relationship between annual income and a spouse's hours of work per week is described in this sample $b_4 = -250.9$, which we interpret to mean that for each additional hour a spouse works per week income decreases on average by \$250.90 when the other variables are constant.

**Number of Family Members Earning Income** In this dataset, the relationship between annual income and the number of family members who earn money is expressed by $b_5 = 958.5$, which tells us that for each additional family member earner annual income increases on average by \$958.50 assuming that the other independent variables are constant.

**Number of Children** The relationship between annual income and number of children is expressed by $b_6 = -1765$, which tells us that in this sample for each additional child annual income decreases on average by \$1765.

## 17-2h Testing the Coefficients

In Chapter 16, we described how to test to determine whether there is sufficient evidence to infer that in the simple linear regression model $x$ and $y$ are linearly related. The null and alternative hypotheses were:

$$H_0: \beta_1 = 0$$
$$H_1: \beta_1 \neq 0$$

The test statistic was:

$$t = \frac{b_1 - \beta_1}{s_{b_1}}$$

which is Student $t$ distributed with $\nu = n - 2$ degrees of freedom.

In the multiple regression model, we have more than one independent variable. For each such variable, we can test to determine whether there is enough evidence of a linear relationship between it and the dependent variable for the entire population when the other independent variables are included in the model.

**Testing the Coefficients**

$$H_0: \beta_i = 0$$
$$H_1: \beta_i \neq 0$$

(for $i = 1, 2, \ldots, k$); the test statistic is:

$$t = \frac{b_i - \beta_i}{s_{b_i}}$$

which is Student $t$ distributed with $\nu = n - k - 1$ degrees of freedom.

To illustrate, we test each of the coefficients in the multiple regression model in the chapter-opening example. The tests that follow are performed just as all other tests in this book have been performed. We set up the null and alternative hypotheses, identify the test statistic, and use the computer to calculate the value of the test statistic and its $p$-value. For each independent variable, we test ($i = 1, 2, 3, 4, 5, 6$):

$$H_0: \beta_i = 0$$
$$H_1: \beta_i \neq 0$$

Refer to page 696 and examine the computer output. The output includes the $t$-tests of $\beta_i$. The results of these tests pertain to the entire population of the United States in 2014. It is also important to add that these test results were determined when the other independent variables were included in the model. We add this statement because a simple linear regression will very likely result in different values of the test statistics and possibly the conclusion.

**Test of $\beta_1$** (Coefficient of age)

Value of the test statistic: $t = 6.28$; $p$-value $= 8.27 \times 10^{-10} \approx 0$

**Test of $\beta_2$** (Coefficient of education)

Value of the test statistic: $t = 9.35$; $p$-value $= 4.45 \times 10^{-19} \approx 0$

**Test of $\beta_3$** (Coefficient of number of hours of work per week)

Value of the test statistic: $t = 9.32$; $p$-value $= 5.55 \times 10^{-19} \approx 0$

**Test of $\beta_4$** (Coefficient of spouse's number of hours of work per week)

Value of the test statistic: $t = -1.97$; $p$-value $= .0496$

**Test of $\beta_5$** (Coefficient of number of earners in family)

Value of the test statistic: $t = .31$; $p$-value $= .7531$

**Test of $\beta_6$** (Coefficient of number of children)

Value of the test statistic: $t = -1.28$; $p$-value $= .2029$

There is sufficient evidence at the 5% significance level to infer that each of the following variables is linearly related to income:

Age
Education
Number of hours of work per week
Spouse's number of hours pf work per week

In this model, there is not enough evidence to conclude that each of the following variables is linearly related to income:

Number of earners in the family
Number of children

Note that this may mean that there is no evidence of a linear relationship between these two independent variables. However, it may also mean that there is a linear relationship between the two variables, but because of a condition called *multicollinearity*, some $t$-test of $\beta_i$ revealed no linear relationship. We will discuss multicollinearity in Section 17-3.

## 17-2i A Cautionary Note about Interpreting the Results

Care should be taken when interpreting the results of this and other regression analyses. We might find that in one model there is enough evidence to conclude that a particular independent variable is linearly related to the dependent variable, but that in another model, no such evidence exists. Consequently, whenever a particular $t$-test is *not* significant, we state that there is not enough evidence to infer that the independent and dependent variable are linearly related *in this model.* The implication is that another model may yield different conclusions.

Furthermore, if one or more of the required conditions are violated, the results may be invalid. In Section 17-3, we introduced the procedures that allow the statistics practitioner to examine the model's requirements. We also remind you that it is dangerous to extrapolate far outside the range of the observed values of the independent variables.

## 17-2j *t*-Tests and the Analysis of Variance

The $t$-tests of the individual coefficients allow us to determine whether $\beta_i \neq 0$ (for $i = 1, 2, \ldots, k$), which tells us whether a linear relationship exists between $x_i$ and $y$. There is a $t$-test for each independent variable. Consequently, the computer automatically performs $k$ $t$-tests. (It actually conducts $k + 1$ $t$-tests, including the one for the intercept $\beta_0$, which we usually ignore.) The $F$-test in the analysis of variance combines these $t$-tests into a single test. That is, we test all the $\beta_i$ at one time to determine whether at least one of them is not equal to 0. The question naturally arises, Why do we need the $F$-test if it is nothing more than the combination of the previously performed $t$-tests? Recall that we addressed this issue earlier. In Chapter 14, we pointed out that we can replace the analysis of variance by a series of $t$-tests of the difference between two means. However, by doing so, we increase the probability of making a Type I error. Which means that even when there is no linear relationship between each of the independent variables and the dependent variable, multiple $t$-tests will likely show some are significant. As a result, you will conclude erroneously that, since at least one $\beta_i$ is not equal to 0, the model is valid. The $F$-test, on the other hand, is performed only once. Because the probability that a Type I error will occur in a single trial is equal to $\alpha$, the chance of erroneously concluding that the model is valid is substantially less with the $F$-test than with multiple $t$-tests.

There is another reason that the $F$-test is superior to multiple $t$-tests. Because of a commonly occurring problem called *multicollinearity*, the $t$-tests may indicate that some independent variables are not linearly related to the dependent variable, when in fact they are. The problem of multicollinearity does not affect the $F$-test, nor does it inhibit us from developing a model that fits the data well. Multicollinearity is discussed in Section 17-3.

## 17-2k The *F*-Test and the *t*-Test in the Simple Linear Regression Model

It is useful for you to know that we can use the $F$-test to test the validity of the simple linear regression model. However, this test is identical to the $t$-test of $\beta_1$. The $t$-test of $\beta_1$ in the simple linear regression model tells us whether that independent variable is linearly related to the dependent variable. However, because there is only one independent variable, the $t$-test of $\beta_1$ also tells us whether the model is valid, which is the purpose of the $F$-test.

The relationship between the $t$-test of $\beta_1$ and the $F$-test can be explained mathematically. Statisticians can show that if we square a $t$-statistic with $\nu$ degrees of freedom we produce an $F$-statistic with 1 and $\nu$ degrees of freedom. (We briefly discussed this relationship in Chapter 14.) To illustrate, consider Example 16.2 on page 638. We found the $t$-test of $\beta_1$ to be $-13.44$, with degrees of freedom equal to 98. The $p$-value was $5.75 \times 10^{-24}$. The output included the analysis of variance table where $F = 180.64$ and the $p$-value was $5.75 \times 10^{-24}$. The $t$-statistic squared is $t^2 = (-13.44)^2 = 180.63$. (The difference is due to rounding errors.) Notice that the degrees of freedom of the $F$-statistic are 1 and 98. Thus, we can use either test to test the validity of the simple linear regression model.

## 17-2l Using the Regression Equation

We can use the multiple regression equation in two ways: We can produce the prediction interval for a particular value of $y$, and we can produce the confidence interval estimate of the expected value of $y$. In Chapter 16, we created an Excel spreadsheet to produce the two intervals. Unfortunately, the calculations for multiple regression are too complex for a spreadsheet. Thus, Excel users will have to forego the pleasure of calculating the intervals.

The good news is that XLSTAT computes the intervals. To illustrate, we'll predict the income of a 50-year-old, with 12 years of education, who works 40 hours per week, whose spouse also works 40 hours per week, 2 earners in the family and has 2 children.

## XLSTAT

| | A | B | C | D | E | F |
|---|---|---|---|---|---|---|
| 1 | Predictions for the new observations (RINCOME): | | | | | |
| 2 | | | | | | |
| 3 | Observation | Pred(RINCOME) | Lower bound 95% | Upper bound 95% | Lower bound 95% | Upper bound 95% |
| 4 | | | (Mean) | (Mean) | (Observation) | (Observation) |
| 5 | PredObs1 | 40,627 | 35,501 | 45,753 | -30,002 | 111,255 |

*INSTRUCTIONS*

1. Conduct a regression analysis. Type the given values of the independent variables into the first row in empty columns. We chose columns I to N.
2. Click **Predictions**. In the **X/Explanatory variables** box check **Quantitative** and type the range of the cells containing the given values of the independent variables. (I1:N1)
3. Click **OK**.

## INTERPRET

The prediction interval is −30,002, 111,255. It is so wide as to be completely useless. To be useful in predicting values, the model must be considerably better. The confidence interval estimate of the expected income of the population is 35,501, 45,753.

## EXERCISES

*The following exercises require the use of a computer and statistical software. Exercises 17.1–17.4 can be solved manually. See Appendix A for the sample statistics.* ***Use a 5% significance level for all tests.***

**17.1** Xr17-01 A developer who specializes in summer cottage properties is considering purchasing a large tract of land adjoining a lake. The current owner of the tract has already subdivided the land into separate building lots and has prepared the lots by removing some of the trees. The developer wants to forecast the value of each lot. From previous experience, she knows that the most important factors affecting the price of a lot are size, number of mature trees, and distance to the lake. From a nearby area, she gathers the relevant data for 60 recently sold lots.

a. Find the regression equation.
b. What is the standard error of estimate? Interpret its value.
c. What is the coefficient of determination? What does this statistic tell you?
d. What is the coefficient of determination, adjusted for degrees of freedom? Why does this value differ from the coefficient of determination? What does this tell you about the model?
e. Test the validity of the model. What does the $p$-value of the test statistic tell you?

f. Interpret each of the coefficients.
g. Test to determine whether each of the independent variables is linearly related to the price of the lot in this model.
h. Predict with 90% confidence the selling price of a 40,000-square-foot lot that has 50 mature trees and is 25 feet from the lake.
i. Estimate with 90% confidence the average selling price of 50,000-square-foot lots that have 10 mature trees and are 75 feet from the lake.

**17.2** Xr17-02 Pat Statsdud, a student ranking near the bottom of the statistics class, decided that a certain amount of studying could actually improve final grades. However, too much studying would not be warranted because Pat's ambition (if that's what one could call it) was to ultimately graduate with the absolute minimum level of work. Pat was registered in a statistics course that had only 3 weeks to go before the final exam and for which the final grade was determined in the following way:

Total mark = 20% (Assignment)
+ 30% (Midterm test)
+ 50% (Final exam)

To determine how much work to do in the remaining 3 weeks, Pat needed to be able to predict the final exam mark on the basis of the assignment mark (worth 20 points) and the midterm mark (worth 30 points). Pat's marks on these were 12/20 and 14/30, respectively. Accordingly, Pat undertook the following analysis. The final exam mark, assignment mark, and midterm test mark for 30 students who took the statistics course last year were collected.

a. Determine the regression equation.
b. What is the standard error of estimate? Briefly describe how you interpret this statistic.
c. What is the coefficient of determination? What does this statistic tell you?
d. Test the validity of the model.
e. Interpret each of the coefficients.
f. Can Pat infer that the assignment mark is linearly related to the final grade in this model?
g. Can Pat infer that the midterm mark is linearly related to the final grade in this model?
h. Predict Pat's final exam mark with 95% confidence.
i. Predict Pat's final grade with 95% confidence.

**17.3** Xr17-03 The president of a company that manufactures drywall wants to analyze the variables that affect demand for his product. Drywall is used to construct walls in houses and offices. Consequently, the president decides to develop a regression model in which the dependent variable is monthly sales of drywall (in hundreds of 4 × 8 sheets) and the independent variables are as follows:

Number of building permits issued in the county
Five-year mortgage rates (in percentage points)
Vacancy rate in apartments (in percentage points)
Vacancy rate in office buildings (in percentage points)

To estimate a multiple regression model, he took monthly observations from the past 2 years.

a. Analyze the data using multiple regression.
b. What is the standard error of estimate? Can you use this statistic to assess the model's fit? If so, how?
c. What is the coefficient of determination, and what does it tell you about the regression model?
d. Test the overall validity of the model.
e. Interpret each of the coefficients.
f. Test to determine whether each of the independent variables is linearly related to drywall demand in this model.
g. Predict next month's drywall sales with 95% confidence if the number of building permits is 50, the 5-year mortgage rate is 9.0%, and the vacancy rates are 3.6% in apartments and 14.3% in office buildings.

**17.4** Xr17-04 The general manager of the Cleveland Indians baseball team is in the process of determining which minor-league players to draft. He is aware that his team needs home-run hitters and would like to find a way to predict the number of home runs a player will hit. Being an astute statistician, he gathers a random sample of players and records the number of home runs each player hit in his first two full years as a major-league player, the number of home runs he hit in his last full year in the minor leagues, his age, and the number of years of professional baseball.

a. Develop a regression model and use a software package to produce the statistics.
b. Interpret each of the coefficients.
c. How well does the model fit?
d. Test the model's validity.
e. Do each of the independent variables belong in the model?
f. Calculate the 95% interval of the number of home runs in the first two years of a player who is 25 years old, has played professional baseball for 7 years, and hit 22 home runs in his last year in the minor leagues.
g. Calculate the 95% interval of the expected number of home runs in the first two years of players who are 27 years old, have played professional baseball for 5 years, and hit 18 home runs in their last year in the minors.

## APPLICATIONS in HUMAN RESOURCES MANAGEMENT

Pavel L Photo and Video/Shutterstock.com

### Severance Pay

In most firms, the entire issue of compensation falls into the domain of the human resources manager. The manager must ensure that the method used to determine compensation contributes to the firm's objectives. Moreover, the firm needs to ensure that discrimination or bias of any kind is not a factor. Another function of the personnel manager is to develop severance packages for employees whose services are no longer needed because of downsizing or merger. The size and nature of severance are rarely part of any working agreement and must be determined by a variety of factors. Regression analysis is often useful in this area.

**17.5** Xr17-05 When one company buys another company, it is not unusual that some workers are terminated. The severance benefits offered to the laid-off workers are often the subject of dispute. Suppose that the Laurier Company recently bought the Western Company and subsequently terminated 20 of Western's employees. As part of the buyout agreement, it was promised that the severance packages offered to the former Western employees would be equivalent to those offered to Laurier employees who had been terminated in the past year. Thirty-six-year-old Bill Smith, a Western employee for the past 10 years, earning \$32,000 per year, was one of those let go. His severance package included an offer of 5 weeks' severance pay. Bill complained that this offer was less than that offered to Laurier's employees when they were laid off, in contravention of the buyout agreement. A statistician was called in to settle the dispute. The statistician was told that severance is determined by three factors: age, length of service with the company, and pay. To determine how generous the severance package had been, a random sample of 50 Laurier ex-employees was taken. For each, the following variables were recorded:

Number of weeks of severance pay
Age of employee
Number of years with the company
Annual pay (in thousands of dollars)

a. Determine the regression equation.
b. Comment on how well the model fits the data.
c. Do all the independent variables belong in the equation? Explain.
d. Perform an analysis to determine whether Bill is correct in his assessment of the severance package.

**17.6** Xr17-06 The admissions officer of a university is trying to develop a formal system to decide which students to admit to the university. She believes that determinants of success include the standard variables—high school grades and SAT scores. However, she also believes that students who have participated in extracurricular activities are more likely to succeed than those who have not. To investigate the issue, she randomly sampled 100 fourth-year students and recorded the following variables:

GPA for the first 3 years at the university (range: 0 to 12)
GPA from high school (range: 0 to 12)
SAT score (range: 400 to 1600)
Number of hours on average spent per week in organized extracurricular activities in the last year of high school

a. Develop a model that helps the admissions officer decide which students to admit and use the computer to generate the usual statistics.
b. What is the coefficient of determination? Interpret its value.
c. Test the overall validity of the model.
d. Test to determine whether each of the independent variables is linearly related to the dependent variable in this model.

e. Determine the 95% interval of the GPA for the first 3 years of university for a student whose high school GPA is 10, whose SAT score is 1200, and who worked an average of 2 hours per week on organized extracurricular activities in the last year of high school.
f. Find the 90% interval of the mean GPA for the first 3 years of university for all students whose high school GPA is 8, whose SAT score is 1100, and who worked an average of 10 hours per week on organized extracurricular activities in the last year of high school.

**17.7** Xr17-07 The marketing manager for a chain of hardware stores needed more information about the effectiveness of the three types of advertising that the chain used. These are localized direct mailing (in which flyers describing sales and featured products are distributed to homes in the area surrounding a store), newspaper advertising, and local television advertisements. To determine which type is most effective, the manager collected 1 week's data from 100 randomly selected stores. For each store, the following variables were recorded:

Weekly gross sales
Weekly expenditures on direct mailing
Weekly expenditures on newspaper advertising
Weekly expenditures on television commercials

All variables were recorded in thousands of dollars.

a. Find the regression equation.
b. What are the coefficient of determination and the coefficient of determination adjusted for degrees of freedom? What do these statistics tell you about the regression equation?
c. What does the standard error of estimate tell you about the regression model?
d. Test the validity of the model.
e. Which independent variables are linearly related to weekly gross sales in this model? Explain.
f. Compute the 95% interval of the week's gross sales if a local store spent $800 on direct mailing, $1,200 on newspaper advertisements, and $2,000 on television commercials.
g. Calculate the 95% interval of the mean weekly gross sales for all stores that spend $800 on direct mailing, $1,200 on newspaper advertising, and $2,000 on television commercials.
h. Discuss the difference between the two intervals found in parts (f) and (g).

**17.8** Xr17-08 For many cities around the world, garbage is an increasing problem. Many North American cities have virtually run out of space to dump the garbage. A consultant for a large American city decided to gather data about the problem. She took a random sample of houses and determined the following:

$Y$ = the amount of garbage per average week (pounds)
$X_1$ = Size of the house (square feet)
$X_2$ = Number of children
$X_3$ = Number of adults who are usually home during the day

a. Conduct a regression analysis.
b. Is the model valid?
c. Interpret each of the coefficients.
d. Test to determine whether each of the independent variables is linearly related to the dependent variable.

**17.9** Xr17-09 The administrator of a school board in a large county was analyzing the average mathematics test scores in the schools under her control. She noticed that there were dramatic differences in scores among the schools. In an attempt to improve the scores of all the schools, she attempted to determine the factors that account for the differences. Accordingly, she took a random sample of 40 schools across the county and, for each, determined the mean test score last year, the percentage of teachers in each school who have at least one university degree in mathematics, the mean age, and the mean annual income (in $1,000s) of the mathematics teachers.

a. Conduct a regression analysis to develop the equation.
b. Is the model valid?
c. Interpret and test the coefficients.
d. Predict with 95% confidence the test score at a school where 50% of the mathematics teachers have mathematics degrees, the mean age is 43, and the mean annual income is $48,300.

**17.10** Xr17-10* Life insurance companies are keenly interested in predicting how long their customers will live because their premiums and profitability depend on such numbers. An actuary for one insurance company gathered data from 100 recently deceased male customers. He recorded the age at death of the customer plus the ages at death of his mother and father, the mean ages at death of his grandmothers, and the mean ages at death of his grandfathers.

a. Perform a multiple regression analysis on these data.
b. Is the model valid?
c. Interpret and test the coefficients.
d. Determine the 95% interval of the longevity of a man whose parents lived to the age of 70, whose grandmothers averaged 80 years, and whose grandfathers averaged 75 years.
e. Find the 95% interval of the mean longevity of men whose mothers lived to 75 years, whose fathers lived to 65 years, whose grandmothers averaged 85 years, and whose grandfathers averaged 75 years.

**17.11** Xr17-11 University students often complain that universities reward professors for research but not for teaching, and they argue that professors react to this situation by devoting more time and energy to the publication of their findings and less time and energy to classroom activities. Professors counter that research and teaching go hand in hand: More research makes better teachers. A student organization at one university decided to investigate the issue. It randomly selected 50 economics professors who are employed by a multicampus university. The students recorded the salaries (in $1,000s) of the professors, their average teaching evaluations (on a 10-point scale), and the total number of journal articles published in their careers. Perform a complete analysis (produce the regression equation, assess it, and report your findings).

**17.12** Xr17-12* One critical factor that determines the success of a catalog store chain is the availability of products that consumers want to buy. If a store is sold out, future sales to that customer are less likely. Accordingly, delivery trucks operating from a central warehouse regularly resupply stores. In an analysis of a chain's operations, the general manager wanted to determine the factors that are related to how long it takes to unload delivery trucks. A random sample of 50 deliveries to one store was observed. The times (in minutes) to unload the truck, the total number of boxes, and the total weight (in hundreds of pounds) of the boxes were recorded.

a. Determine the multiple regression equation.
b. How well does the model fit the data? Explain.
c. Interpret and test the coefficients.
d. Produce a 95% interval of the amount of time needed to unload a truck with 100 boxes weighing 5,000 pounds.
e. Produce a 95% interval of the average amount of time needed to unload trucks with 100 boxes weighing 5,000 pounds.

**17.13** Xr17-13 Lotteries have become important sources of revenue for governments. Many people have criticized lotteries, however, referring to them as a tax on the poor and uneducated. In an examination of the issue, a random sample of 100 adults was asked how much they spend on lottery tickets and was interviewed about various socioeconomic variables. The purpose of this study is to test the following beliefs:

1. Relatively uneducated people spend more on lotteries than do relatively educated people.
2. Older people buy more lottery tickets than younger people.
3. People with more children spend more on lotteries than people with fewer children.
4. Relatively poor people spend a greater proportion of their income on lotteries than relatively rich people.

The following data were recorded:

Amount spent on lottery tickets as a percentage of total household income
Number of years of education
Age
Number of children
Personal income (in thousands of dollars)

a. Develop the multiple regression equation.
b. Is the model valid?
c. Test each of the beliefs. What conclusions can you draw?

**17.14** Xr17-14* The MBA program at a large university is facing a pleasant problem—too many applicants. The current admissions policy requires students to have completed at least 3 years of work experience and an undergraduate degree with a B-average or better. Until 3 years ago, the school admitted any applicant who met these requirements. However, because the program recently converted from a 2-year program (four semesters) to a 1-year program (three semesters), the number of applicants has increased substantially. The dean, who teaches statistics courses, wants to raise the admissions standards by developing a method that more accurately predicts how well an applicant will perform in the MBA program. She believes that the primary determinants of success are the following:

Undergraduate grade point average (GPA)
Graduate Management Admissions Test (GMAT) score
Number of years of work experience

She randomly sampled students who completed the MBA and recorded their MBA program GPA, as well as the three variables listed here.

a. Develop a multiple regression model.
b. Test the model's validity.
c. Test to determine which of the independent variables is linearly related to MBA GPA.

**17.15** Xr17-15 With voter turnout during presidential elections around 50%, a vital task for politicians is to try to predict who will actually vote. A variable used to determine who is likely to vote was created and defined as follows. DEFINITE: 1 = Definitely will not vote; 2, 3, 4, 5, 6, 7, 8, 9, 10 = Definitely will vote. A pollster conducted a survey that recorded the variable as well as age, education, and income. Develop a regression model to predict intention to vote using the following demographic independent variables:

a. Determine the regression equation.
b. Test the model's validity.
c. Test to determine whether there is sufficient evidence to infer a linear relationship between the dependent variable and each independent variable.

**17.16** Xr17-16 Refer to Exercise 17.15. The pollster also recorded the following variables in addition to the variable DEFINITE.

Number of days in previous week watching national news on television (DAYS1)

Number of days in previous week watching local television news in afternoon or early evening (DAYS2)

Number of days in previous week watching local television news in late evening (DAYS3)

Number of days in previous week reading a daily newspaper (DAYS4)

Number of days in previous week reading a daily newspaper on the Internet (DAYS5)

Number of days in previous week listening to news on radio (DAYS6)

The purpose of this survey is to answer this question, "Does watching news on television or reading newspapers provide indicators of who will vote?" Conduct a regression analysis with intention to vote (DEFINITE) as the dependent variable.

a. Compute the regression equation.
b. Is there enough evidence to conclude that the model is valid?
c. Test each slope coefficient.

## APPLICATIONS in OPERATIONS MANAGEMENT

Ken Wolter/Shutterstock.com

### Location Analysis

Location analysis is one function of operations management. Deciding where to locate a plant, warehouse, or retail outlet is a critical decision for any organization. A large number of variables must be considered in this decision problem. For example, a production facility must be located close to suppliers of raw resources and supplies, skilled labor, and transportation to customers. Retail outlets must consider the type and number of potential customers. In the next example, we describe an application of regression analysis to find profitable locations for a motel chain.

**17.17** Xr17-17 La Quinta Motor Inns is a moderately priced chain of motor inns located across the United States. Its market is the frequent business traveler. The chain recently launched a campaign to increase market share by building new inns. The management of the chain is aware of the difficulty in choosing locations for new motels. Moreover, making decisions without adequate information often results in poor decisions. Consequently, the chain's management acquired data on 100 randomly selected inns belonging to La Quinta. The objective was to predict which sites are likely to be profitable.

To measure profitability, La Quinta used *operating margin*, which is the ratio of the sum of profit, depreciation, and interest expenses divided by total revenue. (Although occupancy is often used as a measure of a motel's success, the company statistician concluded that occupancy was too unstable, especially during economic turbulence.) The higher the operating margin, the greater the success of the inn. La Quinta defines profitable inns as those with an operating margin in excess of 50%; unprofitable inns are those with margins of less than 30%. After a discussion with a number of experienced managers, La Quinta decided to select one or two independent variables from each of the following categories: competition, market awareness, demand generators, demographics, and physical location. To measure the degree of competition, they determined the total number of motel and hotel rooms within 3 miles of each La Quinta inn. Market awareness was measured by the number of miles to the closest competing motel. Two variables that represent sources of customers were chosen. The amount of office space and college and university enrollment in the surrounding community are demand generators. Both of these are measures of economic activity. A demographic variable that describes the community is the median household income. Finally, as a measure of the physical qualities of the location La Quinta chose the distance to the downtown core. These data are stored using the following format:

Column 1: $y$ = Operating margin, in percent
Column 2: $x_1$ = Total number of motel and hotel rooms within 3 miles of La Quinta inn
Column 3: $x_2$ = Number of miles to closest competition
Column 4: $x_3$ = Office space in thousands of square feet in surrounding community
Column 5: $x_4$ = College and university enrollment (in thousands) in nearby university or college
Column 6: $x_5$ = Median household income (in \$thousands) in surrounding community
Column 7: $x_6$ = Distance (in miles) to the downtown core

Adapted from Sheryl E. Kimes and James A. Fitzsimmons, "Selecting Profitable Hotel Sites at La Quinta Motor Inns," *INTERFACES* 20 March–April 1990, pp. 12–20.

a. Develop a regression analysis.
b. Test to determine whether there is enough evidence to infer that the model is valid.
c. Test each of the slope coefficients.
d. Interpret the coefficients.
e. Predict with 95% confidence the operating margin of a site with the following characteristics:
   There are 3,815 rooms within 3 miles of the site, the closest other hotel or motel is .9 miles away, the amount of office space is 476,000 square feet, there is one college and one university with a total enrollment of 24,500 students, the median income in the area is \$35,000, and the distance to the downtown core is 11.2 miles.
f. Refer to part (e). Estimate with 95% confidence the mean operating margin of all La Quinta inns with those characteristics.

## General Social Survey Exercises

*Excel Data Analysis users: We remind you that any row that contains at least one empty cell (in dependent and independent variables column) must be removed.* ***Conduct all tests at the 5% significance level.***

**17.18** GSS2014* How does the amount of education of one's parents (PAEDUC, MAEDUC) affect your education (EDUC)?
a. Develop a regression model.
b. Test the validity of the model.
c. Test the two slope coefficients.
d. Interpret the coefficients.

**17.19** GSS2014* What determines people's opinion on the following question? Should the government reduce income differences between rich and poor (EQWLTH: 1 = Government should reduce differences; 2, 3, 4, 5, 6, 7 = No government action).
a. Develop a regression analysis using demographic variables age, (AGE), education (EDUC), income (RINCOME), and weekly hours of work (HRS1).
b. Test the model's validity.
c. Test each of the slope coefficients.
d. Interpret the coefficient of determination.

**17.20** GSS2014* The Nielsen Ratings estimate the number of televisions tuned to various channels. However, television executives need more information. The General Social Survey may be the source of this information. Respondents were asked to report the number of hours per average day of television viewing (TVHOURS). Conduct a regression analysis using the independent variables age (AGE), education (EDUC), hours of work (HRS1), and number of children (CHILDS).

a. Test the model's validity.
b. Interpret the slope coefficients.
c. Test each slope coefficient.
d. Determine the coefficient of determination and describe what it tells you.

**17.21** GSS2014* What determines people's opinion on the following question, Should the government improve the standard of living of poor people (HELPPOOR: 1 = Government act; 2, 3, 4, 5 = People should help themselves)?
a. Develop a regression analysis using demographic variables age, (AGE), education (EDUC), income (RINCOME), and weekly hours of work (HRS1).
b. Test the model's validity.
c. Test each of the slope coefficients.
d. Interpret the coefficient of determination.

## Survey of Consumer Finances Exercises

**17.22** SCF2013:\MC* How does age and education affect income among middle-class households? To answer the question, conduct a regression analysis of the dependent variable INCOME using the independent variables AGE and years of education (EDUC).
a. Estimate the regression coefficients.
b. Test the model's validity.
c. Test to determine whether there is evidence of a positive linear relationship between income and education.
d. What does the coefficient of determination tell you?

**17.23** SCF2013:\MC* How are middle class households' expenditures on food eaten at home affected by the age, education, and income of the head of the household? To answer the question conduct a regression analysis using FOODHOME as the dependent variable and AGE, EDUC, and INCOME as independent variables.
a. Determine the regression coefficients.
b. Is there enough evidence to infer that the model is valid?
c. Test each coefficient to determine whether each independent variable is linearly related to the dependent variable.

**17.24** SCF2013:\MC* Repeat Exercise 17.23 for expenditures on food away from home (FOODAWAY).

# 17-3 Regression Diagnostics—II

In Section 16-6, we discussed how to determine whether the required conditions are unsatisfied. The same procedures can be used to diagnose problems in the multiple regression model. Here is a brief summary of the diagnostic procedure we described in Chapter 16.

Calculate the residuals and check the following:

1. *Is the error variable nonnormal?* Draw the histogram of the residuals.
2. *Is the error variance constant?* Plot the residuals versus the predicted values of $y$.
3. *Are the errors independent (time-series data)?* Plot the residuals versus the time periods.
4. *Are there observations that are inaccurate or do not belong to the target population?* Double-check the accuracy of outliers and influential observations.

If the error is nonnormal and/or the variance is not a constant, several remedies can be attempted. These are beyond the level of this book.

Outliers and influential observations are checked by examining the data in question to ensure accuracy.

Nonindependence of a time series can sometimes be detected by graphing the residuals and the time periods and looking for evidence of autocorrelation. In Section 17-4, we introduce the Durbin–Watson test, which tests for one form of autocorrelation. We will offer a corrective measure for nonindependence.

FIGURE **17.4** **Negative First-Order Autocorrelation**

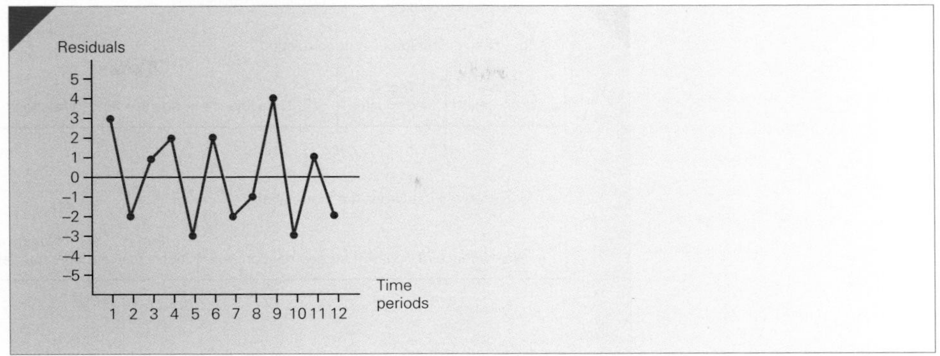


Table 8 in Appendix B is designed to test for positive first-order autocorrelation by providing values of $d_L$ and $d_U$ for a variety of values of $n$ and $k$ and for $\alpha = .01$ and .05.

The decision is made in the following way. If $d < d_L$, we conclude that there is enough evidence to show that positive first-order autocorrelation exists. If $d > d_U$, we conclude that there is not enough evidence to show that positive first-order autocorrelation exists. And if $d_L \leq d \leq d_U$, the test is inconclusive. The recommended course of action when the test is inconclusive is to continue testing with more data until a conclusive decision can be made.

For example, to test for positive first-order autocorrelation with $n = 20$, $k = 3$, and $\alpha = .05$, we test the following hypotheses:

$H_0$: There is no first-order autocorrelation.

$H_1$: There is positive first-order autocorrelation.

The decision is made as follows:

If $d < d_L = 1.00$, reject the null hypothesis in favor of the alternative hypothesis.

If $d > d_U = 1.68$, do not reject the null hypothesis.

If $1.00 \leq d \leq 1.68$, the test is inconclusive.

To test for negative first-order autocorrelation, we change the critical values. If $d > 4 - d_L$, we conclude that negative first-order autocorrelation exists. If $d < 4 - d_U$, we conclude that there is not enough evidence to show that negative first-order autocorrelation exists. If $4 - d_U \leq d \leq 4 - d_L$, the test is inconclusive.

We can also test simply for first-order autocorrelation by combining the two one-tail tests. If $d < d_L$ or $d > 4 - d_L$, we conclude that autocorrelation exists. If $d_U \leq d \leq 4 - d_U$, we conclude that there is no evidence of autocorrelation. If $d_L \leq d \leq d_U$ or $4 - d_U \leq d \leq 4 - d_L$, the test is inconclusive. The significance level will be $2\alpha$ (where $\alpha$ is the one-tail significance level). Figure 17.5 describes the range of values of $d$ and the conclusion for each interval.

For time-series data, we add the Durbin–Watson test to our list of regression diagnostics. In other words, we determine whether the error variable is normally distributed with constant variance (as we did in Section 17-3), we identify outliers and (if our software allows it) influential observations that should be verified, and we conduct the Durbin–Watson test.

FIGURE **17.5** **Durbin-Watson Test**

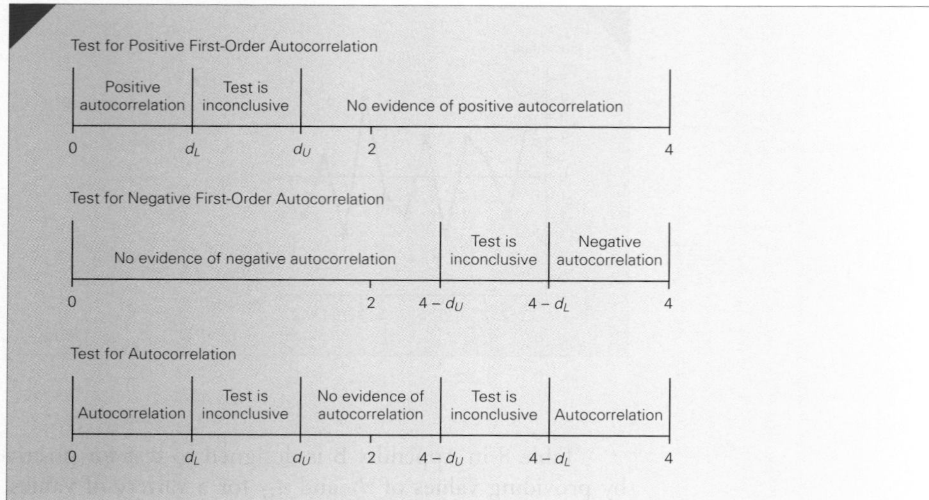


EXAMPLE 17.1

DATA Xm17-01

## Christmas Week Ski Lift Sales

Christmas week is a critical period for most ski resorts. Because many students and adults are free from other obligations, they are able to spend several days indulging in their favorite pastime, skiing. A large proportion of gross revenue is earned during this period. A ski resort in Vermont wanted to determine the effect that weather had on its sales of lift tickets. The manager of the resort collected data on the number of lift tickets sold during Christmas week ($y$), the total snowfall in inches ($x_1$), and the average temperature in degrees Fahrenheit ($x_2$) for the past 20 years. Develop the multiple regression model and diagnose any violations of the required conditions.

SOLUTION:

The model is

$$y = \beta_0 + \beta_1 x_1 + \beta_2 x_2 + \varepsilon$$

Excel does not perform the Durbin-Watson test.

### XLSTAT

| | A | B | C | D | E | F |
|---|---|---|---|---|---|---|
| 1 | **Regression of variable Tickets:** | | | | | |
| 2 | | | | | | |
| 3 | Goodness of fit statistics (Tickets): | | | | | |
| 4 | Observations | 20 | | | | |
| 5 | Sum of weights | 20 | | | | |
| 6 | DF | 17 | | | | |
| 7 | R² | 0.1200 | | | | |
| 8 | Adjusted R² | 0.0165 | | | | |
| 9 | MSE | 2,929,836 | | | | |
| 10 | RMSE | 1,712 | | | | |
| 11 | DW | 0.5931 | | | | |
| 12 | | | | | | |
| 13 | Analysis of variance (Tickets): | | | | | |
| 14 | Source | DF | Sum of squares | Mean squares | F | Pr > F |
| 15 | Model | 2 | 6,793,798 | 3,396,899 | 1.159 | 0.3373 |
| 16 | Error | 17 | 49,807,214 | 2,929,836 | | |
| 17 | Corrected Total | 19 | 56,601,012 | | | |
| 18 | | | | | | |
| 19 | Model parameters (Tickets): | | | | | |
| 20 | Source | Value | Standard error | t | Pr > \|t\| | |
| 21 | Intercept | 8308 | 903.7 | 9.19 | < 0.0001 | |
| 22 | Snowfall | 74.59 | 51.57 | 1.45 | 0.1663 | |
| 23 | Temperature | −8.75 | 19.70 | −0.44 | 0.6625 | |

## INTERPRET

As you can see, the coefficient of determination is small ($R^2 = 12\%$) and the $p$-value of the $F$-test is .3373, both of which indicate that the model is poor. We used Excel to draw the histogram (Figure 17.6) of the residuals and plot the predicted values of $y$ versus the residuals in Figure 17.7. Because the observations constitute a time series, we also used Excel to plot the time periods (years) versus the residuals (Figure 17.8).

FIGURE **17.6** **Histogram of Residuals in Example 17.1**

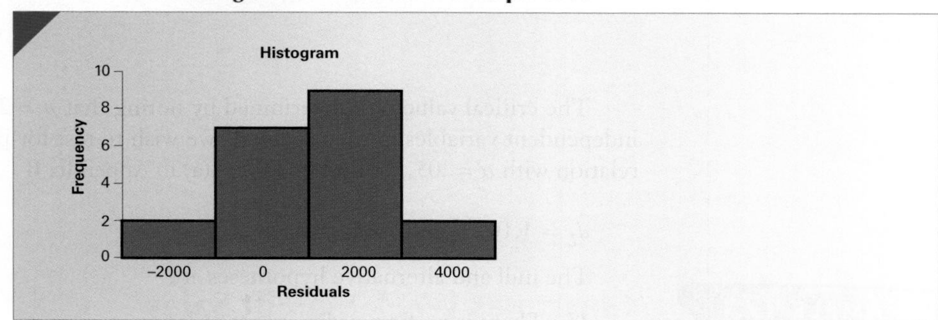


The histogram reveals that the error may be normally distributed.

FIGURE **17.7** **Plot of Predicted Values versus Residuals in Example 17.1**

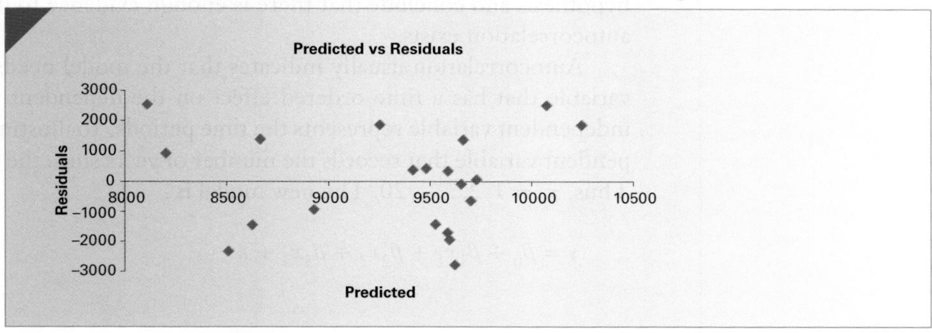


There does not appear to be any evidence of heteroscedasticity.

FIGURE **17.8** **Plot of Time Periods versus Residuals in Example 17.1**

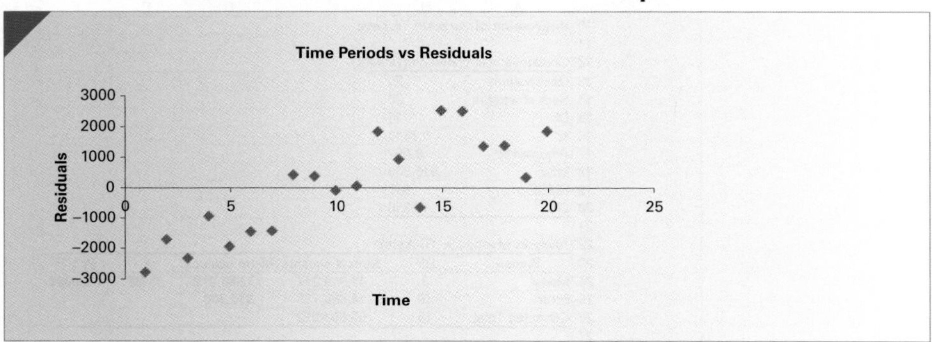


This graph reveals a serious problem. There is a strong relationship between consecutive values of the residuals, which indicates that the requirement that the errors are independent has been violated. To confirm this diagnosis, we instructed XLSTAT to calculate the Durbin–Watson statistic.

**XLSTAT**

| 11 | DW | 0.5931 |
|---|---|---|

The Durbin–Watson statistic will be in the goodness-of-fit statistics.

*INSTRUCTIONS*

Run the regression. Click **Outputs** and check **Predictions and residuals** and **Studentized residuals.**

The critical values are determined by noting that $n = 20$ and $k = 2$ (there are two independent variables in the model). If we wish to test for positive first-order autocorrelation with $\alpha = .05$, we find in Table 8(a) in Appendix B

$$d_L = 1.10 \quad \text{and} \quad d_U = 1.54$$

The null and alternative hypotheses are

$H_0$: There is no first-order autocorrelation.

$H_1$: There is positive first-order autocorrelation.

The rejection region is $d < d_L = 1.10$. Because $d = .5931$, we reject the null hypothesis and conclude that there is enough evidence to infer that positive first-order autocorrelation exists.

Autocorrelation usually indicates that the model needs to include an independent variable that has a time-ordered effect on the dependent variable. The simplest such independent variable represents the time periods. To illustrate, we included a third independent variable that records the number of years since the year the data were gathered. Thus, $x_3 = 1, 2, \ldots, 20$. The new model is

$$y = \beta_0 + \beta_1 x_1 + \beta_2 x_2 + \beta_3 x_3 + \varepsilon$$

**XLSTAT**

| | A | B | C | D | E | F |
|---|---|---|---|---|---|---|
| 10 | **Regression of variable Tickets:** | | | | | |
| 11 | | | | | | |
| 12 | Goodness of fit statistics (Tickets): | | | | | |
| 13 | Observations | 20 | | | | |
| 14 | Sum of weights | 20 | | | | |
| 15 | DF | 16 | | | | |
| 16 | R² | 0.7410 | | | | |
| 17 | Adjusted R² | 0.692 | | | | |
| 18 | MSE | 916,300 | | | | |
| 19 | RMSE | 957 | | | | |
| 20 | DW | 1.8850 | | | | |
| 21 | | | | | | |
| 22 | Analysis of variance (Tickets): | | | | | |
| 23 | Source | DF | Sum of squares | Mean squares | F | Pr > F |
| 24 | Model | 3 | 41,940,217 | 13,980,072 | 15.26 | **< 0.0001** |
| 25 | Error | 16 | 14,660,795 | 916,300 | | |
| 26 | Corrected Total | 19 | 56,601,012 | | | |
| 27 | | | | | | |
| 28 | Model parameters (Tickets): | | | | | |
| 29 | Source | Value | Standard error | t | Pr > \|t\| | |
| 30 | Intercept | 5966 | 631.3 | 9.45 | **< 0.0001** | |
| 31 | Snowfall | 70.18 | 28.85 | 2.43 | **0.0271** | |
| 32 | Temperature | −9.23 | 11.02 | −0.84 | 0.4145 | |
| 33 | Time | 230.0 | 37.13 | 6.19 | **< 0.0001** | |

As we did before, we calculate the residuals and conduct regression diagnostics using Excel. The results are shown in Figure 17.9–17.11.

FIGURE **17.9** **Histogram of Residuals in Example 17.1 (Time Variable Included)**

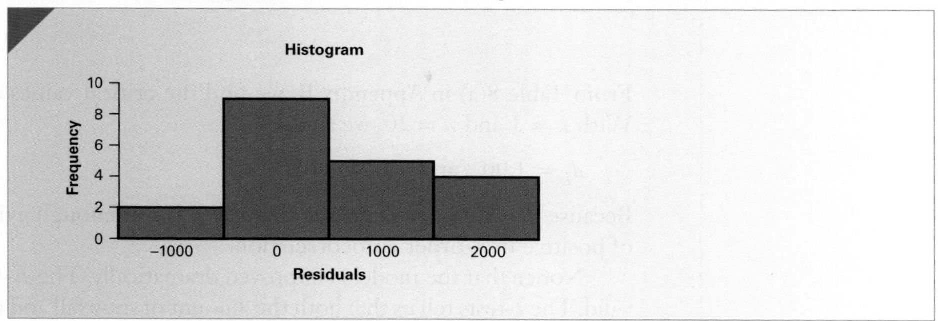


The histogram reveals that the error may be normally distributed.

FIGURE **17.10** **Plot of Predicted Values versus Residuals in Example 17.1 (Time Variable Included)**

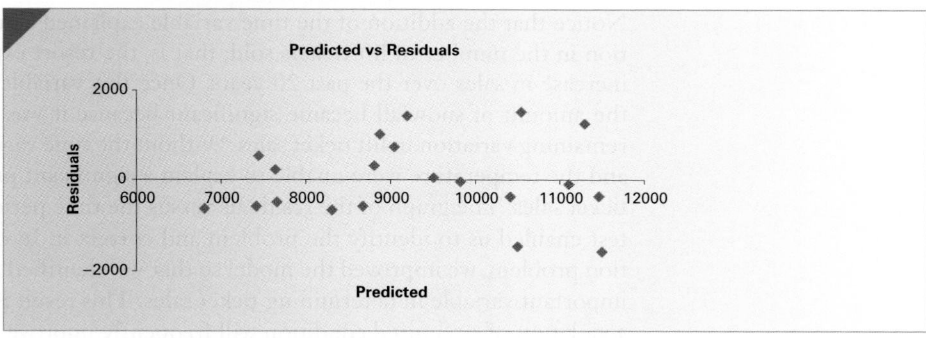


The error variable variance appears to be constant.

FIGURE **17.11** **Plot of Time Periods versus Residuals in Example 17.1 (Time Variable Included)**

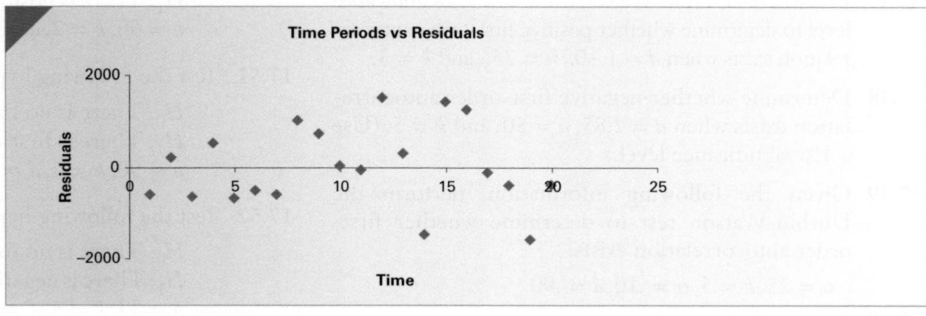


There is no sign of autocorrelation. To confirm our diagnosis, we conducted the Durbin–Watson test.

**XLSTAT**

| 20 | DW | 1.8850 |
|---|---|---|

From Table 8(a) in Appendix B, we find the critical values of the Durbin–Watson test. With $k = 3$ and $n = 20$, we find

$$d_L = 1.00 \quad \text{and} \quad d_U = 1.68$$

Because $d > 1.68$, we conclude that there is not enough evidence to infer the presence of positive first-order autocorrelation.

Notice that the model is improved dramatically. The $F$-test tells us that the model is valid. The $t$-tests tell us that both the amount of snowfall and time are significantly linearly related to the number of lift tickets. This information could prove useful in advertising for the resort. For example, the resort could emphasize any recent snowfall in its advertising. If no new snow has fallen, the resort might emphasize its snow-making facilities.

## 17-4b Developing an Understanding of Statistical Concepts

Notice that the addition of the time variable explained a large proportion of the variation in the number of lift tickets sold; that is, the resort experienced a relatively steady increase in sales over the past 20 years. Once this variable was included in the model, the amount of snowfall became significant because it was able to explain some of the remaining variation in lift ticket sales. Without the time variable, the amount of snowfall and the temperature were unable to explain a significant proportion of the variation in ticket sales. The graph of the residuals versus the time periods and the Durbin–Watson test enabled us to identify the problem and correct it. In overcoming the autocorrelation problem, we improved the model so that we identified the amount of snowfall as an important variable in determining ticket sales. This result is quite common. Correcting a violation of a required condition will frequently improve the model.

## Exercises

**17.47** Perform the Durbin-Watson test at the 5% significance level to determine whether positive first-order autocorrelation exists when $d = 1.10$, $n = 25$, and $k = 3$.

**17.48** Determine whether negative first-order autocorrelation exists when $d = 2.85$, $n = 50$, and $k = 5$. (Use a 1% significance level.)

**17.49** Given the following information, perform the Durbin-Watson test to determine whether first-order autocorrelation exists:

$n = 25, k = 5, \alpha = .10, d = .90$

**17.50** Test the following hypotheses with $\alpha = .05$.

$H_0$: There is no first-order autocorrelation.
$H_1$: There is positive first-order autocorrelation.
$n = 50, k = 2, d = 1.38$

**17.51** Test the following hypotheses with $\alpha = .02$.

$H_0$: There is no first-order autocorrelation.
$H_1$: There is first-order autocorrelation.
$n = 90, k = 5, d = 1.60$

**17.52** Test the following hypotheses with $\alpha = .05$.

$H_0$: There is no first-order autocorrelation.
$H_1$: There is negative first-order autocorrelation.
$n = 33, k = 4, d = 2.25$

*The following exercises require a computer and software.*

**17.53** Xr17-53 Observations of variables $y$, $x_1$, and $x_2$ were taken over 100 consecutive time periods.

a. Conduct a regression analysis of these data.
b. Plot the residuals versus the time periods. Describe the graph.
c. Perform the Durbin-Watson test. Is there evidence of autocorrelation? Use $\alpha = .10$.
d. If autocorrelation was detected in Part c, propose an alternative regression model to remedy the problem. Use the computer to generate the statistics associated with this model.
e. Redo Parts b and c. Compare the two models.

**17.54** Xr17-54 Weekly sales of a company's product ($y$) and those of its main competitor ($x$) were recorded for one year.

a. Conduct a regression analysis of these data.
b. Plot the residuals versus the time periods. Does there appear to be autocorrelation?
c. Perform the Durbin-Watson test. Is there evidence of autocorrelation? Use $\alpha = .10$.
d. If autocorrelation was detected in Part c, propose an alternative regression model to remedy the problem. Use the computer to generate the statistics associated with this model.
e. Redo Parts b and c. Compare the two models.

**17.55** Refer to Exercise 17.3. Is there evidence of positive first-order autocorrelation?

**17.56** Refer to Exercise 16.131. Determine whether there is evidence of first-order autocorrelation.

**17.57** Xr17-57 The manager of a tire store in Minneapolis has been concerned with the high cost of inventory. The current policy is to stock all the snow tires that are predicted to sell over the entire winter at the beginning of the season (end of October). The manager can reduce inventory costs by having suppliers deliver snow tires regularly from October to February. However, he needs to be able to predict weekly sales to avoid stockouts that will ultimately lose sales. To help develop a forecasting model, he records the number of snow tires sold weekly during the last winter and the amount of snowfall (in inches) in each week.

a. Develop a regression model and use a software package to produce the statistics.
b. Perform a complete diagnostic analysis to determine whether the required conditions are satisfied.
c. if one or more conditions are unsatisfied, attempt to remedy the problem.
d. Use whatever procedures you wish to assess how well the new model fits the data.
e. Interpret and test each of the coefficients.

## CHAPTER SUMMARY

The multiple regression model extends the model introduced in Chapter 16. The statistical concepts and techniques are similar to those presented in simple linear regression. We assess the model in three ways: standard error of estimate, the coefficient of determination (and the coefficient of determination adjusted for degrees of freedom), and the $F$-test of the analysis of variance. We can use the $t$-tests of the coefficients to determine whether each of the independent variables is linearly related to the dependent variable. As we did in Chapter 16, we showed how to diagnose violations of the required conditions and to identify other problems. We introduced multicollinearity and demonstrated its effect and its remedy. Finally, we presented the Durbin–Watson test to detect first-order autocorrelation.

### IMPORTANT TERMS:

Response surface 694
Coefficient of determination adjusted for degrees of freedom 698
Multicollinearity 713
Durbin–Watson test 715
First-order autocorrelation 715

### SYMBOLS:

| Symbol | Pronounced | Represents |
|---|---|---|
| $\beta_i$ | Beta sub $i$ or beta $i$ | Coefficient of $i$th independent variable |
| $b_i$ | $b$ sub $i$ or $b\,i$ | Sample coefficient |

## FORMULAS:

Standard error of estimate

$$s_\varepsilon = \sqrt{\frac{\text{SSE}}{n-k-1}}$$

Test statistic for $\beta_i$

$$t = \frac{b_i - \beta_i}{s_{b_i}}$$

Coefficient of determination

$$R^2 = \frac{s_{xy}^2}{s_x^2 s_y^2} = 1 - \frac{\text{SSE}}{\sum(y_i - \bar{y})^2}$$

Adjusted coefficient of determination

$$\text{Adjusted } R^2 = 1 - \frac{\text{SSE}/(n-k-1)}{\sum(y_i - \bar{y})^2/(n-1)}$$

Mean square for error

$$\text{MSE} = \text{SSE}/k$$

Mean square for regression

$$\text{MSR} = \text{SSR}/(n-k-1)$$

$F$-statistic

$$F = \text{MSR/MSE}$$

Durbin–Watson statistic

$$d = \frac{\sum_{i=1}^{m}(e_i - e_{i-1})^2}{\sum_{i=1}^{n} e_i^2}$$

## COMPUTER OUTPUT AND INSTRUCTIONS:

| Technique | Excel |
|---|---|
| Regression | 696 |
| Prediction interval | 705 |
| Durbin–Watson statistic | 720 |

# Chapter Exercises

*The following exercises require the use of a computer and statistical software.* ***Use a 5% significance level.***

**17.58** Xr17-58 The agronomist referred to in Exercise 16.133 believed that the amount of rainfall as well as the amount of fertilizer used would affect the crop yield. She redid the experiment in the following way. Thirty greenhouses were rented. In each, the amount of fertilizer and the amount of water were varied. At the end of the growing season, the amount of corn was recorded.

a. Determine the sample regression line and interpret the coefficients.
b. Do these data allow us to infer that there is a linear relationship between the amount of fertilizer and the crop yield?
c. Do these data allow us to infer that there is a linear relationship between the amount of water and the crop yield?
d. What can you say about the fit of the multiple regression model?
e. Is it reasonable to believe that the error variable is normally distributed with constant variance?
f. Predict the crop yield when 100 kilograms of fertilizer and 1,000 liters of water are applied. Use a confidence level of 95%.

**17.59** Xr16-12* Exercise 16.12 addressed the problem of determining the relationship between the price of apartment buildings and number of square feet. Hoping to improve the predictive capability of the model, the real estate agent also recorded the number of apartments, the age, and the number of floors.

a. Calculate the regression equation.
b. Is the model valid?
c. Compare your answer with that of Exercise 16.12.

**17.60** Xr16-16* In Exercise 16.16, a statistics practitioner examined the relationship between office rents and the city's office vacancy rate. The model appears to be quite poor. It was decided to add another variable that measures the state of the economy. The city's unemployment rate was chosen for this purpose.

a. Determine the regression equation.
b. Determine the coefficient of determination and describe what this value means.
c. Test the model's validity in explaining office rent.
d. Determine which of the two independent variables is linearly related to rents.
e. Determine whether the error is normally distributed with a constant variance.
f. Determine whether there is evidence of autocorrelation.
g. Predict with 95% confidence the office rent in a city whose vacancy rate is 10% and whose unemployment rate is 7%.

## CASE 17.1 An Analysis of Mutual Fund Managers, Part 1*

JohnKwan/Shutterstock.com

DATA C17-01

There are thousands of mutual funds available (see page 161 for a brief introduction to mutual funds). There is no shortage of sources of information about them. Newspapers regularly report the value of each unit, mutual fund companies and brokers advertise extensively, and there are books on the subject. Many of the advertisements imply that individuals should invest in the advertiser's mutual fund because it has performed well in the past. Unfortunately, there is little evidence to infer that past performance is a predictor of the future. However, it may be possible to acquire useful information by examining the managers of mutual funds. Several researchers have studied the issue. One project gathered data concerning the performance of 2,029 funds.

The performance of each fund was measured by its risk-adjusted excess return, which is the difference between the return on investment of the fund and a return that is considered a standard. The standard is based on a variety of variables, including the risk-free rate.

Four variables describe the fund manager: age, tenure (how many years the manager has been in charge), whether the manager had an MBA (1 = yes, 0 = no), and a measure of the quality of the manager's education [the average Scholastic Achievement Test (SAT) score of students at the university where the manager received his or her undergraduate degree].

Conduct an analysis of the data. Discuss how the average SAT score of the manager's alma mater, whether he or she has an MBA, and his or her age and tenure are related to the performance of the fund.

*This case is based on "Are Some Mutual Fund Managers Better Than Others? Cross-Sectional Patterns in Behavior and Performance," Judith Chevalier and Glenn Ellison, Working Paper 5852, National Bureau of Economic Research.

## CASE 17.2 An Analysis of Mutual Fund Managers, Part 2

RTimages/Shutterstock.com

DATA C17-02a C17-02b

In addition to analyzing the relationship between the managers' characteristic and the performance of the fund, researchers wanted to determine whether the same characteristics are related to the behavior of the fund. In particular, they wanted to know whether the risk of the fund and its management expense ratio (MER) were related to the manager's age, tenure, university SAT score, and whether he or she had an MBA.

In Section 4-6, we introduced the market model wherein we measure the systematic risk of stocks by the stock's beta. The beta of a portfolio is the average of the betas of the stocks that make up the portfolio. File C17-02a stores the same managers' characteristics as those in file C17-01. However, the first column contains the betas of the mutual funds.

To analyze the management expense ratios, it was decided to include a measure of the size of the fund. The logarithm of the funds' assets (in $millions) was recorded with the MER. These data are stored in file C17-02b.

Analyze both sets of data and write a brief report of your findings.

# APPENDIX 17 / REVIEW OF CHAPTERS 12 TO 17

Table A17.1 presents a list of inferential methods presented thus far, and Figure A17.1 depicts a flowchart designed to help students identify the correct statistical technique.

**TABLE A17.1 Summary of Statistical Techniques in Chapters 12 to 17**

| |
|---|
| $t$-test of $\mu$ |
| Estimator of $\mu$ (including estimator of $N\mu$) |
| $\chi^2$ test of $\sigma^2$ |
| Estimator of $\sigma^2$ |
| $z$-test of $p$ |
| Estimator of $p$ (including estimator of $Np$) |
| Equal-variances $t$-test of $\mu_1 - \mu_2$ |
| Equal-variances estimator of $\mu_1 - \mu_2$ |
| Unequal-variances $t$-test of $\mu_1 - \mu_2$ |
| Unequal-variances estimator of $\mu_1 - \mu_2$ |
| $t$-test of $\mu_D$ |
| Estimator of $\mu_D$ |
| $F$-test of $\sigma_1^2/\sigma_2^2$ |
| Estimator of $\sigma_1^2/\sigma_2^2$ |
| $z$-test of $p_1 - p_2$ (Case 1) |
| $z$-test of $p_1 - p_2$ (Case 2) |
| Estimator of $p_1 - p_2$ |
| One-way analysis of variance (including multiple comparisons) |
| Two-way (randomized blocks) analysis of variance |
| Two-factor analysis of variance |
| $\chi^2$-goodness-of-fit test |
| $\chi^2$-test of a contingency table |
| Simple linear regression and correlation (including $t$-tests of $\beta_1$ and $\rho$, and prediction and confidence intervals) |
| Multiple regression (including $t$-tests of $\beta_i$, $F$-test, and prediction and confidence intervals) |

FIGURE **A17.1** **Flowchart of Techniques in Chapters 12 to 17**

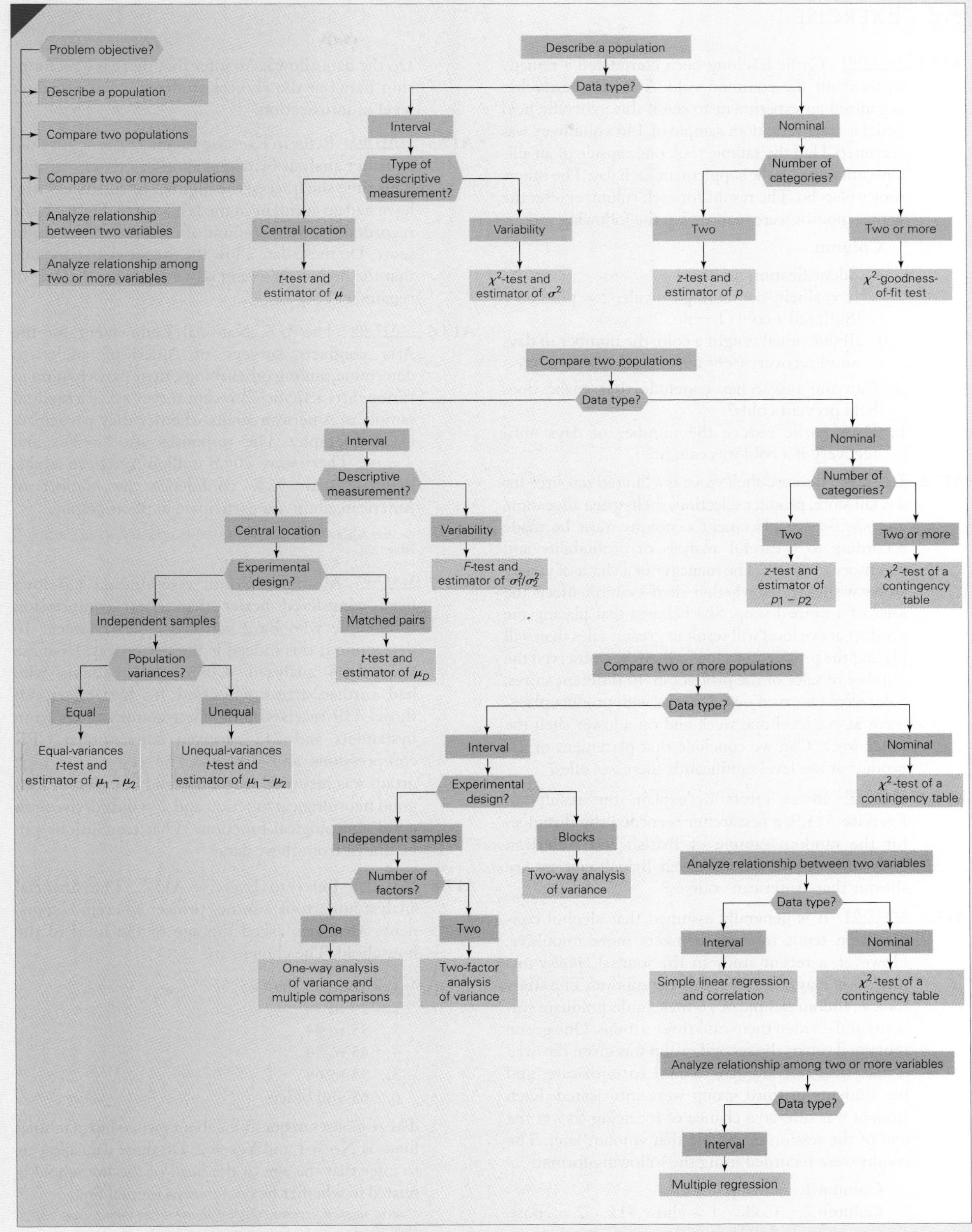

## EXERCISE

**A17.1** XrA17-01 Garlic has long been considered a remedy to ward off the common cold. A British researcher organized an experiment to see if this generally held belief is true. A random sample of 146 volunteers was recruited. Half the sample took one capsule of an allicin-containing garlic supplement each day. The others took a placebo. The results for each volunteer after the winter months were recorded in the following way.

**Column**

1. Identification number
2. 1 = allicin-containing capsule; 2 = placebo
3. Suffered a cold (1 = no, 2 = yes)
4. If individual caught a cold, the number of days until recovery (999 was recorded if no cold)

a. Can the researcher conclude that garlic does help prevent colds?

b. Does garlic reduce the number of days until recovery if a cold was caught?

**A17.2** XrA17-02 Because shelf space is a limited resource for a retail store, product selection, shelf-space allocation, and shelf-space placement decisions must be made according to a careful analysis of profitability and inventory turnover. The manager of a chain of variety stores wishes to see whether shelf location affects the sales of a canned soup. She believes that placing the product at eye level will result in greater sales than will placing the product on a lower shelf. She observed the number of sales of the product in 40 different stores. Sales were observed over 2 weeks, with product placement at eye level one week and on a lower shelf the other week. Can we conclude that placement of the product at eye level significantly increases sales?

**A17.3** XrA17-03 In an effort to explain the results of Exercise A15.9, a researcher recorded the distances for the random sample of British and American golf courses. Can we infer that British courses are shorter than American courses?

**A17.4** XrA17-04 It is generally assumed that alcohol consumption tends to make drinkers more impulsive. However, a recent study in the journal *Alcohol and Alcoholism* may contradict this assumption. The study took a random sample of 76 male undergraduate students and divided them into three groups. One group remained sober; the second group was given flavored drinks with not enough alcohol to intoxicate; and the students in third group were intoxicated. Each student was offered a chance of receiving $15 at the end of the session or double that amount later. The results were recorded using the following format:

Column 1: Group number

Column 2: Code 1 = chose $15, 2 = chose $30 later

Do the data allow us to infer that there is a relationship between the choices students make and their level of intoxication?

**A17.5** XrA17-05 Refer to Exercise 13.35. The executive did a further analysis by taking another random sample. This time she tracked the number of customers who have had an accident in the last 5 years. For each she recorded the total amount of repairs and the credit score. Do these data allow the executive to conclude that the higher the credit score the lower the cost of repairs will be?

**A17.6** XrA17-06 The U.S. National Endowment for the Arts conducts surveys of American adults to determine, among other things, their participation in various arts activities. A recent survey asked a random sample of American adults whether they participate in photography. The responses are 1 = Yes and 2 = no. There were 205.8 million American adults. Estimate with 95% confidence the number of American adults are participate in photography.

(*Source:* Adapted from the *Statistical Abstract of the United States, 2006*, Table 1228.)

**A17.7** XrA17-07 Mouth-to-mouth resuscitation has long been considered better than chest compression for people who have suffered a heart attack. To determine if this indeed is the better way, Japanese researchers analyzed 4,068 adult patients who had cardiac arrest witnessed by bystanders. Of those, 439 received only chest compressions from bystanders and 712 received conventional CPR compressions and breaths. The results for each group was recorded where 1 = did not survive with good neurological function and 2 = did survive with good neurological function. What conclusions can be drawn from these data?

**A17.8** XrA17-08 Refer to Exercise A15.7. The financial analyst undertook another project wherein respondents were also asked the age of the head of the household. The choices are

1. Younger than 25
2. 25 to 34
3. 35 to 44
4. 45 to 54
5. 55 to 64
6. 65 and older

The responses to questions about ownership of mutual funds is No = 1 and Yes = 2. Do these data allow us to infer that the age of the head of the household is related to whether he or she owns mutual funds?

(*Source:* Adapted from the *Statistical Abstract of the United States, 2006*, Table 1200.)

**A17.9** XrA17-09 Over one decade (1995–2005), the number of hip and knee replacement surgeries increased by 87%. Because the costs of hip and knee replacements are so expensive, private health-insurance and government-operated health-care plans have become more concerned. To get more information, random samples of people who had hip replacements in 1995 and in 2005 were drawn. From the files, the ages of the patients were recorded. Is there enough evidence to infer that the ages of people who require hip replacements are getting smaller?

(*Source:* Canadian Joint Replacement Registry.)

**A17.10** XrA17-10 Refer to Exercise A17.9. Weight is a major factor that determines whether a person will need a hip or knee replacement and at what age. To learn more about the topic, a medical researcher randomly sampled individuals who had hip replacement (code = 1) and knee replacement (code = 2) and one of the following categories:

1. Underweight
2. Normal range
3. Overweight but not obese
4. Obese

Do the data allow the researcher to conclude that weight and the joint needing replacement are related?

**A17.11** XrA17-11 Television shows with large amounts of sex or violence tend to attract more viewers. Advertisers want large audiences, but they also want viewers to remember the brand names of their products. A study was undertaken to determine the effect that shows with sex and violence have on their viewers. A random sample of 328 adults was divided into three groups. Group 1 watched violent programs, group 2 watched sexually explicit shows, and group 3 watched neutral shows. The researchers spliced nine 30-second commercials for a wide range of products. After the show, the subjects were quizzed to see if they could recall the brand name of the products. They were also asked to name the brands 24 hours later. The number of correct answers was recorded. Conduct a test to determine whether differences exist between the three groups of viewers and which type of program does best in brand recall. Results were published in the *Journal of Applied Psychology* (*National Post*, August 16, 2004).

**A17.12** XrA17-12 In an effort to explain to customers why their electricity bills have been so high lately, and how customers could save money by reducing the thermostat settings on both space heaters and water heaters, a public utility commission has collected total kilowatt consumption figures for last year's winter months, as well as thermostat settings on space and water heaters, for 100 homes.

a. Determine the regression equation.
b. Determine the coefficient of determination and describe what it tells you.
c. Test the validity of the model.
d. Find the 95% interval of the electricity consumption of a house whose space heater thermostat is set at 70 and whose water heater thermostat is set at 130.
e. Calculate the 95% interval of the average electricity consumption for houses whose space heater thermostat is set at 70 degrees Fahrenheit and whose water heater thermostat is set at 130 degrees Fahrenheit.

**A17.13** XrA17-13 An economist wanted to learn more about total compensation packages. She conducted a survey of 858 workers and asked all to report their hourly wages or salaries, their total benefits, and whether the companies they worked for produced goods or services. Determine whether differences exist between goods-producing and services-producing firms in terms of hourly wages and total benefits.

(*Source:* Adapted from the *Statistical Abstract of the United States, 2006*, Table 637.)

**A17.14** XrA17-14 Professional athletes in North America are paid very well for their ability to play games that amateurs play for fun. To determine the factors that influence a team to pay a hockey player's salary, an MBA student randomly selected 50 hockey players who played in the 1992–1993 and 1993–1994 seasons. He recorded their salaries at the end of the 1993–1994 season as well as a number of performance measures in the previous two seasons. The following data were recorded.

Columns 1 and 2: Games played in 1992–1993 and 1993–1994
Columns 3 and 4: Goals scored in 1992–1993 and 1993–1994
Columns 5 and 6: Assists recorded in 1992–1993 and 1993–1994
Columns 7 and 8: Plus/minus score in 1992–1993 and 1993–1994
Columns 9 and 10: Penalty minutes served in 1992–1993 and 1993–1994
Column 11: Salary in U.S. dollars

(Plus/minus is the number of goals scored by the player's team minus the number of goals scored by the opposing team while the player is on the ice.) Develop a model that analyzes the relationship between salary and the performance measures. Describe your findings. (The author wishes to thank Gordon Barnett for writing this exercise.)

**A17.15** XrA17-15 The risks associated with smoking are well known. Virtually all physicians recommend that their patients quit. This raises the question, What are the risks for people who quit smoking compared to continuing smokers and those who have never smoked? In a study described in the *Journal of Internal Medicine* [Feb. 2004, 255(2): 266–272], researchers took samples of each of the following groups.

Group 1: Never smokers
Group 2: Continuing smokers
Group 3: Smokers who quit

At the beginning of the 10-year research project, there were 238 people who had never smoked and 155 smokers. Over the year, 39 smokers quit. The weight gain, increase in systolic blood pressure (SBP), and increase in diastolic blood pressure (DBP) were measured and recorded. Determine whether differences exist between the three groups in terms of weight gain, increases in systolic blood pressure, and increases in diastolic blood pressure and which groups differ.

**A17.16** XrA17-16 A survey was conducted among Canadian farmers, who were each asked to report the number of acres in his or her farm. There were a total of 229, 373 farms in Canada in 2006. Estimate with 95% confidence the total amount of area (in acres) that was farmed in Canada in 2006.

(*Source:* Statistics Canada).

## GENERAL SOCIAL SURVEY EXERCISES

***Conduct all tests at the 5% significance level. Use a 95% confidence level for estimates.***

In 2012, there were 221,963,000 Americans aged 21 years or more.

**A17.17** GSS2012* The survey asked the following question: "Is it government's responsibility to help pay for doctor and hospital bills?" The responses were HELPSICK: 1 = Government should help; 2, 3, 4, 5 = People should help themselves). Is there enough statistical evidence to infer that there are differences among the five categories of educational attainment (DEGREE: 0 = Left high school, 1 = High school, 2 = Junior college, 3 = Bachelor's degree, 4 = Graduate)?

**A17.18** GSS2012* The survey asked the following question: "I'm going to show you a seven-point scale on which political views that people might hold arranged from extremely liberal to extremely conservative. Where would you place yourself on this scale?" Estimate the number of Americans who are liberal (POLVIEWS: 1 = Extremely liberal, 2 = Liberal, 3 = Slightly liberal).

**A17.19** GSS2012* Are American women more liberal than American men? If so we should see evidence from the General Social Survey. Is there enough evidence to conclude that there are differences in political philosophies (POLVIEWS3: 1 = Liberal, 2 = Moderate, 3 = Conservative) between men and women (SEX: 1 = Male, 2 = Female)?

**A17.20** GSS2012* Is it true that as we age we become more conservative? If this is true we would expect that conservatives would be older than liberals and independents. Analyze the data to determine whether there is enough evidence to conclude that differences in age (AGE) exist between the three political philosophies (POLVIEWS3: 1 = Liberal, 2 = Moderate, 3 = Conservative).

**A17.21** GSS2012* Do conservatives oppose gun control while liberals support it? Conduct a test to determine whether there is sufficient evidence to conclude that the three political parties (PARTYID3: 1 = Democrat, 2 = Independent, 3 = Republican) differ in their support for gun control (GUNLAW: 1 = Support, 2 = Oppose).

**A17.22** GSS2012* Who is more likely to have completed a graduate degree, men or women? Conduct a test to determine whether there is enough evidence to infer that men and women (SEX: 1 = Male, 2 = Female) differ in their completion of graduate degrees (DEGREE: 4 = Graduate).

**A17.23** GSS2012* Are there differences between Democrats, Independents, and Republicans (PARTYID3) in their answers to the following question: "Should government do more or less to solve country's problems (HELPNOT: 1 = Government should do more; 2, 3, 4, 5 = Government does too much). Conduct a test to determine whether there is enough evidence to conclude that differences exist.

**A17.24** GSS2012* There are many advantages to self-employment (WRKSLF: 1 = self-employed; 2 = someone else) including the ability to decide how hard and how often to work. Does that mean that self-employed individuals work less than other workers (HRS1)? Conduct a test to provide an answer.

**A17.25** GSS2012* Does political philosophy affect support for capital punishment? Is there enough evidence to conclude that support for capital punishment (CAPPUN: 1 = Favor, 2 = Oppose) differs between the three political points of view (POLVIEWS3: 1 = Liberal, 2 = Moderate, 3 = Conservative)?

**A17.26** GSS2012* Does being unemployed for any period of time affect an individual's political persuasion? Determine whether there is enough evidence to infer that Americans who have been unemployed in the last 10 years (UNEMP: 1 = Yes, 2 = No) have different party affiliations (PARTYID3: 1 = Democrat, 2 = Independent, 3 = Republican) than those who have not been unemployed.

**A17.27** GSS2012* Do men and women differ in their belief that they pay too much income tax? Conduct a test to determine whether there is enough evidence to conclude that men and women (SEX: 1 = Male, 2 = Female) differ in their responses to the tax question (TAX: = Too high, 2 = About right, 3 = Too low).

**A17.28** GSS2012* Do married men and women have different perceptions of their marriage? The survey asked the following question: "Taking all things together, how would you describe your marriage (HAPMAR: 1= Very happy, 2 = Pretty happy, 3 = Not too happy)?" Is there enough evidence to conclude that men and women differ (SEX: 1 = Male, 2 = Female)?

**A17.29** GSS2012* Do people have an overconfidence attitude about their financial situation compared to others? Estimate the number of American adults who say that they belong in the upper class (CLASS: 4 = Upper class).

**A17.30** GSS2012* Do most people love their jobs? The survey asked respondents: "On the whole, how satisfied are you with the work you do?" Estimate the number of American workers who are very satisfied (SATJOB: 1 = Very satisfied).

**A17.31** GSS2012* Are Americans more educated? Conduct a test to determine whether there is enough evidence to conclude that the average American has completed at least a high school education (12 years of school) (EDUC).

**A17.32** GSS2012* Many aspects of life, including jobs, become routine and perhaps boring. The General Social Survey asked respondents: "In general, do you find life... Is there enough evidence to infer that the majority find life exciting (LIFE: 1 = Exciting)?"

**A17.33** GSS2012* One of the questions in the survey was "Does the Earth go around the Sun or does the Sun go around the Earth?" (EARTHSUN: 1 = Earth around Sun, 2 = Sun around Earth, 8 = Don't know, 9 = No answer). Estimate the number of Americans who knew the answer is 1.

**A17.34** GSS2012* Is there sufficient evidence to conclude that as income (RINCOME) increases Americans are less likely to believe that government should reduce income inequality (EQWLTH: 1 = Government should reduce differences; 2, 3, 4, 5, 6, 7 = No government action)?

**A17.35** GSS2012* Is the number of years of education of individuals affected by the educational attainment of their fathers? To answer this question, is there enough evidence to conclude that years of education (EDUC) is positively related to the years of education of fathers (PAEDUC)?

## Survey of Consumer Finances

***Conduct all tests at the 5% significance level. Use a 95% confidence level for estimates.***

**According to the U.S. Census, there were 220,958,853 adults in the United States in 2010.**

**A17.36** SCF2010:\MC* Do middle-class households headed by men (HHSEX: 1 = male, 2 = female) spend more money on food away from home than their female counterparts (FOODAWAY)? Conduct a test to answer the question.

**A17.37** SCF2010:\All* In 2007–2009, the United States was hit with a financial crisis brought on by a crash in the housing market. How has this impacted the proportion of families who own their home in 2010? Estimate the proportion of home ownership (HOUSECL: 1 = own).

**A17.38** SCF2010:\UC The upper class in the 2010 survey had household net worth between $1,345,975 and $7,402,095. Households in this net worth category have large amounts to invest in the stock market. Estimate the mean investment in the stock market by upper class households (STOCKS).

**A17.39** SCF2010:\UC* According to the U.S. Census, the average family spent $3921 on food eaten at home (FOODHOME). Is there enough evidence to infer that the average upper-class household spent more than the average family?

**A17.40** SCF2010:\All* The survey asked whether the household had declared bankruptcy in the previous 5 years (BNKRUPLAST5: 1 = Yes). Is there enough evidence to conclude that male and female (HHSEX: 1 = Male, 2 = Female) heads of households differ?

**A17.41** SCF2010:\All* In 2010, banks were still in trouble because of the housing meltdown. As a result, they were increasing their standards for credit cards and loans. Estimate the proportion of people who were turned down for credit in the previous 5 years (TURNDOWN: 1).

**A17.42** SCF2010:\All* Does education affect how people spend their food dollars? Answer the question by determining whether there is enough statistical evidence to infer that there are differences in expenditures for food at home (FOODHOME) between the four categories of education (EDCL 1 = No high school diploma, 2 = High school diploma, 3 = Some college, 4 = College degree).

**A17.43** SCF2010:\All* Are there differences between male and female (HHSEX: 1 = Male, 2 = Female) heads of households with respect to family structure (FAMSTRUCT: 1 = Not married or living with partner + children, 2 = Not married or living with partner + no children+ head of household under 55, 3 = Not married or living with partner + no children + head of household 55 or older, 4 = Married or living with partner + children, 5 = Married or living with partner + no children)? Conduct a test to answer the question.

## CASE A17.1 Testing a More Effective Device to Keep Arteries Open

A stent is a metal mesh cylinder that holds a coronary artery open after a blockage has been removed. However, in many patients the stents, which are made from bare metal, become blocked as well. One cause of the reoccurrence of blockages is the body's rejection of the foreign object. In a study published in the *New England Journal of Medicine* (January 2004), a new polymer-based stent was tested. After insertion, the new stents slowly release a drug (paclitaxel) to prevent the rejection problem. A sample of 1,314 patients who were receiving a stent in a single, previously untreated coronary artery blockage was recruited. A total of 652 were randomly assigned to receive a bare-metal stent, and 662 to receive an identical-looking polymer drug-releasing stent. The results were recorded in the following way:

Column 1: Patient identification number
Column 2: Stent type (1 = bare metal, 2 = polymer based)
Column 3: Reference-vessel diameter (the diameter of the artery that is blocked, in millimeters)
Column 4: Lesion length (the length of the blockage, in millimeters)

Reference-vessel diameters and lesion lengths were measured before the stents were inserted.

The following data were recorded 12 months after the stents were inserted.

Column 5: Blockage reoccurrence after 9 months (2 = yes, 1 = no)
Column 6: Blockage that needed to be reopened (2 = yes, 1 = no)
Column 7: Death from cardiac causes (2 = yes, 1 = no)
Column 8: Stroke caused by stent (2 = yes, 1 = no)

a. Using the variables stored in columns 3 through 8, determine whether there is enough evidence to infer that the polymer-based stent is superior to the bare-metal stent.
b. As a laboratory researcher in the pharmaceutical company write a report that describes this experiment and the results.

DA CA1

## CASE A17.2 Automobile Crashes and the Ages of Drivers*

Setting premiums for insurance is a complex task. If the premium is too high, the insurance company will lose customers; if it is too low, the company will lose money. Statistics plays a critical role in almost all aspects of the insurance business. As part of a statistical analysis, an insurance company in Florida studied the relationship between the severity of car crashes and the ages of the drivers. A random sample of crashes in 2002 in the state of Florida was drawn. For each crash, the age category of the driver was recorded as well as whether the driver was injured or killed. The data were stored as follows:

Column 1: Crash number
Column 2: Age category

1. 5 to 34
2. 35 to 44
3. 45 to 54
4. 55 to 64
5. 65 and over

Column 3: Medical status of driver

1 = Uninjured
2 = Injured (but not killed)
3 = Killed

a. Is there enough evidence to conclude that age and medical status of the driver in car crashes are related?
b. Estimate with 95% confidence the proportion of all Florida drivers in crashes in 2002 who were uninjured.

DATA CA17-0

*Adapted from Florida Department of Highway Safety and Vehicles, as reported in the *Miami Herald*, January 1, 2004, p. 2B.

Zastolskiy Victor/Shutterstock.com

# MODEL BUILDING

**CHAPTER OUTLINE**



## General Social Survey: Variables That Affect Income II

DATA GSS2014*

In the Chapter 17 opening example, we found that one's income is affected by age, education, number of hours of work per week, and spouse's number of hours of work per week. Determine whether income is also affected by gender and race.

Tyler Olson/Shutterstock.com

**On page 746, we will provide our answer.**

## INTRODUCTION

Chapters 16 and 17 introduced the techniques and concepts of regression analysis. We discussed how the model is developed, interpreted, assessed, and diagnosed for violations of required conditions. However, there is more to regression analysis. In this chapter, we demonstrate why this procedure is one of the most powerful and commonly used techniques in statistics. Regression analysis allows the statistics practitioner to use mathematical models to realistically describe relationships between the dependent variable and the independent variables.

In Section 18-1, we introduce models in which the relationship between the dependent variable and the independent variables may not be linear. Section 18-2 introduces indicator variables, which allow us to use nominal independent variables. We describe pay equity, an important human resources management application that employs nominal independent variables in Section 18-3. In Section 18-4, we introduce stepwise regression, which enables the statistics practitioner to include the independent variables that yield the best fitting models. Finally, Section 18-5 discusses how to properly use regression analysis in building models.

## 18-1 POLYNOMIAL MODELS

Chapter 17 introduced the multiple regression model:

$$y = \beta_0 + \beta_1 x_1 + \beta_2 x_2 + \cdots + \beta_k x_k + \varepsilon$$

We included variables $x_1, x_2, \ldots, x_k$ because we believed that these variables were each linearly related to the dependent variable. In this section, we discuss models where the independent variables may be functions of a smaller number of predictor variables. The simplest form of the **polynomial model** is described in the box.

**Polynomial Model with One Predictor Variable**

$$y = \beta_0 + \beta_1 x + \beta_2 x^2 + \cdots + \beta_p x^p + \varepsilon$$

Technically, this is a multiple regression model with $p$ independent variables. However, all independent variables are based on only one variable, which we label the **predictor variable**; that is, $x_1 = x, x_2 = x^2, \ldots, x_p = x^p$. In this model, $p$ is the **order** of the equation. For reasons that we discuss later, we rarely propose a model whose order is greater than 3. However, it is worthwhile to devote individual attention to situations where $p = 1, 2$, and 3.

### 18-1a First-Order Model

When $p = 1$, we have the now-familiar simple linear regression model introduced in Chapter 16. It is also called the **first-order** polynomial model.

$$y = \beta_0 + \beta_1 x + \varepsilon$$

Obviously, this model is chosen when the statistics practitioner believes that there is a straight-line relationship between the dependent and independent variables over the range of the values of $x$.

## 18-1b Second-Order Model

With $p = 2$, the polynomial model is

$$y = \beta_0 + \beta_1 x + \beta_2 x^2 + \varepsilon$$

When we plot $x$ versus $y$, the graph is shaped like a parabola, as shown in Figures 18.1 and 18.2. The coefficient $\beta_0$ represents the intercept where the response surface strikes the $y$-axis. The signs of $\beta_1$ and $\beta_2$ control the position of the parabola relative to the $y$-axis. If $\beta_1 = 0$, for example, the parabola is symmetric and centered around $x = 0$. If $\beta_1$ and $\beta_2$ have the same sign, the parabola shifts to the left. If $\beta_1$ and $\beta_2$ have opposite signs, the parabola shifts to the right. The coefficient $\beta_2$ describes the curvature. If $\beta_2 = 0$, there is no curvature. If $\beta_2$ is negative, the graph is concave (as in Figure 18.1). If $\beta_2$ is positive, the graph is convex (as in Figure 18.2). The greater the absolute value of $\beta_2$, the greater the rate of curvature, as can be seen in Figure 18.3.

FIGURE **18.1** **Second-Order Model with $\beta_2 < 0$**

FIGURE **18.2** **Second-Order Model with $\beta_2 > 0$**

FIGURE **18.3** **Second-Order Model with Various Values of $\beta_2$**

## 18-1c Third-Order Model

By setting $p = 3$, we produce the third-order model

$$y = \beta_0 + \beta_1 x + \beta_2 x^2 + \beta_3 x^3 + \varepsilon$$

Figures 18.4 and 18.5 depict this equation, whose curvature can change twice.

FIGURE **18.4** **Third-Order Model with $\beta_3 < 0$**

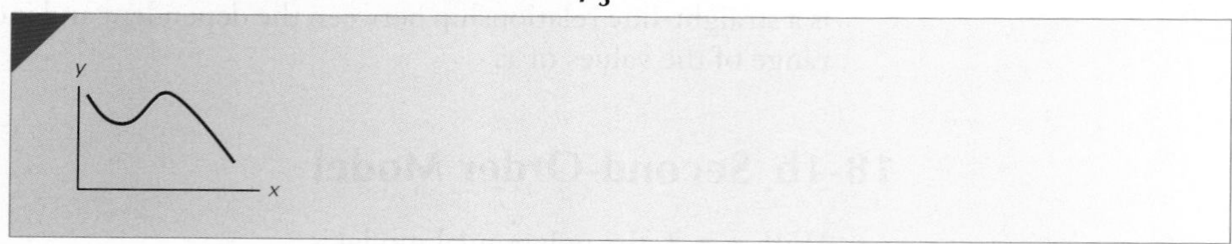


FIGURE **18.5** **Third-Order Model with $\beta_3 > 0$**

As you can see, when $\beta_3$ is negative, $y$ is decreasing over the range of $x$, and when $\beta_3$ is positive, $y$ increases. The other coefficients determine the position of the curvature changes and the point at which the curve intersects the $y$-axis.

The number of real-life applications of this model is quite small. Statistics practitioners rarely encounter problems involving more than one curvature reversal. Therefore, we will not discuss any higher order models.

## 18-1d Polynomial Models with Two Predictor Variables

If we believe that two predictor variables influence the dependent variable, we can use one of the following polynomial models. The general form of this model is rather cumbersome, so we will not show it. Instead we discuss several specific examples.

## 18-1e First-Order Model

The first-order model is represented by

$$y = \beta_0 + \beta_1 x_1 + \beta_2 x_2 + \varepsilon$$

This model is used whenever the statistics practitioner believes that, on average, $y$ is linearly related to each of $x_1$ and $x_2$, and the predictor variables do not interact. (Recall that we introduced interaction in Chapter 14.) This means that the effect of one predictor variable on $y$ is independent of the value of the second predictor variable. For example, suppose that the sample regression line of the first-order model is

$$\hat{y} = 5 + 3x_1 + 4x_2$$

If we examine the relationship between $y$ and $x_1$ for several values of $x_2$ (say, $x_2 = 1, 2,$ and 3), we produce the following equations.

| $x_2$ | $\hat{y} = 5 + 3x_1 + 4x_2$ |
|---|---|
| 1 | $\hat{y} = 9 + 3x_1$ |
| 2 | $\hat{y} = 13 + 3x_1$ |
| 3 | $\hat{y} = 17 + 3x_1$ |

The only difference in the three equations is the intercept. (See Figure 18.6.) The coefficient of $x_1$ remains the same, which means that the effect of $x_1$ on $y$ remains the same no matter what the value of $x_2$. (We could also have shown that the effect of $x_2$ on $y$ remains the same no matter what the value of $x_1$.) As you can see from Figure 18.6, the first-order model with no interaction produces parallel straight lines.

FIGURE **18.6** **First-Order Model with Two Independent Variables: No Interaction**

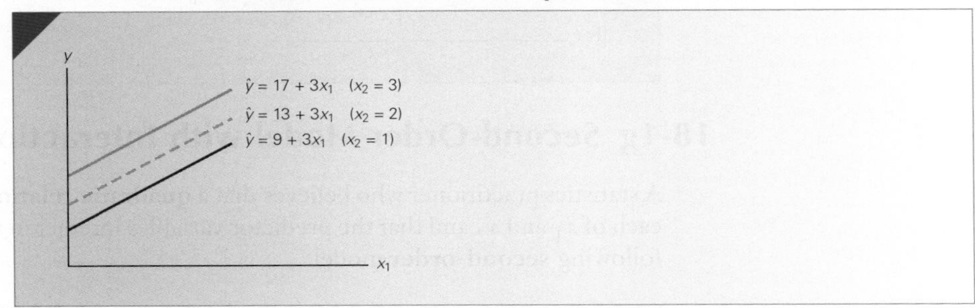


A statistics practitioner who thinks that the effect of one predictor variable on $y$ is influenced by the other predictor variable can use the model described next.

## 18-1f First-Order Model with Two Predictor Variables and Interaction

**Interaction** means that the effect of $x_1$ on $y$ is influenced by the value of $x_2$. (It also means that the effect of $x_2$ on $y$ is influenced by $x_1$.)

**First-Order Model with Interaction**

$$y = \beta_0 + \beta_1 x_1 + \beta_2 x_2 + \beta_3 x_1 x_2 + \varepsilon$$

Suppose that the sample regression line is

$$\hat{y} = 5 + 3x_1 + 4x_2 - 2x_1 x_2$$

If we examine the relationship between $y$ and $x_1$ for $x_2 = 1, 2$, and 3, we produce the following table of equations:

| $x_2$ | $\hat{y} = 5 + 3x_1 + 4x_2 - 2x_1x_2$ |
|---|---|
| 1 | $\hat{y} = 9 + x_1$ |
| 2 | $\hat{y} = 13 - x_1$ |
| 3 | $\hat{y} = 17 - 3x_1$ |

As you can see, not only is the intercept different but also the coefficient of $x_1$ varies. Obviously, the effect of $x_1$ on $y$ is influenced by the value of $x_2$. Figure 18.7 depicts these equations. The straight lines are clearly not parallel.

FIGURE **18.7** First-Order Model with Interaction

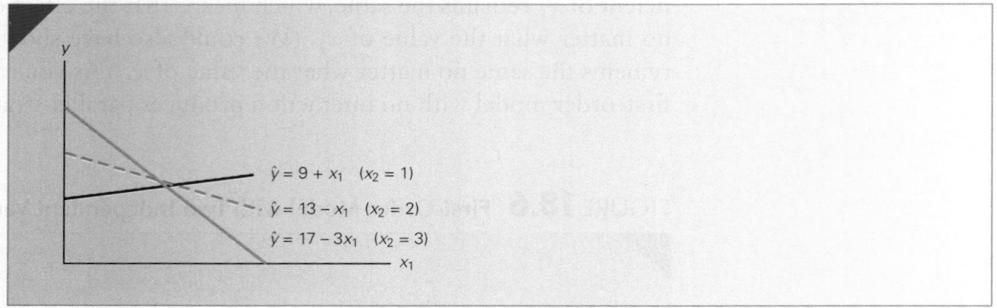


## 18-1g Second-Order Model with Interaction

A statistics practitioner who believes that a **quadratic relationship** exists between $y$ and each of $x_1$ and $x_2$ and that the predictor variables interact in their effect on $y$ can use the following **second-order** model.

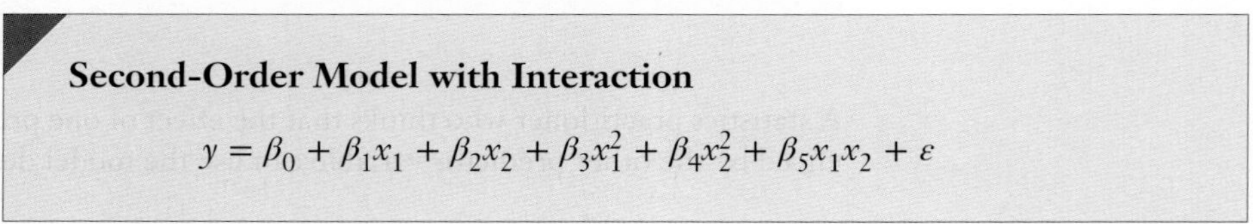

**Second-Order Model with Interaction**

$$y = \beta_0 + \beta_1 x_1 + \beta_2 x_2 + \beta_3 x_1^2 + \beta_4 x_2^2 + \beta_5 x_1 x_2 + \varepsilon$$

Figures 18.8 and 18.9, respectively, depict this model without and with the interaction term.

FIGURE **18.8** Second-Order Model without Interaction

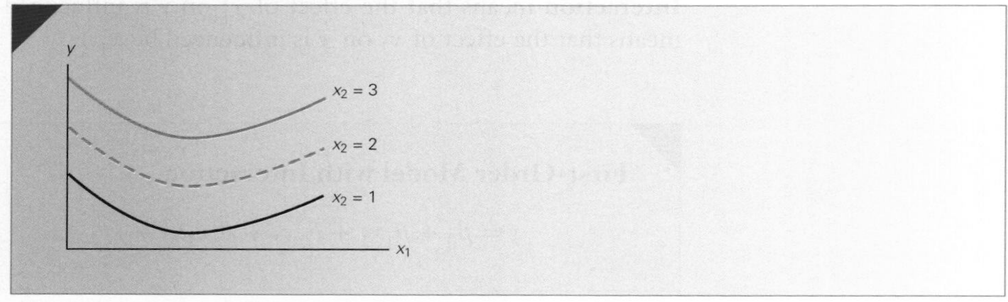


FIGURE **18.9** Second-Order Model with Interaction

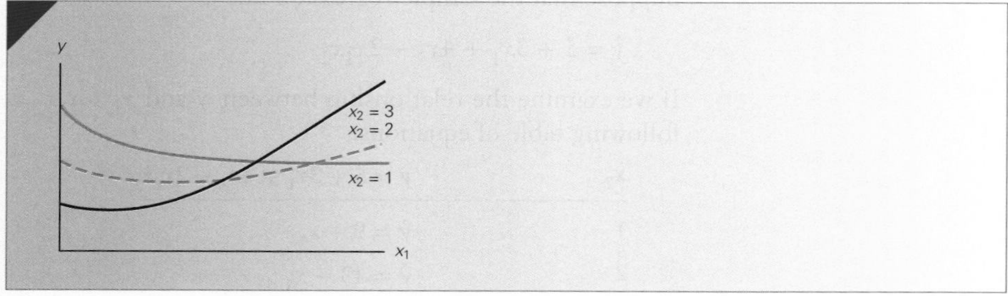


Now that we've introduced several different models, how do we know which model to use? The answer is that we employ a model based on our knowledge of the variables involved and then test that model using the statistical techniques presented in this and the preceding chapters.

## EXAMPLE 18.1 Selecting Sites for a Fast-Food Restaurant, Part 1

In trying to find new locations for their restaurants, fast-food restaurant chains like McDonald's and Wendy's usually consider a number of factors. Suppose that an analyst working for a fast-food restaurant chain has been asked to construct a regression model that will help identify new locations that are likely to be profitable. The analyst knows that this type of restaurant has, as its primary market, middle-income adults and their children, particularly those between the ages of 5 and 12. Which model should the analyst propose?

SOLUTION:

The dependent variable is gross revenue or net profit. The predictor variables will be mean annual household income and the mean age of children in the restaurant's neighborhood. The relationship between the dependent variable and each predictor variable is probably quadratic. In other words, members of relatively poor or relatively affluent households are less likely to eat at this chain's restaurants because the restaurants attract mostly middle-income customers. Figure 18.10 depicts the hypothesized relationship.

FIGURE **18.10** **Relationship between Annual Gross Revenue and Mean Household Income**

A similar relationship can be proposed for revenue and age. Neighborhoods where the mean age of children is either quite low or quite high will probably produce lower revenues than in similar areas where the mean age lies in the middle of the 5-to-12 range.

The question of whether to include the interaction term is more difficult to answer. When in doubt, it is probably best to include it. Thus, the model to be tested is

$$y = \beta_0 + \beta_1 x_1 + \beta_2 x_2 + \beta_3 x_1^2 + \beta_4 x_2^2 + \beta_5 x_1 x_2 + \varepsilon$$

where

$y$ = Annual gross sales

$x_1$ = Mean annual household income in the neighborhood

$x_2$ = Mean age of children in the neighborhood

## EXAMPLE 18.2 Selecting Sites for a Fast-Food Restaurant, Part 2

DATA Xm18-02

To determine whether the second-order model with interaction is appropriate, the analyst in Example 18.1 selected 25 areas at random. Each area consists of approximately 5,000 households, as well as one of her employer's restaurants and three competing fast-food restaurants. The previous year's annual gross sales, the mean annual household income, and the mean age of children (the latter two figures are available from the latest census) were recorded; some of these data are listed here (the file also contains $x_1^2$, $x_2^2$, and $x_1x_2$). What conclusions can be drawn from these data?

| Area | Annual Gross Revenue ($ Thousands) $y$ | Mean Annual Household ($ Thousands) $x_1$ | Mean Age of Children $x_2$ |
|---|---|---|---|
| 1 | $1,128 | $23.5 | 10.5 |
| 2 | 1,005 | 17.6 | 7.2 |
| 3 | 1,212 | 26.3 | 7.6 |
| ⋮ | ⋮ | ⋮ | ⋮ |
| 25 | 950 | 17.8 | 6.1 |

SOLUTION:

We'll use Excel (XLSTAT's printout is similar) to produce the regression analysis shown here.

## EXCEL Data Analysis

| | A | B | C | D | E | F |
|---|---|---|---|---|---|---|
| 1 | SUMMARY OUTPUT | | | | | |
| 2 | | | | | | |
| 3 | *Regression Statistics* | | | | | |
| 4 | Multiple R | 0.9521 | | | | |
| 5 | R Square | 0.9065 | | | | |
| 6 | Adjusted R Square | 0.8819 | | | | |
| 7 | Standard Error | 44.70 | | | | |
| 8 | Observations | 25 | | | | |
| 9 | | | | | | |
| 10 | ANOVA | | | | | |
| 11 | | *df* | *SS* | *MS* | *F* | *Significance F* |
| 12 | Regression | 5 | 368,140 | 73,628 | 36.86 | 3.86E-09 |
| 13 | Residual | 19 | 37,956 | 1,998 | | |
| 14 | Total | 24 | 406,096 | | | |
| 15 | | | | | | |
| 16 | | *Coefficients* | *Standard Error* | *t Stat* | *P-value* | |
| 17 | Intercept | −1134.0 | 320.0 | −3.54 | 0.0022 | |
| 18 | Income | 173.20 | 28.20 | 6.14 | 6.66E-06 | |
| 19 | Age | 23.55 | 32.23 | 0.73 | 0.4739 | |
| 20 | Income sq | −3.726 | 0.542 | −6.87 | 1.48E-06 | |
| 21 | Age sq | −3.869 | 1.179 | −3.28 | 0.0039 | |
| 22 | (Income)( Age) | 1.967 | 0.944 | 2.08 | 0.0509 | |

## INTERPRET

From the computer output, we determine that the value of the coefficient of determination ($R^2$) is 90.65%, which tells us that the model fits the data quite well. The value of the $F$-statistic is 36.86, which has a $p$-value of approximately 0. This confirms that the model is valid.

Care must be taken when interpreting the $t$-tests of the coefficients in this type of model. Not surprisingly, each variable will be correlated with its square, and the interaction variable will be correlated with both of its components. As a consequence, multicollinearity distorts the $t$-tests of the coefficients in some cases, making it appear that some of the components should be eliminated from the model. However, in most such applications, the objective is to forecast the dependent variable and multicollinearity does not affect the model's fit or forecasting capability.

## EXERCISES

**18.1** Graph $y$ versus $x_1$ for $x_2 = 1, 2,$ and 3 for each of the following equations.

a. $y = 1 + 2x_1 + 4x_2$

b. $y = 1 + 2x_1 + 4x_2 - x_1x_2$

**18.2** Graph $y$ versus $x_1$ for $x_2 = 2, 4,$ and 5 for each of the following equations.

a. $y = 0.5 + 1x_1 - 0.7x_2 - 1.2x_1^2 + 1.5x_2^2$

b. $y = 0.5 + 1x_1 - 0.7x_2 - 1.2x_1^2 + 1.5x_2^2 + 2x_1x_2$

*The following exercises require the use of a computer and software. Exercise 18.3–18.5 can be solved manually. See Appendix A.*

**18.3** Xr18-03 The general manager of a supermarket chain believes that sales of a product are influenced by the amount of space the product is allotted on shelves. If true, this would have great significance, because the more profitable items could be given more shelf space. The manager realizes that sales volume would likely increase with more space only up to a certain point. Beyond that point, sales would likely flatten and perhaps decrease (because customers are often dismayed by very large displays). To test his belief, the manager records the number of boxes of detergent sold during 1 week in 25 stores in the chain. For each store, he records the shelf space (in inches) allotted to the detergent.

a. Write the equation that represents the model.

b. Discuss how well the model fits.

### APPLICATIONS in ECONOMICS

Dustin Dennis/Shutterstock.com

#### Demand Curve

The law of supply and demand states that other things being equal, the higher the price of a product or service, the lower is the quantity demanded. The relationship between quantity and price is called a *demand curve*. Generally, such a curve is modeled by a quadratic equation. To estimate the demand curve, we measure the demand at several different prices and then employ regression analysis to calculate the coefficients of the model.

**18.4** Xr18-04 A fast-food restaurant chain whose menu features hamburgers and chicken sandwiches is about to add a fish sandwich to its menu. There was considerable debate among the executives about the likely demand and what the appropriate price should be. A recently hired economics graduate observed that the demand curve would reveal a great deal about the relationship between price and demand. She convinced the executives to conduct an experiment. A random sample of 20 restaurants was drawn. The restaurants were almost identical in terms of sales and in the demographics of the surrounding area. At each restaurant, the fish sandwich was sold at a different price. The number of sandwiches sold over a 7-day period and the price were recorded. A first-order model and a second-order model were proposed.

a. Write the equation for each model.

b. Use regression analysis to estimate the coefficients and other statistics for each model.

c. Which model seems to fit better? Explain.

d. Use the better model to calculate the point prediction for weekly sales when the price is \$2.95.

## APPLICATIONS in OPERATIONS MANAGEMENT

Image Source/Getty Images

### Learning Curve

A well-established phenomenon in operations management is the *learning curve,* which describes how quickly new workers learn to do their jobs. A number of mathematical models are used to describe the relationship between time on the job and productivity. Regression analysis allows the operations manager to select the appropriate model and use it to predict when workers achieve their highest level of productivity.

**18.5** Xr18-05 A person starting a new job always takes a certain amount of time to adjust fully. In repetitive-task situations, such as on an assembly line, significant productivity gains can occur within a few days. In an experiment to study this phenomenon, the average amount of time required for a new employee to install electronic components in a computer was measured for her first 10 days. These data are shown here.

| **Day** | 1 | 2 | 3 | 4 | 5 | 6 | 7 | 8 | 9 | 10 |
|---|---|---|---|---|---|---|---|---|---|---|
| **Mean times (minutes)** | 40 | 41 | 36 | 38 | 33 | 32 | 30 | 32 | 29 | 30 |

A first-order model and a second-order model were proposed.
a. Write the equation for each model.
b. Analyze both models. Determine whether they are valid.
c. Which model fits better? Explain.

**18.6** Xr17-14* Refer to Exercise 17.14. The dean of the school of business wanted to improve the regression model, which was developed to describe the relationship between MBA program GPA and undergraduate GPA, GMAT score, and years of work experience. The dean now believes that an interaction effect may exist between undergraduate GPA and the GMAT test score.
a. Write the equation that describes the model.
b. Use a computer to generate the regression statistics. Use whatever statistics you deem necessary to assess the model's fit. Is this model valid?
c. Compare your results with those achieved in the original example.

**18.7** Xr18-07 The manager of the food concession at a major league baseball stadium wanted to be able to predict the attendance of a game 24 hours in advance to prepare the correct amount of food for sale. He believed that the two most important factors were the home team's winning percentage and the visiting team's winning percentage. In order to examine his beliefs, he collected the attendance figures, the home team's winning percentage, and the visiting team's winning percentage for 40 randomly selected games from all the teams in the league.
a. Conduct a regression analysis using a first-order model with interaction.
b. Do these results indicate that your model is valid? Explain.

**18.8** Xr18-08 The manager of a large hotel on the Riviera in southern France wanted to forecast the monthly vacancy rate (as a percentage) during the peak season. After considering a long list of potential variables, she identified two variables that she believed were most closely related to the vacancy rate: The average daily temperature and the value of the currency in American dollars. She collected data for 25 months.
a. Perform a regression analysis using a first-order model with interaction.
b. Perform a regression analysis using a second-order model with interaction.
c. Which model fits better? Explain.

**18.9** Xr18-09 The coach and the general manager of a team in the National Hockey League are trying to decide what kinds of players to draft. To help in making their decision, they need to know which variables are most closely related to the goals differential—the difference between the number of goals their team scores and the number of goals scored by their team's opponents. (A positive differential means that their team wins, and a negative differential is a loss.) After some consideration, they decide that there are two important variables: The percentage of face-offs won and the penalty-minutes differential. The latter variable is the difference between the number of penalty minutes assessed against their team and the number of penalty minutes assessed against their team's opponents. The data from 100 games were recorded.

a. Perform a regression analysis using a first-order model with interaction.
b. Is this model valid?
c. Should the interaction term be included?

**18.10** Xr18-10 The production manager of a chemical plant wants to determine the roles that temperature and pressure play in the yield of a particular chemical produced at the plant. From past experience, she believes that when pressure is held constant, lower and higher temperatures tend to reduce the yield. When temperature is held constant, higher and lower pressures tend to increase the yield. She does not have any idea about how the yield is affected by various combinations of pressure and temperature. She observes 80 batches of the chemical in which the pressure and temperature were allowed to vary.

a. Which model should be used? Explain.
b. Conduct a regression analysis using the model you specified in part (a).
c. Assess how well the model fits the data.

## 18-2 Nominal Independent Variables

When we introduced regression analysis, we pointed out that all the variables must be interval. But in many real-life cases, one or more independent variables are nominal. For example, suppose that the used-car dealer in Example 16.2 believed that the color of a car is a factor in determining its auction price. Color is clearly a nominal variable. If we assign numbers to each possible color, these numbers will be completely arbitrary, and using them in a regression model will usually be pointless. For example, suppose the dealer believes the colors that are most popular, white and silver, are likely to lead to different prices than other colors. Accordingly, he assigns a code of 1 to white cars, a code of 2 to silver cars, and a code of 3 to all other colors. If we now conduct a multiple regression analysis using odometer reading and color as independent variables, the following results would be obtained. (File Xm16-02* contains these data. Interested readers can produce the following regression equation.)

$$\hat{y} = 17.342 - .0671x_1 - .0434x_2$$

Aside from the inclusion of the variable $x_2$, this equation is very similar to the one we produced in the simple regression model ($\hat{y} = 17.250 - .0669x$). The $t$-test of color ($t$-statistic $= -1.11$, and $p$-value $= .2694$) indicates that there is not enough evidence to infer that color is not linearly related to price. There are two possible explanations for this result. First, there is no relationship between color and price. Second, color is a factor in determining the car's price, but the way in which the dealer assigned the codes to the colors made detection of that fact impossible—that is, the dealer treated the nominal variable, color, as an interval variable. To further understand why we cannot use nominal data in regression analysis, try to interpret the coefficient of color. Such an effort is similar to attempting to interpret the mean of a sample of nominal data. It is futile. Even though this effort failed, it is possible to include nominal variables in the regression model. This is accomplished through the use of *indicator variables*.

An **indicator variable** (also called a **dummy variable**) is a variable that can assume either one of only two values (usually 0 and 1), where 1 represents the existence of a certain condition and 0 indicates that the condition does not hold. In this illustration, we would create two indicator variables to represent the color of the car:

$$I_1 = \begin{cases} 1 & \text{(if color is white)} \\ 0 & \text{(if color is not white)} \end{cases}$$

and

$$I_2 = \begin{cases} 1 & \text{(if color is silver)} \\ 0 & \text{(if color is not silver)} \end{cases}$$

Notice that we need only two indicator variables to represent the three categories. A white car is represented by $I_1 = 1$ and $I_2 = 0$. A silver car is represented by $I_1 = 0$ and $I_2 = 1$. Because cars that are painted some other color are neither white nor silver, they are represented by $I_1 = 0$ and $I_2 = 0$. It should be apparent that we cannot have $I_1 = 1$ and $I_2 = 1$, as long as we assume that no Toyota Camry is two-toned.

The effect of using these two indicator variables is to create three equations, one for each of the three colors. As you're about to discover, we can use the equations to determine how the car's color relates to its auction selling price.

In general, to represent a nominal variable with $m$ categories, we must create $m - 1$ indicator variables. The last category represented by $I_1 = I_2 = \cdots = I_{m-1} = 0$ is called the **omitted category**.

## 18-2a Interpreting and Testing the Coefficients of Indicator Variables

In file Xm16-02a, we stored the values of $I_1$ and $I_2$. We then performed a multiple regression analysis using the variables odometer reading ($x$), $I_1$, and $I_2$.

### EXCEL Data Analysis

| | A | B | C | D | E | F |
|---|---|---|---|---|---|---|
| 1 | SUMMARY OUTPUT | | | | | |
| 2 | | | | | | |
| 3 | *Regression Statistics* | | | | | |
| 4 | Multiple R | 0.8371 | | | | |
| 5 | R Square | 0.7008 | | | | |
| 6 | Adjusted R Square | 0.6914 | | | | |
| 7 | Standard Error | 0.3043 | | | | |
| 8 | Observations | 100 | | | | |
| 9 | | | | | | |
| 10 | ANOVA | | | | | |
| 11 | | *df* | *SS* | *MS* | *F* | *Significance F* |
| 12 | Regression | 3 | 20.81 | 6.94 | 74.95 | 4.65E-25 |
| 13 | Residual | 96 | 8.89 | 0.0926 | | |
| 14 | Total | 99 | 29.70 | | | |
| 15 | | | | | | |
| 16 | | *Coefficients* | *Standard Error* | *t Stat* | *P-value* | |
| 17 | Intercept | 16.837 | 0.197 | 85.42 | 2.28E-92 | |
| 18 | Odometer | −0.0591 | 0.0051 | −11.67 | 4.04E-20 | |
| 19 | I-1 | 0.0911 | 0.0729 | 1.25 | 0.2143 | |
| 20 | I-2 | 0.3304 | 0.0816 | 4.05 | 0.0001 | |

INTERPRET

The regression equation is

$$\hat{y} = 16.837 - .0591x + .0911I_1 + .3304I_2$$

The intercept and the coefficient of odometer reading are interpreted in the usual manner. The intercept ($b_0 = 16.837$) is meaningless in the context of this problem. The coefficient of the odometer reading ($b_1 = -.0591$) tells us that for each additional mile on the odometer, the auction price decreases an average of 5.91 cents, holding the color constant. Now examine the remaining two coefficients:

$$b_2 = .0911$$
$$b_3 = .3304$$

Recall that we interpret the coefficients in a multiple regression model by holding the other variables constant. In this example, we interpret the coefficient of $I_1$ as follows. In this sample, a white Camry sells for .0911 thousand or $91.10 on average more than other colors (nonwhite, nonsilver) with the same odometer reading. A silver car sells for $330.40 on average more than other colors with the same odometer reading. The reason both comparisons are made with other colors is that such cars are represented by $I_1 = I_2 = 0$. Thus, for a nonwhite and nonsilver car, the equation becomes

$$\hat{y} = 16.837 - .0591x + .0911(0) + .3304(0)$$

which is

$$\hat{y} = 16.837 - .0591x$$

For a white car ($I_1 = 1$ and $I_2 = 0$), the regression equation is

$$\hat{y} = 16.837 - .0591x + .0911(1) + .3304(0)$$

which is

$$\hat{y} = 16.928 - .0591x$$

Finally, for a silver car ($I_1 = 0$ and $I_2 = 1$), the regression equation is

$$\hat{y} = 16.837 - .0591x + .0911(0) + .3304(1)$$

which simplifies to

$$\hat{y} = 17.167 - .0591x$$

Figure 18.11 depicts the graph of price versus odometer reading for the three different color categories. Notice that the three lines are parallel (with slope = −.0591) while the intercepts differ.

**FIGURE 18.11 Price Versus Odometer Reading for Three Colors**

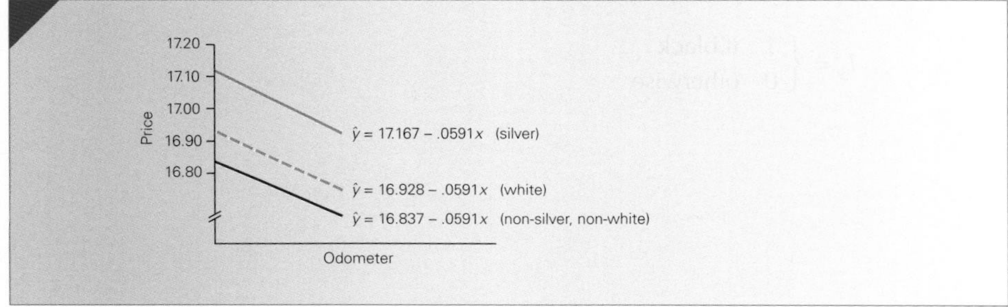

We can also perform $t$-tests on the coefficients of $I_1$ and $I_2$. However, because the variables $I_1$ and $I_2$ represent different groups (the three color categories), these $t$-tests allow us to draw inferences about the differences in auction selling prices between the groups for the entire population of similar 3-year-old Toyota Camrys.

The test of the coefficient of $I_1$, which is $\beta_2$, is conducted as follows:

$H_0$: $\beta_2 = 0$
$H_1$: $\beta_2 \neq 0$

Test statistic: $t = 1.25$, $p$-value $= .2143$

There is insufficient evidence to infer that white Camrys have a different mean selling price than do Camrys in the omitted category in the population of 3-year-old Camrys with the same odometer reading.

To determine whether silver-colored Camrys sell for a different price than Camrys in the other color category, we test

$H_0$: $\beta_3 = 0$
$H_1$: $\beta_3 \neq 0$

Test statistic: $t = 4.05$, $p$-value $= .0001$

We can conclude that there are differences in the mean auction selling prices between all 3-year-old, silver-colored Camrys and the omitted color category with the same odometer readings.

## General Social Survey: Variables that Affect Income II

Tyler Olson/Shutterstock.com

To include the nominal variables gender and race in a multiple regression model, we need to create two sets of indicator variables. The first is to represent gender.
For gender let:

$$I_1 = \begin{cases} 1 & \text{if male} \\ 0 & \text{if female} \end{cases}$$

For race let:

$$I_2 = \begin{cases} 1 & \text{if white} \\ 0 & \text{otherwise} \end{cases}$$

$$I_3 = \begin{cases} 1 & \text{if black} \\ 0 & \text{otherwise} \end{cases}$$

## EXCEL Data Analysis

| | A | B | C | D | E | F | G |
|---|---|---|---|---|---|---|---|
| 1 | SUMMARY OUTPUT | | | | | | |
| 2 | | | | | | | |
| 3 | *Regression Statistics* | | | | | | |
| 4 | Multiple R | 0.6115 | | | | | |
| 5 | R Square | 0.3740 | | | | | |
| 6 | Adjusted R Square | 0.3639 | | | | | |
| 7 | Standard Error | 35,096 | | | | | |
| 8 | Observations | 446 | | | | | |
| 9 | | | | | | | |
| 10 | ANOVA | | | | | | |
| 11 | | *df* | *SS* | *MS* | *F* | *Significance F* | |
| 12 | Regression | 7 | 322,244,322,457 | 46,034,903,208 | 37.38 | 5.44E-41 | |
| 13 | Residual | 438 | 539,482,462,437 | 1,231,695,120 | | | |
| 14 | Total | 445 | 861,726,784,894 | | | | |
| 15 | | | | | | | |
| 16 | | *Coefficients* | *Standard Error* | *t Stat* | *P-value* | *Lower 95%* | *Upper 95%* |
| 17 | Intercept | −112,407 | 14,523 | −7.74 | 6.93E-14 | −140,950 | −83,865 |
| 18 | I-1 | 14,879 | 3617 | 4.11 | 4.65E-05 | 7770 | 21989 |
| 19 | I-2 | 5552 | 6789 | 0.82 | 0.4139 | −7791 | 18896 |
| 20 | I-3 | −3977 | 8478 | −0.47 | 0.6392 | −20639 | 12685 |
| 21 | AGE | 820.4 | 146.7 | 5.59 | 3.97E-08 | 532 | 1109 |
| 22 | EDUC | 5637 | 592.3 | 9.52 | 1.21E-19 | 4473 | 6801 |
| 23 | HRS1 | 969.4 | 120.5 | 8.05 | 8.01E-15 | 733 | 1206 |
| 24 | SPHRS1 | −141.9 | 128.2 | −1.11 | 0.2688 | −394 | 110 |

### INTERPRET

The model has improved slightly; the coefficient of determination has increased from .3456 to .3740 and the standard error decreased from 35,841 to 35,096.

The coefficient of variable $I_1$ is 14,879, which tells us that in this sample men earn an average $14,879 more than women when the comparison is made holding the other independent variables constant. Here is how we interpret this number. Assume that this is the population coefficient (and not the sample coefficient). Imagine populations of men and women who are identical in terms of the other independent variables (race, age, education, hours of work, spouse's hours of work, number of children, and number of family earners). And now when we compare incomes, the men earn on average $18,794 more than the women.

The *t*-test of the coefficient is $t = 4.11$ and with a *p*-value of 0. We conclude that there is enough evidence that, in the United States in 2014, average incomes of men and women were different when the other variables were held constant.

The coefficient of $I_2$ is 5,552. This number means that in this sample white people earn an average of $5,552 more than the other category, which is nonwhite and nonblack holding the other variables constant. However, the *t*-statistic is .82 and its *p*-value is .4139. There is not enough evidence to infer that the mean income of the population of white people is different from the mean income of the population of nonwhite, nonblack people.

The coefficient of $I_3$ is −3,977. In this sample, black people earn an average of $3,977 less than the other category holding the other variables constant. The *t*-test value is −.47 and its *p*-value is .6392. There is not enough evidence to conclude that, in 2014, the mean income of black people was different from the mean income of nonwhite, nonblack people.

Notice that because two of the indicator variables were not statistically significant this model is only slightly better than the model in Chapter 17.

## EXERCISES

**18.11** How many indicator variables must be created to represent a nominal independent variable that has five categories?

**18.12** Create and identify indicator variables to represent the following nominal variables.

a. Religious affiliation (Catholic, Protestant, and others)
b. Working shift (8 A.M. to 4 P.M., 4 P.M. to 12 midnight, and 12 midnight to 8 A.M.)
c. Supervisor (Jack Jones, Mary Brown, George Fosse, and Elaine Smith)

**18.13** In a study of computer applications, a survey asked which microcomputer a number of companies used. The following indicator variables were created.

$$I_1 = \begin{cases} 1 & \text{(if IBM)} \\ 0 & \text{(if not)} \end{cases} \qquad I_2 = \begin{cases} 1 & \text{(if Macintosh)} \\ 0 & \text{(if not)} \end{cases}$$

Which computer is being referred to by each of the following pairs of values?

a. $I_1 = 0; I_2 = 1$
b. $I_1 = 1; I_2 = 0$
c. $I_1 = 0; I_2 = 0$

*The following exercises require the use of a computer and software. Exercises 18.16 and 18.17 can be solved manually. See Appendix A.*

**18.14** Xr17-14* Refer to Exercise 17.14. After considering the results of the initial study, the dean realized that she may have omitted an important variable—the type of undergraduate degree. She returned to her sample of students and recorded the type of undergraduate degree using the following codes:

1 = BA

2 = BBA (including similar business or management degrees)

3 = BEng or BSc

4 = Other (including no undergraduate degree)

These data were included with the data from the original example. Can the dean conclude that the undergraduate degree is a factor in determining how well a student performs in the MBA program?

**18.15** Xr17-14* Refer to Exercise 17.14.

a. Predict with 95% confidence the MBA program GPA of a BEng whose undergraduate GPA was 9.0, whose GMAT score as 700, and who has had 10 years of work experience.
b. Repeat part (a) for a BA student.

**18.16** Xr17-10* Refer to Exercise 17.10, where a multiple regression analysis was performed to predict men's longevity based on the parents' and grandparents' longevity. In addition to these data, suppose that the actuary also recorded whether the man was a smoker (1 = yes and 0 = no).

a. Use regression analysis to produce the statistics for this model.
b. Compare the equation you just produced to that produced in Exercise 18.10. Describe the differences.
c. Are smoking and length of life related? Explain.

**18.17** Xr18-17 The manager of an amusement park would like to be able to predict daily attendance in order to develop more accurate plans about how much food to order and how many ride operators to hire. After some consideration, he decided that the following three factors are critical:

Yesterday's attendance
Weekday or weekend
Predicted weather

He then took a random sample of 40 days. For each day, he recorded the attendance, the previous day's attendance, day of the week, and weather forecast. The first independent variable is interval, but the other two are nominal. Accordingly, he created the following sets of indicator variables:

$$I_1 = \begin{cases} 1 & \text{(if weekend)} \\ 0 & \text{(if not)} \end{cases}$$

$$I_2 = \begin{cases} 1 & \text{(if mostly sunny is predicted)} \\ 0 & \text{(if not)} \end{cases}$$

$$I_3 = \begin{cases} 1 & \text{(if rain is predicted)} \\ 0 & \text{(if not)} \end{cases}$$

a. Conduct a regression analysis.
b. Is this model valid? Explain.
c. Can we conclude that weather is a factor in determining attendance?
d. Do these results provide sufficient evidence that weekend attendance is, on average, larger than weekday attendance?

**18.18** Xr16-06* Recall Exercise 16.6 where a statistics practitioner analyzed the relationship between the length of a commercial and viewers' memory of the commercial's product. However, in the experiment not only was the length varied but also the type of commercial. There were three types: humorous (1), musical (2), and serious (3). The memory test scores, lengths, and type of commercial (using the codes in parentheses) were recorded.

a. Perform a regression analysis using the codes provided in the data file.
b. Can we infer that the memory test score is related to the type of commercial? Test with $\alpha = .05$.
c. Create indicator variables to describe the type of commercial and perform another regression analysis.
d. Repeat part (b) using the second model.
e. Discuss the reasons for the differences between parts (b) and (d).

**18.19** Xr17-12* Refer to Exercise 17.12 where the amount of time to unload a truck was analyzed. The manager realized that another variable, the time of day, may affect unloading time. He recorded the following codes: 1 = morning, 2 = early afternoon, and 3 = late afternoon.

a. Run a regression using the codes for time of day.
b. Create indicator variables to represent time of day. Perform a regression analysis with these new variables.
c. Which model fits better? Explain.
d. Is time of day related to time to unload?

**18.20** Xr18-20 Profitable banks are ones that make good decisions on loan applications. *Credit scoring* is the statistical technique that helps banks make that decision. However, many branches overturn credit scoring recommendations, whereas other banks do not use the technique. In an attempt to determine the factors that affect loan decisions, a statistics practitioner surveyed 100 banks and recorded the percentage of bad loans (any loan that is not completely repaid), the average size of the loan, and whether a scorecard is used, and if so, whether scorecard recommendations are overturned more than 10% of the time. These results are stored in columns 1 (percentage good loans), 2 (average loan), and 3 (code 1 = no scorecard, 2 = scorecard overturned more than 10% of the time, and 3 = scorecard overturned less than 10% of the time).

a. Create indicator variables to represent the codes.
b. Perform a regression analysis.
c. How well does the model fit the data?
d. Is multicollinearity a problem?
e. Interpret and test the coefficients. What does this tell you?
f. Predict with 95% confidence the percentage of bad loans for a bank whose average loan is \$10,000 and that does not use a scorecard.

**18.21** Xr18-21 Refer to Exercise 16.132, where a simple linear regression model was used to analyze the relationship between welding machine breakdowns and the age of the machine. The analysis proved to be so useful to company management that it decided to expand the model to include other machines. Data were gathered for two other machines. These data as well as the original data were recorded in the following way:

Column 1: Cost of repairs
Column 2: Age of machine
Column 3: Machine (1 = welding machine; 2 = lathe; 3 = stamping machine)

a. Develop a multiple regression model.
b. Interpret the coefficients.
c. Can we conclude that welding machines cost less to repair than other machines?

**18.22** Xr16-139* Refer to Exercise 16.139. The gender of the student was recorded where 1 = male and 0 = female.

a. Does the inclusion of gender improve the model?
b. Predict with 95% confidence the height of a female whose index finger is 6.5 cm long.
c. Predict with 95% confidence the height of a male whose index finger is 6.5 cm long.
d. Is this model likely to be useful? Explain.

## APPLICATIONS in HUMAN RESOURCES MANAGEMENT

iStockphoto.com/terex

### Performance Measurement

Most aspects of workers' performance fall into the domain of the human resources or personnel department. An important performance measurement is the attendance record of each worker. Personnel managers need to know what factors are likely to influence a worker to be absent more frequently than the norm. This can enable the manager to determine whether

(Continued)

someone should be hired in the first place. Once hired, the manager needs to be able to influence workers' attitudes and performance.

**18.23** Xr18-23 Absenteeism is a serious employment problem in most countries. It is estimated that absenteeism reduces potential output by more than 10%. Two economists launched a research project to learn more about the problem. They randomly selected 100 organizations to participate in a 1-year study. For each organization, they recorded the average number of days absent per employee and several variables thought to affect absenteeism. The following data were recorded:

Column 1: Average number of days absent per employee
Column 2: Average employee wage
Column 3: Percentage of part-time employees
Column 4: Percentage of unionized employees
Column 5: Availability of shiftwork (1 = yes; 0 = no)
Column 6: Union–management relationship (1 = good; 0 = not good)

a. Conduct a regression analysis.
b. Can we infer at the 5% significance level that the availability of shiftwork is related to absenteeism?
c. Is there enough evidence at the 5% significance level to infer that in organizations where the union–management relationship is good, absenteeism is lower?

(The authors are grateful to James Fong and Diana Mansour for developing this exercise.)

## General Social Survey Exercises

**18.24** GSS2014* a. Conduct a regression analysis with income (RINCOME) as the dependent variable and age (AGE), education (EDUC), number of hours of work (HRS1), and whether someone worked for him or herself (WRKSLF: 1 = Self, 2 = Someone else) as independent variables.
b. Interpret the coefficient of WRKSLF.
c. Is there sufficient evidence to infer that people who work for themselves earn larger incomes after removing the effect of age, education, and weekly hours of work?

**18.25** GSS2014* Develop a multiple regression model with the position on the question, should the government reduce income differences (EQWLTH: 1 = Government should reduce income differences; 2, 3, 4, 5, 6, 7 = No government action) as the dependent variable and age (AGE), education (EDUC), income (RINCOME), weekly hours of work (HRS1), and party (PARTYID3: 1 = Democrat, 2 = Independent, 3 = Republican) as independent variables.

a. Is there sufficient evidence to infer that Democrats are more likely than Independents to believe that government should reduce income differences after removing the effects of age, income, education, and weekly hours?
b. Is there sufficient evidence to infer that Republicans are more likely than Independents to believe that government should take no action to reduce income differences after removing the effects of age, income, education, and weekly hours?

**18.26** GSS2014* Repeat Exercise 18.25 using political views (POLVIEWS3: 1 = Liberal, 2 = Moderate, 3 = Conservative) instead of political party.
a. Is there sufficient evidence to infer that liberals are more likely than moderates to believe that government should reduce income differences after removing the effects of age, income, education, and weekly hours?

b. Is there sufficient evidence to infer that conservatives are more likely than moderates to believe that government should take no action to reduce income differences after removing the effects of age, income, education, and weekly hours?

**18.27** GSS2014* Can we infer that men and women (SEX: 1 = Male, 2 = Female) differ in the amount of television per day (TVHOURS) after removing the effects of age (AGE) and education (EDUC)?

**18.28** GSS2014* Conduct a regression analysis with position on the question, should the government help poor people? Use (HELPPOOR: 1 = Government action; 2, 3, 4, 5 = People should help themselves) as the dependent variable and age (AGE), education (EDUC), income (RINCOME), weekly work hours (HRS1), and political views (POLVIEWS3: 1 = Liberal, 2 = Moderate, 3 = Conservative) as independent variables.

a. Is there sufficient evidence to infer that liberals are more likely than moderates to believe that government should help poor people after removing the effects of age, income, education, and weekly hours?
b. Is there sufficient evidence to infer that conservatives are more likely than moderates to believe that people should help themselves after removing the effects of age, income, education, and weekly hours?

**18.29** GSS2014* Can we infer that there are differences in income (RINCOME) between people who work for the government and people who work for private employers (WRKGOVT: 1 = Government, 2 = Private) after removing the effects of age (AGE), education (EDUC), and weekly hours of work (HRS1)?

**18.30** GSS2014* Conduct a regression analysis with number of hours of television per day (TVHOURS) to determine whether there is enough evidence to infer that there are differences between the three race categories (RACE: 1 = White, 2 = Black, 3 = Other) after removing the effects of age (AGE) and education (EDUC).

**18.31** GSS2014* Conduct a regression analysis with position on the question, should the government help poor people (HELPPOOR: 1 = Government action; 2, 3, 4, 5 = People should help themselves) as the dependent variable and age (AGE), income (RINCOME), education (EDUC), weekly work hours (HRS1), and party (PARTYID3: 1 = Democrat, 2 = Independent, 3 = Republican) as independent variables.

a. Is there sufficient evidence to infer that Democrats are more likely than Independents to believe that government should help poor people after removing the effects of age, income, education, and weekly hours?
b. Is there sufficient evidence to infer that Republicans are more likely than Independents to believe that people should help themselves after removing the effects of age, income, education, and weekly hours?

**18.32** GSS2014* Can we infer that there are differences in income (RINCOME) between Americans born in the United States and those born elsewhere (BORN: 1 = United States, 2 = Elsewhere), after removing the effects of age (AGE), education (EDUC), and weekly hours of work (HRS1)?

**18.33** GSS2014* To determine the effect of union membership run a regression with income (RINCOME) as the dependent variable and age (AGE), education (EDUC), number of hours worked per week (HRS1), and union membership (UNION:1 = Respondent belongs, 2 = Spouse belongs, 3 = Both belong, 4 = Neither belong). Is there sufficient evidence that union membership for the respondent, spouse, or both affects income after removing the effects of age, education, and hours worked?

## 18-3 (Optional) Applications in Human Resources Management: Pay Equity

In the history of North America, there are many examples of racial, ethnic, and gender discrimination. In the last three decades, there have been a number of endeavors designed to eliminate discriminatory practices and to right past wrongs. One of these efforts is pay equity, a program that attempts to correct discrimination in the way workers are paid. Our goal in this section is to describe the statistical component of the pay equity issue.

There are two forms of pay equity. The first is "equal pay for equal work." This form is relatively straightforward, arguing that if two individuals do the same job with similar qualifications and experience, they should be paid the same. In many jurisdictions, it is illegal to violate equal pay for equal work. The second form is "equal pay for work of equal value." This form is controversial for several reasons, including the use of subjectively assigned measures of qualifications and working conditions.

Regression analysis is used extensively in pay-equity cases. However, the methodology used in equal-pay-for-equal-work cases differs from that used for equal-pay-for-work-of-equal-value cases. The following example illustrates how statistical analyses can be utilized for the former.

## EXAMPLE 18.3 Testing for Pay Equity: Equal Pay for Equal Work

DATA Xm18-03

A large firm employing tens of thousands of workers has been accused of discriminating against its female managers. The accusation is based on a random sample of 100 managers. The mean annual salary of the 38 female managers is $76,189, whereas the mean annual salary of the 62 male managers is $97,832. A statistical analysis reveals that the $t$-test of the difference between two means yields a $p$-value of less than 1%, which provides overwhelming evidence that male managers are paid more than female managers. In rebuttal, the president of the firm points out that the company has a strict policy of equal pay for equal work and that the difference may be the result of other variables. Accordingly, he found and recorded the number of years of education and the number of years of experience for each of the 100 managers in the sample. Also recorded are the salary and gender (0 = female, 1 = male). The president wanted to know whether a regression analysis would shed some light on the issue.

### SOLUTION:

Using salary as the dependent variable, a multiple regression analysis was performed with the results shown here.

### EXCEL Data Analysis

| | A | B | C | D | E | F |
|---|---|---|---|---|---|---|
| 1 | SUMMARY OUTPUT | | | | | |
| 2 | | | | | | |
| 3 | *Regression Statistics* | | | | | |
| 4 | Multiple R | 0.8326 | | | | |
| 5 | R Square | 0.6932 | | | | |
| 6 | Adjusted R Square | 0.6836 | | | | |
| 7 | Standard Error | 16,274 | | | | |
| 8 | Observations | 100 | | | | |
| 9 | | | | | | |
| 10 | ANOVA | | | | | |
| 11 | | *df* | *SS* | *MS* | *F* | *Significance F* |
| 12 | Regression | 3 | 57,434,095,083 | 19,144,698,361 | 72.29 | 1.55E-24 |
| 13 | Residual | 96 | 25,424,794,888 | 264,841,613 | | |
| 14 | Total | 99 | 82,858,889,971 | | | |
| 15 | | | | | | |
| 16 | | *Coefficients* | *Standard Error* | *t Stat* | *P-value* | |
| 17 | Intercept | −5835 | 16083 | −0.36 | 0.7175 | |
| 18 | Education | 2119 | 1018 | 2.08 | 0.0401 | |
| 19 | Experience | 4099 | 317 | 12.92 | 9.89E-23 | |
| 20 | Gender | 1851 | 3703 | 0.50 | 0.6183 | |

INTERPRET

The model fits quite well. The coefficient of determination is .6932, which tells the president that 69.32% of the variation in salaries is explained by the model. The $F$-statistic is 72.29, which has a $p$-value of 0. There is overwhelming evidence to allow us to infer that the model is valid.

The $p$-values of the $t$-tests to determine whether there is evidence of a linear relationship between salary and each of education, experience, and gender are .0401, 0, and .6183, respectively. Both the years of education and the years of experience are linearly related to salary. However, the $t$-test of the slope for gender tells us that there is not enough evidence to infer that the mean salaries of all the firm's male and female managers with the same amount of education and experience differ. In other words, on average, the female managers in this firm have less education and experience than their male counterparts, which explains their lower mean salary. Before the regression analysis, we calculated the difference in sample mean salaries to be $97,832 – $76,189 = $21,643. After removing the effects of education and experience in this sample that difference was reduced to $1, 851, which is statistically insignificant.

## 18-3a Regression Analysis for Equal-Pay-for-Work-of-Equal-Value Cases

Cases involving the issue of equal pay for work of equal value are much more difficult. The issue generally revolves around female-dominated and male-dominated jobs. The former refers to jobs that are generally held by women (e.g., secretaries) and the latter refers to jobs generally held by men (e.g., maintenance workers). Women's groups claim that male-dominated jobs are more highly paid. Here the issue is not underpaying women who are doing exactly the same jobs performed by men. Instead, the issue is that women's jobs are undervalued. Thus, it is necessary to evaluate jobs.

Several jurisdictions have enacted laws requiring pay equity for work of equal value. One such jurisdiction is the province of Manitoba. The Manitoba Pay Equity Act is mandatory in the province's civil service, crown corporations, hospitals, and universities. The act defines gender-dominated job classes as ones with at least 10 workers where at least 70% are of the same gender. The act requires that all such jobs be evaluated to determine whether female-dominated jobs are undervalued and underpaid compared to male-dominated jobs.

Although regression analysis is employed, there are major differences between the technique described in Example 18.3 and the one used in this case. Rather than estimate a regression model that explains how several related variables affect pay, we need to develop a job evaluation system. The system is used to assign a score to each job, which is then used as an independent variable in regression where pay is again the dependent variable. The regression analysis can be conducted in several ways. The simple linear regression equation can be estimated using the male-dominated jobs only. The coefficients are then used to calculate the "correct" female-dominated job pay rates. The difference between the so-called correct and actual pay rates represents the degree of underpayment. Alternatively, a regression analysis with both male- and female-dominated jobs can be employed. An indicator variable representing gender is included. The value of the indicator variable's coefficient represents the difference between male- and female-dominated jobs and the degree of underpayment. The following example illustrates the latter type of analysis, which was adapted from the province of Manitoba Pay Equity Act manuals that describe the law and how it is to be administered.

## EXAMPLE 18.4 Testing for Pay Equity: Equal Pay for Work of Equal Value

In a university, a total of eight jobs are identified as gender dominated. The female-dominated jobs are cleaner, secretary, and workers in the book store and cafeteria. The male-dominated jobs are maintenance worker, security guard, gardener, and technician. Perform a pay-equity analysis to determine whether and to what degree female-dominated jobs are undervalued and underpaid.

SOLUTION:

The hourly pay rates are as follows:

| Job Categories | Pay Rate |
|---|---|
| Maintenance | 13.55 |
| Security | 15.65 |
| Gardener | 13.80 |
| Technician | 19.90 |
| Cleaner | 11.85 |
| Secretary | 14.75 |
| Bookstore | 18.90 |
| Cafeteria | 13.30 |

After some consideration, the following factors were selected as part of the job evaluation system:

Knowledge and training
Responsibility
Mental effort
Physical effort
Working conditions

Each factor is assigned a weight that reflects its importance. The weights (which must sum to 1) are 25%, 23%, 22%, 15%, and 15%, respectively.

A score for each job is determined by assigning a value between 1 and 10 for each of the five factors and then multiplying by the weight. Smaller values represent less-demanding requirements or better conditions.

The male-dominated jobs are evaluated as follows:

| Factors | Weight | Maintenance | Security | Gardener | Technician |
|---|---|---|---|---|---|
| Knowledge and training | .25 | 1 | 2 | 3 | 9 |
| Responsibility | .23 | 2 | 7 | 1 | 7 |
| Mental effort | .22 | 2 | 3 | 1 | 8 |
| Physical effort | .15 | 7 | 1 | 6 | 4 |
| Working conditions | .15 | 7 | 4 | 8 | 1 |
| Total score | | 3.25 | 3.52 | 3.30 | 6.37 |

As you can see, the scores assigned to the maintenance workers and gardeners reflect relatively small demands on knowledge, training, and mental effort but high demands on physical effort and poor working conditions. The technician, on the other hand, has excellent working conditions but requires a high level of knowledge and training.

The evaluations of the female-dominated jobs are as follows:

| Factors | Weight | Cleaner | Secretary | Bookstore | Cafeteria |
|---|---|---|---|---|---|
| Knowledge and training | .25 | 1 | 6 | 4 | 2 |
| Responsibility | .23 | 2 | 7 | 7 | 2 |
| Mental effort | .22 | 2 | 6 | 7 | 2 |
| Physical effort | .15 | 7 | 3 | 2 | 5 |
| Working conditions | .15 | 5 | 1 | 1 | 6 |
| Total score | | 2.95 | 5.03 | 4.60 | 3.05 |

As was the case with the male-dominated jobs, the scores for the female-dominated jobs are based on a subjective assessment of the requirements and work that the jobs entail.

The score and an indicator variable are used as independent variables in a regression analysis with pay as the dependent variable. The following data are used in the regression analysis:

| Job Categories | Pay Rate | Score | Gender |
|---|---|---|---|
| Maintenance | 13.55 | 3.25 | 1 |
| Security | 15.65 | 3.52 | 1 |
| Gardener | 13.80 | 3.30 | 1 |
| Technician | 19.90 | 6.37 | 1 |
| Cleaner | 11.85 | 2.95 | 0 |
| Secretary | 14.75 | 5.03 | 0 |
| Bookstore | 18.90 | 4.60 | 0 |
| Cafeteria | 13.30 | 3.05 | 0 |

where

$$\text{Gender} = \begin{cases} 1 & \text{if male-dominated job} \\ 0 & \text{if female-dominated job} \end{cases}$$

The results of the regression are shown below.

## EXCEL Data Analysis

| | A | B | C | D | E | F |
|---|---|---|---|---|---|---|
| 1 | SUMMARY OUTPUT | | | | | |
| 2 | | | | | | |
| 3 | *Regression Statistics* | | | | | |
| 4 | Multiple R | 0.8515 | | | | |
| 5 | R Square | 0.7251 | | | | |
| 6 | Adjusted R Square | 0.6152 | | | | |
| 7 | Standard Error | 1.75 | | | | |
| 8 | Observations | 8 | | | | |
| 9 | | | | | | |
| 10 | ANOVA | | | | | |
| 11 | | *df* | *SS* | *MS* | *F* | *Significance F* |
| 12 | Regression | 2 | 40.39 | 20.19 | 6.59 | 0.0396 |
| 13 | Residual | 5 | 15.31 | 3.06 | | |
| 14 | Total | 7 | 55.70 | | | |
| 15 | | | | | | |
| 16 | | *Coefficients* | *Standard Error* | *t Stat* | *P-value* | |
| 17 | Intercept | 7.15 | 2.31 | 3.10 | 0.0270 | |
| 18 | Score | 1.93 | 0.547 | 3.54 | 0.0166 | |
| 19 | Gender | 0.633 | 1.242 | 0.51 | 0.6318 | |

INTERPRET

We cannot apply the usual statistical inference because the eight observations represent the entire population under consideration. Instead we simply use the coefficients of interest. In this case we discover that male-dominated jobs are paid an average of .63 more than female-dominated jobs after adjusting for the value of each job. If we accept the validity of this analysis (see Exercises 18.29 and 18.30), we conclude that the holders of female-dominated jobs need to have their pay rates increased by 63 cents per hour.

## Exercises

*The following exercises require a computer and software.*

**18.34** Xr18-34 Pay equity for men and women has been an ongoing source of conflict for a number of years in North America. Suppose that a statistics practitioner is investigating the factors that affect salary differences between male and female university professors. He believes that the following variables have some impact on a professor's salary:

Number of years since first degree

$$\text{Highest degree} = \begin{cases} 1 \text{ if Highest degree is a Ph.D.} \\ 0 \text{ if Highest degree is not a Ph.D.} \end{cases}$$

Average score on teaching evaluations
Number of articles published in refereed journals

$$\text{Gender} = \begin{cases} 1 & \text{if Professor is male} \\ 0 & \text{if Professor is female} \end{cases}$$

A random sample of 100 university professors was taken and the following data were recorded:

Column 1: Annual salary
Column 2: Number of years since first degree
Column 3: Highest degree
Column 4: Mean score on teaching evaluation
Column 5: Number of articles published
Column 6: Gender

a. Can the statistics practitioner conclude that the model is valid?
b. Can the statistics practitioner conclude at the 5% significance level that there is gender discrimination?

*An Excel spreadsheet,* ***Pay Equity*** *(stored in the* ***Excel Workbooks*** *folder), was created to perform the analysis described in Example 18.4. The jobs, pay rates, job scores, and the values of the indicator variable are shown at the bottom of the sheet. These data were used as inputs in the regression analysis. The worksheet is set up so that any change in the factor scores and/or weights automatically changes the job scores at the bottom of the page.*

**18.35** Re-do Example 18.4. Change the weights for knowledge and training to 15% and for working conditions to 25%. What effect does this have on the conclusion? Briefly explain why the result was predictable.

**18.36** Re-do Example 18.4 by assigning your own values to each factor and to the weights. What conclusion did you reach?

**18.37** Discuss how the factor values and weights affect the final result. Explain the strengths and weaknesses of the statistical analysis.

## 18-4 (Optional) Stepwise Regression

In Section 17-3 we introduced multicollinearity and described the problems that it causes by distorting the $t$-tests of the coefficients. If one of the objectives of the regression analysis is to determine whether and how each independent variable is related to the dependent variable, it is necessary to reduce the extent of multicollinearity.

As we discussed in Section 17-3, one of the ways to reduce multicollinearity is to include independent variables that appear to be uncorrelated with each other. A correlation matrix is usually produced to determine the correlation coefficients for each pair of variables. In many cases the correlation matrix will not be able to identify whether multicollinearity is a serious problem because there are many ways for variables to be related. For example, one variable may be a function of several other variables. Consequently, a correlation matrix may not reveal the problem. In this section, we introduce *stepwise regression*, a procedure that eliminates correlated independent variables.

**Stepwise regression** is an iterative procedure that adds and deletes one independent variable at a time. The decision to add or delete a variable is made on the basis of whether that variable improves the model. XLSTAT features this and related procedures. Excel does not.

## 18-4a Stepwise Regression Procedure

The procedure begins by computing the simple regression model for each independent variable. The independent variable with the largest $F$-statistic (which in a simple regression model is the $t$-statistic squared) or, equally, with the smallest $p$-value is chosen as the first entering variable. The standard is called the *$F$-to-enter*. If no independent variable exceeds the $F$-to-enter, the procedure ceases with no regression model produced. If at least one variable exceeds the standard, the procedure continues. It then considers whether the model would be improved by adding a second independent variable. It examines all such models to determine which is best and whether the $F$-statistic of the second variable (with the first variable already in the equation) is greater than the $F$-to-enter.

If two independent variables are highly correlated, only one of them will enter the equation. Once the first variable is included, the added explanatory power of the second variable will be minimal and its $F$-statistic will not be large enough to enter the model. In this way, multicollinearity is reduced.

The procedure continues by deciding whether to add another independent variable at each step. The computer also checks to see whether the inclusion of previously added variables is warranted. At each step the $p$-values of all variables are computed and compared to the *$F$-to-remove*. If a variable's $F$-statistic falls below this standard, it is removed from the equation. These steps are repeated until no more variables are added or removed.

To illustrate, we'll use the General Social Survey of 2012 where we conducted a regression analysis and discovered the problem of multicollinearity (see page 713).

Excel does not offer stepwise regression as one of its options. We use XLSTAT.

### XLSTAT

| | A | B | C | D | E | F | G |
|---|---|---|---|---|---|---|---|
| 1 | **Regression of variable INCOME:** | | | | | | |
| 2 | Summary of the variables selection INCOME: | | | | | | |
| 3 | | | | | | | |
| 4 | Nbr. of variables | Variables | Variable IN/OUT | Status | MSE | R² | Adjusted R² |
| 5 | 1 | EDUC | EDUC | IN | 1,222,873,630 | 0.2008 | 0.1984 |
| 6 | 2 | EDUC / HRS1 | HRS1 | IN | 1,074,097,086 | 0.3001 | 0.2960 |
| 7 | 3 | AGE / EDUC / HRS1 | AGE | IN | 1,052,978,541 | 0.3159 | 0.3098 |
| 8 | | | | | | | |
| 9 | Model parameters (INCOME): | | | | | | |
| 10 | | | | | | | |
| 11 | Source | Value | Standard error | t | Pr > \|t\| | Lower bound (95%) | Upper bound (95%) |
| 12 | Intercept | -84,462 | 12,042 | -7.01 | **< 0.0001** | -108,149 | -60,775 |
| 13 | AGE | 420.7 | 150.7 | 2.79 | **0.006** | 124.4 | 717.1 |
| 14 | EDUC | 5,352 | 559.1 | 9.57 | **< 0.0001** | 4,252 | 6,451 |
| 15 | HRS1 | 913.3 | 128.1 | 7.13 | **< 0.0001** | 661 | 1,165 |
| 16 | SPHRS1 | 0.000 | 0.000 | | | | |
| 17 | EARNRS | 0.000 | 0.000 | | | | |
| 18 | CHILDS | 0.000 | 0.000 | | | | |

*INSTRUCTIONS*

Run a regression analysis and click **Options**, check **Model selection**, and choose **Stepwise**. Note that we have heavily edited the printout.

INTERPRET

The regression equation is:

$$\hat{y} = -84{,}462 + 421 \text{ AGE} + 5362 \text{ EDUC} + 913 \text{ HRS1}$$

All of these independent variables are shown to be linearly related to income.

Compare this equation to the one produced in Chapter 17 and you find that the coefficients and test results are very similar. The main difference is that the three variables that were not significant in the equation in Chapter 17 are not included in the stepwise regression result.

## EXERCISES

*The following exercises require the use of a computer and statistical software.*

**18.38** Xr17-16 Refer to Exercise 17.16.
a. Use stepwise regression to compute the regression equation.
b. Compare the output with that produced in Exercise 17.16.

**18.39** Xr17-17 Refer to Exercise 17.17
a. Use stepwise regression to compute the regression equation.
b. Compare the output with that produced in Exercise 17.17.

## GENERAL SOCIAL SURVEY EXERCISES

**18.40** GSS2014* Refer to Exercise 17.20. Use stepwise regression to calculate the equation.

**18.41** GSS2014* Refer to Exercise 17.21. Use stepwise regression to answer the question.

**18.42** SCF2013:\MC* Refer to Exercise 17.24. Run a stepwise regression and report the differences between this regression and the one in Exercise 17.24.

## 18-5 MODEL BUILDING

At this point, we have described several different regression models. You now have the use of nominal predictor variables and the tools to describe a variety of nonlinear relationships. In this section, we describe how the statistics practitioner builds a model.

Regression analysis is used either to determine how one or more predictor variables are related to a dependent variable or to predict the value of the dependent variable and estimate its expected value. Although the process differs between the two objectives, there are many similarities in the approach.

Here is the procedure that is employed in the building of a model.

## 18-5a Procedure for Building a Model

1. *Identify the dependent variable.* Clearly define the variable that you wish to analyze or predict. For example, if you want to forecast sales, decide whether it is to be the number of units sold, gross revenue, or perhaps net profits. In addition, decide whether to forecast weekly, monthly, or annual figures.

2. *List potential predictors.* Using your knowledge of the dependent variable, produce a list of predictors that may be related to the dependent variable. Although we cannot establish a causal relationship, we should attempt to include predictor variables that cause changes in the dependent variable. Bear in mind the problems caused by multicollinearity and the cost of gathering, storing, and processing data. Be selective in your choices. It is best to use the fewest independent variables that produce a satisfactory model.

3. *Gather the required observations for the potential models.* A general rule is that there should be at least six observations for each independent variable used in the equation.

4. *Identify several possible models.* Once again, use your knowledge of the dependent variable and predictor variables to formulate a model. For example, if you believe that a predictor variable affects the dependent variable, but you are uncertain about the form of the relationship, then formulate first- and second-order models with and without interaction. It may be helpful to draw a scatter diagram of the dependent variable and each predictor variable to discover the nature of the relationship.

5. *Use statistical software to estimate the models.* Use one or more of the variable selection methods described in the previous section to determine which variables to include in the model. If the objective is to determine which predictor variables are related to the dependent variable, you will need to ensure that multicollinearity is not a problem. If it is, attempt to reduce the number of independent variables.

6. *Determine whether the required conditions are satisfied.* If not, attempt to correct the problem. At this point, you may have several "equal" models from which to choose.

7. *Use your judgment and the statistical output to select the best model.* This may be the most difficult part of the process. There may be a model that fits best, but another one may be a better predictor, and yet another may feature fewer variables and, thus, be easier to work with. Experience with regression helps. Taking another statistics course is likely your best strategy.

## CHAPTER SUMMARY

This chapter completes our discussion of the regression technique, which began in Chapter 17. We presented several additional models for predicting the value of one variable on the basis of other variables. Polynomial models with one and two independent variables were presented. We discussed how indicator variables allow us to use nominal variables and we described how indicator variables are used in pay equity discussions. Logistic regression was introduced to address the problem of a nominal dependent variable. To help choose the model that is best for our purposes, we introduced stepwise regression. We completed the chapter by providing some advice on how statisticians build models.

### IMPORTANT TERMS:

Polynomial model 734
Predictor variable 734
Order 734
First-order 734
Interaction 737
Quadratic relationship 738
Second-order 738
Indicator variable 744
Dummy variable 744
Omitted category 744
Stepwise regression 757

### SYMBOLS:

| Symbol | Pronounced | Represents |
|---|---|---|
| $I_i$ | *I* sub *i* or *I i* | Indicator variable |

### COMPUTER OUTPUT AND INSTRUCTIONS:

| Technique | XLSTAT |
|---|---|
| Stepwise regression | 757 |

## CHAPTER EXERCISES

*The following exercises require the use of a computer and statistical software. Use a 5% significance level.*

**18.43** Xr18-43 Car designers have been experimenting with ways to improve gas mileage for many years. An important element in this research is the way in which a car's speed affects how quickly fuel is burned. Competitions whose objective is to drive the farthest on the smallest amount of gas have determined that low speeds and high speeds are inefficient. Designers would like to know which speed burns gas most efficiently. As an experiment, 50 identical cars are driven at different speeds and the gas mileage measured.

a. Write the equation of the model you think is appropriate.
b. Perform a regression analysis using your model.
c. How well does it fit?

**18.44** Xr18-44 The number of car accidents on a particular stretch of highway seems to be related to the number of vehicles that travel over it and the speed at which they are traveling. A city alderman has decided to ask the county sheriff to provide him with statistics covering the last few years, with the intention of examining these data statistically so that he can (if possible) introduce new speed laws that will reduce traffic accidents. Using the number of accidents as the dependent variable, he obtains estimates of the number of cars passing along a stretch of road and their average speeds (in miles per hour). The observations for 60 randomly selected days were recorded.

a. Which model should the alderman use? Explain.
b. Conduct a regression analysis using a first-order model with interaction.
c. Is the model valid?

**18.45** Refer to Exercise 18.44.
a. Estimate a second-order model with interaction.
b. Is this model valid in predicting the number of accidents? Test at the 10% significance level.

**18.46** Xr18-46 After analyzing whether the number of ads is related to the number of customers, the manager in Exercise 16.99 decided to determine whether the advertising made any difference. As a result, he reorganized the experiment. Each week he advertised several times per week, but in only one of the advertising media. He again recorded the weekly number of customers, the number of ads, and the media of that week's advertisement (1 = Newspaper, 2 = Radio, 3 = Television).
a. Create indicator variables to describe the advertising medium.
b. Conduct a regression analysis. Test to determine whether the model is valid.
c. Does the advertising medium make a difference? Explain.

**18.47** Xr18-47 A baseball fan has been collecting data from a newspaper on the various American League teams. She wants to explain each team's winning percentage as a function of its batting average and its earned run average plus an indicator variable for whether the team fired its manager within the last 12 months (1 = Fired manager, and 0 = Did not fire manager). The data for 50 randomly selected teams over the last five seasons were recorded.
a. Perform a regression analysis using a first-order model (no interaction).
b. Do these data provide sufficient evidence that a team that fired its manager within the last 12 months wins less frequently than a team that did not fire its manager?

**18.48** Xr18-48 A growing segment of the textile industry in the United States is based on piecework, wherein workers are paid for each unit they produce, instead of receiving an hourly wage. The manager of one such company has observed that inexperienced workers perform quite poorly, but they usually improve quickly. However, very experienced workers do not perform as well as expected. Analysts attribute this phenomenon to boredom. More experienced workers grow weary of the monotonous work and become less productive. In an attempt to learn more about piecework labor, a statistics practitioner took a random sample of workers with varying years of experience and counted the number of units each produced in 8 hours.
a. Write the equation of the model that you think would fit.
b. Perform a regression analysis using your model.
c. Describe how well the model fits.

**18.49** Xr18-49 The maintenance of swimming pools is quite costly because of all the chlorine that is needed to keep the water clear and relatively free of germs. A chain of hotels (all with outdoor pools) seeking to reduce costs decided to analyze the factors that determine how much chlorine is needed. They commissioned a chemist to conduct an analysis. It is believed that the speed at which chlorine in a pool is depleted is dependent on the temperature of the water (higher temperature uses chlorine faster); pH level, which is a measure of the acidity of the water (pH ranges from 0 to 14, where 0 is very acidic and 14 is very alkaline; levels around 7.5 use the least chlorine); and weather (sunshine uses up chlorine). The chemist conducted the following experiment. The percentage of chlorine depletion during 8-hour days was recorded under varying conditions of pH level, water temperature, and weather conditions. These data were recorded in the following way:

Column 1: Percentage of chlorine depletion over 8 hours
Column 2: Temperature (degrees Fahrenheit)
Column 3: pH level
Column 4: 1 = Mainly cloudy, 2 = Sunny, 3 = Partly sunny

a. Write the equation of the model that you would suggest.
b. Use regression analysis to estimate the model's coefficients.
c. Test to determine whether the model is valid.
d. Can we infer that higher temperatures deplete chlorine more quickly?
e. Is there evidence to infer that the belief about the relationship between chlorine depletion and pH level is correct?
f. Can we infer that weather is a factor in chlorine depletion?

iStockphoto.com/clu

# NONPARAMETRIC STATISTICS

## CHAPTER OUTLINE



## General Social Survey

### Do Democrats, Independents, and Republicans Differ in the Number of Times per Week They Read Newspapers?

DATA GSS2014*

Because of the way politics have evolved, it appears that campaigns for president start at least two years before the actual election. And of course there are elections for representatives every two years. This means that politics is part of the regular news that appears in newspapers across the country. In the business of politics, it is important to know where voters are getting their information. Historically, newspapers have been critical to political campaigns because almost all newspapers make recommendations about whom to vote for. This raises the question,

Kiyoshi Ota/Getty Images

(See Solution on page 795.)

Do supporters of the three political affiliations (PARTYID3: 1 = Democrat, 2 = Independent, 3 = Republican) read newspapers with the same frequency? One of the questions asked in the 2014 General Social Survey was, How often do you read the newspaper (NEWS: 1 = Every day, 2 = A few times a week, 3 = Once a week, 4 = Less than once a week, 5 = Never)? After we introduce the appropriate statistical technique, we will provide our answer (see page 795).

## INTRODUCTION

Throughout this book, we have presented statistical techniques that are used when the data are either interval or nominal. In this chapter, we introduce statistical techniques that deal with ordinal data. We will introduce three methods that compare two populations, two procedures used to compare two or more populations, and a technique to analyze the relationship between two variables. As you've seen when we compare two or more populations of interval data, we measure the difference between means. However, as we discussed in Chapter 2, when the data are ordinal, the mean is not an appropriate measure of location. As a result, the methods in this chapter do not enable us to test the difference in population means; instead, we will test characteristics of populations without referring to specific parameters. For this reason, these techniques are called **nonparametric techniques**. Rather than testing to determine whether the population means differ, we will test to determine whether the *population locations* differ.

Although nonparametric methods are designed to test ordinal data, they have another area of application. The statistical tests described in Sections 13-1 and 13-3 and in Chapter 14 require that the populations be normally distributed. If the data are extremely nonnormal, the $t$-tests and $F$-test are invalid. Fortunately, nonparametric techniques can be used instead. For this reason, nonparametric procedures are often (perhaps more accurately) called **distribution-free statistics**. The techniques presented here can be used when the data are interval and the required condition of normality is unsatisfied. In such circumstances, we will treat the interval data as if they were ordinal. For this reason, even when the data are interval and the mean is the appropriate measure of location, we will choose instead to test population locations.

Figure 19.1 depicts the distributions of two populations when their locations are the same. Notice that because we don't know (or care) anything about the shape of the distributions, we represent them as nonnormal. Figure 19.2 describes a circumstance when the location of population 1 is to the right of the location of population 2. The location of population 1 is to the left of the location of population 2 in Figure 19.3.

FIGURE **19.1** **Population Locations Are the Same**

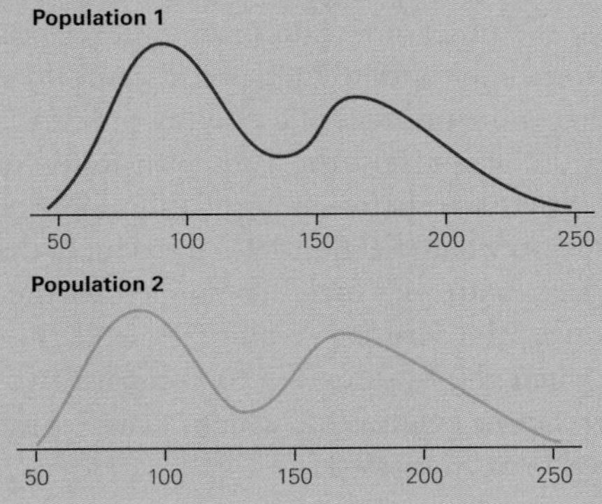

FIGURE **19.2** **Location of Population 1 Is to the Right of the Location of Population 2**

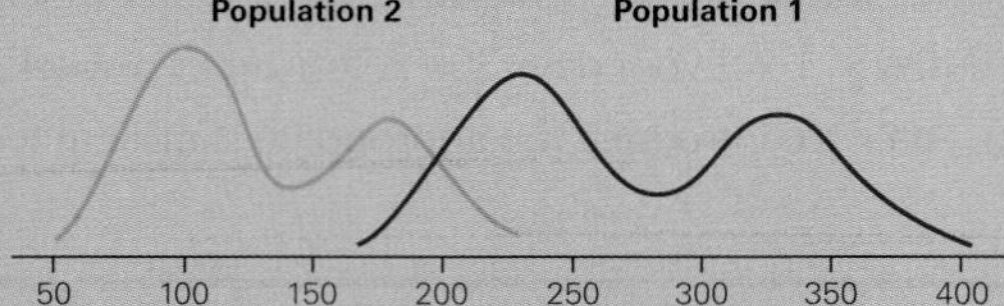


FIGURE **19.3** **Location of Population 1 Is to the Left of the Location of Population 2**

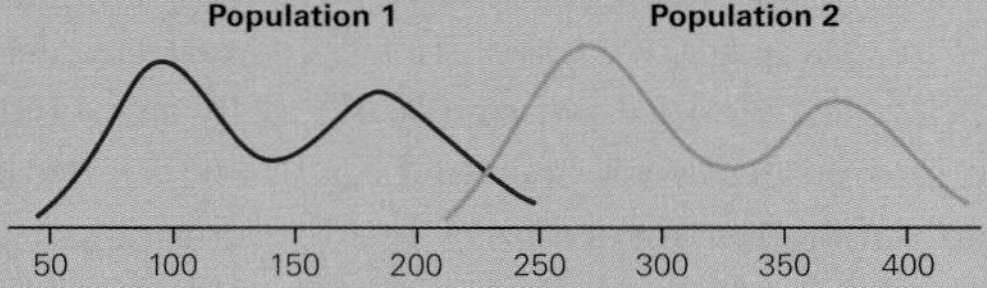


When the problem objective is to compare two populations, the null hypothesis will state

$H_0$: The two population locations are the same

The alternative hypothesis can take on any one of the following three forms.

1. If we want to know whether there is sufficient evidence to infer that there is a difference between the two populations, the alternative hypothesis is

   $H_1$: The location of population 1 is different from the location of population 2

2. If we want to know whether we can conclude that the random variable in population 1 is larger in general than the random variable in population 2 (see Figure 19.2), the alternative hypothesis is

   $H_1$: The location of population 1 is to the right of the location of population 2

3. If we want to know whether we can conclude that the random variable in population 1 is smaller in general than the random variable in population 2 (see Figure 19.3), the alternative hypothesis is

   $H_1$: The location of population 1 is to the left of the location of population 2

As you will see, nonparametric tests utilize a ranking procedure as an integral part of the calculations. You've actually dealt with such a process already in this book. In Chapter 4, we introduced the median as a measure of central location. The median is computed by placing the observations in order and selecting the observation that falls in the middle. Thus, the appropriate measure of central location of ordinal data is the median, a statistic that is the product of a ranking process.

In the next section, we present the Wilcoxon Rank Sum Test employed when we wish to test for the differences between population locations when the data are generated from independent samples. Section 19-2 introduces the sign test and the Wilcoxon signed Rank Sum Test, both of which are applied to the matched pairs experiment. Section 19-3 introduces the Kruskal–Wallis Test and the Friedman Test, procedures that are employed when the objective is to compare two or more populations. The Spearman rank correlation coefficient, which analyzes the relationship between two variables, is presented in Section 19-4.

## 19-1 / WILCOXON RANK SUM TEST

The test we introduce in this section deals with problems with the following characteristics:

1. The problem objective is to compare two populations.
2. The data are either ordinal or interval where the normality requirement necessary to perform the equal-variances $t$-test of $\mu_1 - \mu_2$ is unsatisfied.
3. The samples are independent.

To illustrate how to compute the test statistic for the **Wilcoxon Rank Sum Test** for independent samples, we offer the following example.

EXAMPLE 19.1

### Wilcoxon Rank Sum Test

Suppose that we want to determine whether the following observations drawn from two populations allow us to conclude at the 5% significance level that the location of population 1 is to the left of the location of population 2.

| | | | |
|---|---|---|---|
| Sample 1: | 22 | 23 | 20 |
| Sample 2: | 18 | 27 | 26 |

We want to test the following hypotheses:

$H_0$: The two population locations are the same.

$H_1$: The location of population 1 is to the left of the location of population 2.

### Test Statistic

The first step is to rank all six observations, with rank 1 assigned to the smallest observation and rank 6 to the largest.

| Sample 1 | Rank | Sample 2 | Rank |
|---|---|---|---|
| 22 | 3 | 18 | 1 |
| 23 | 4 | 27 | 6 |
| 20 | 2 | 26 | 5 |
| | $T_1 = 9$ | | $T_2 = 12$ |

Observe that 18 is the smallest number, so it receives a rank of 1; 20 is the second-smallest number, and it receives a rank of 2. We continue until rank 6 is assigned to 27, which is the largest of the observations. In case of ties, we average the ranks of the tied observations. The second step is to calculate the sum of the ranks of each sample. The rank sum of sample 1, denoted as $T_1$, is 9. The rank sum of sample 2, denoted as $T_2$, is 12.

(Note that $T_1$ plus $T_2$ must equal the sum of the integers from 1 to 6, which is 21.) We can use either rank sum as the test statistic. We arbitrarily select $T_1$ as the test statistic and label it $T$. The value of the test statistic in this example is $T = T_1 = 9$.

## Sampling Distribution of the Test Statistic

A small value of $T$ indicates that most of the smaller observations are in sample 1 and that most of the larger observations are in sample 2. This would imply that the location of population 1 is to the left of the location of population 2. Therefore, in order for us to conclude statistically that this is the case, we need to show that $T$ is small. The definition of "small" comes from the sampling distribution of $T$. As we did in Section 9-1 when we derived the sampling distribution of the sample mean, we can derive the sampling distribution of $T$ by listing all possible values of $T$. In Table 19.1, we show all possible rankings of two samples of size 3.

TABLE **19.1** **All Possible Ranks and Rank Sums of Two Samples of Size 3**

| RANKS OF SAMPLE 1 | RANK SUM | RANKS OF SAMPLE 2 | RANK SUM |
|---|---|---|---|
| 1, 2, 3 | 6 | 4, 5, 6 | 15 |
| 1, 2, 4 | 7 | 3, 5, 6 | 14 |
| 1, 2, 5 | 8 | 3, 4, 6 | 13 |
| 1, 2, 6 | 9 | 3, 4, 5 | 12 |
| 1, 3, 4 | 8 | 2, 5, 6 | 13 |
| 1, 3, 5 | 9 | 2, 4, 6 | 12 |
| 1, 3, 6 | 10 | 2, 4, 5 | 11 |
| 1, 4, 5 | 10 | 2, 3, 6 | 11 |
| 1, 4, 6 | 11 | 2, 3, 5 | 10 |
| 1, 5, 6 | 12 | 2, 3, 4 | 9 |
| 2, 3, 4 | 9 | 1, 5, 6 | 12 |
| 2, 3, 5 | 10 | 1, 4, 6 | 11 |
| 2, 3, 6 | 11 | 1, 4, 5 | 10 |
| 2, 4, 5 | 11 | 1, 3, 6 | 10 |
| 2, 4, 6 | 12 | 1, 3, 5 | 9 |
| 2, 5, 6 | 13 | 1, 3, 4 | 8 |
| 3, 4, 5 | 12 | 1, 2, 6 | 9 |
| 3, 4, 6 | 13 | 1, 2, 5 | 8 |
| 3, 5, 6 | 14 | 1, 2, 4 | 7 |
| 4, 5, 6 | 15 | 1, 2, 3 | 6 |

If the null hypothesis is true and the two population locations are identical, then it follows that each possible ranking is equally likely. Because there are 20 different possibilities, each value of $T$ has the same probability, namely, 1/20. Notice that there is one value of 6, one value of 7, two values of 8, and so on. Table 19.2 summarizes the values of $T$ and their probabilities, and Figure 19.4 depicts this sampling distribution.

TABLE **19.2** **Sampling Distribution of *T* with Two Samples of Size 3**

| $T$ | $P(T)$ |
|---|---|
| 6 | 1/20 |
| 7 | 1/20 |
| 8 | 2/20 |
| 9 | 3/20 |
| 10 | 3/20 |
| 11 | 3/20 |
| 12 | 3/20 |
| 13 | 2/20 |
| 14 | 1/20 |
| 15 | 1/20 |
| Total | 1 |

FIGURE **19.4** **Sampling Distribution of *T* with Two Samples of Size 3**

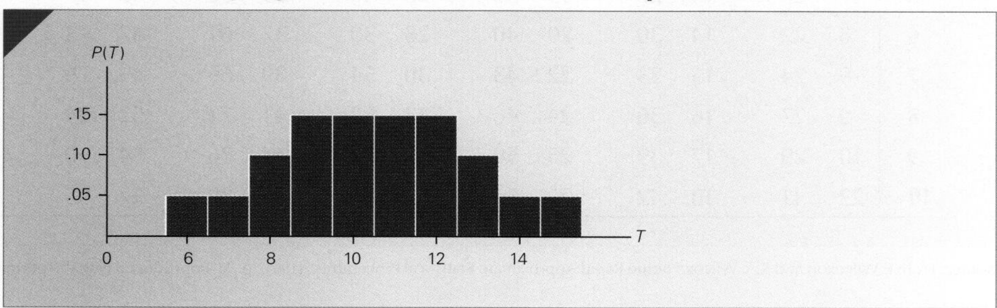


From this sampling distribution we can see that $P(T \leq 6) = P(T = 6) = 1/20 = .05$. Because we're trying to determine whether the value of the test statistic is small enough for us to reject the null hypothesis at the 5% significance level, we specify the rejection region as $T \leq 6$. Because $T = 9$, we cannot reject the null hypothesis.

Statisticians have generated the sampling distribution of $T$ for various combinations of sample sizes. The critical values are provided in Table 9 in Appendix B and reproduced here as Table 19.3. Table 19.3 provides values of $T_L$ and $T_U$ for sample sizes between 3 and 10 ($n_1$ is the size of sample 1, and $n_2$ is the size of sample 2). The values of $T_L$ and $T_U$ in part (a) of the table are such that

$$P(T \leq T_L) = P(T \geq T_U) = .025$$

The values of $T_L$ and $T_U$ in part (b) of the table are such that

$$P(T \leq T_L) = P(T \geq T_U) = .05$$

Part (a) is used either in a two-tail test with $\alpha = .05$ or in a one-tail test with $\alpha = .025$. Part (b) is employed either in a two-tail test with $\alpha = .10$ or in a one-tail test with $\alpha = .05$. Because no other values are provided, we are restricted to those values of $\alpha$.

TABLE **19.3** **Critical Values of the Wilcoxon Rank Sum Test**

(a) $\alpha = .025$ one-tail; $\alpha = .05$ two-tail

| $n_2 \backslash n_1$ | 3 | | 4 | | 5 | | 6 | | 7 | | 8 | | 9 | | 10 | |
|---|---|---|---|---|---|---|---|---|---|---|---|---|---|---|---|---|
| | $T_L$ | $T_U$ | $T_L$ | $T_U$ | $T_L$ | $T_U$ | $T_L$ | $T_U$ | $T_L$ | $T_U$ | $T_L$ | $T_U$ | $T_L$ | $T_U$ | $T_L$ | $T_U$ |
| **4** | 6 | 18 | 11 | 25 | 17 | 33 | 23 | 43 | 31 | 53 | 40 | 64 | 50 | 76 | 61 | 89 |
| **5** | 6 | 21 | 12 | 28 | 18 | 37 | 25 | 47 | 33 | 58 | 42 | 70 | 52 | 83 | 64 | 96 |
| **6** | 7 | 23 | 12 | 32 | 19 | 41 | 26 | 52 | 35 | 63 | 44 | 76 | 55 | 89 | 66 | 104 |
| **7** | 7 | 26 | 13 | 35 | 20 | 45 | 28 | 56 | 37 | 68 | 47 | 81 | 58 | 95 | 70 | 110 |
| **8** | 8 | 28 | 14 | 38 | 21 | 49 | 29 | 61 | 39 | 73 | 49 | 87 | 60 | 102 | 73 | 117 |
| **9** | 8 | 31 | 15 | 41 | 22 | 53 | 31 | 65 | 41 | 78 | 51 | 93 | 63 | 108 | 76 | 124 |
| **10** | 9 | 33 | 16 | 44 | 24 | 56 | 32 | 70 | 43 | 83 | 54 | 98 | 66 | 114 | 79 | 131 |

(b) $\alpha = .05$ one-tail; $\alpha = .10$ two-tail

| $n_2 \backslash n_1$ | 3 | | 4 | | 5 | | 6 | | 7 | | 8 | | 9 | | 10 | |
|---|---|---|---|---|---|---|---|---|---|---|---|---|---|---|---|---|
| | $T_L$ | $T_U$ | $T_L$ | $T_U$ | $T_L$ | $T_U$ | $T_L$ | $T_U$ | $T_L$ | $T_U$ | $T_L$ | $T_U$ | $T_L$ | $T_U$ | $T_L$ | $T_U$ |
| **3** | 6 | 15 | 11 | 21 | 16 | 29 | 23 | 37 | 31 | 46 | 39 | 57 | 49 | 68 | 60 | 80 |
| **4** | 7 | 17 | 12 | 24 | 18 | 32 | 25 | 41 | 33 | 51 | 42 | 62 | 52 | 74 | 63 | 87 |
| **5** | 7 | 20 | 13 | 27 | 19 | 36 | 26 | 46 | 35 | 56 | 45 | 67 | 55 | 80 | 66 | 94 |
| **6** | 8 | 22 | 14 | 30 | 20 | 40 | 28 | 50 | 37 | 61 | 47 | 73 | 57 | 87 | 69 | 101 |
| **7** | 9 | 24 | 15 | 33 | 22 | 43 | 30 | 54 | 39 | 66 | 49 | 79 | 60 | 93 | 73 | 107 |
| **8** | 9 | 27 | 16 | 36 | 24 | 46 | 32 | 58 | 41 | 71 | 52 | 84 | 63 | 99 | 76 | 114 |
| **9** | 10 | 29 | 17 | 39 | 25 | 50 | 33 | 63 | 43 | 76 | 54 | 90 | 66 | 105 | 79 | 121 |
| **10** | 22 | 31 | 18 | 42 | 26 | 54 | 35 | 67 | 46 | 80 | 57 | 95 | 69 | 111 | 83 | 127 |

*Source:* From F. Wilcoxon and R.A. Wilcox, "Some Rapid Approximate Statistical Procedures" (1964), p. 28. Reproduced with the permission of American Cyanamid Company.

Although it is possible to derive the sampling distribution of the test statistic for any other sample sizes, the process can be quite tedious. Fortunately it is also unnecessary. Statisticians have shown that when the sample sizes are larger than 10, the test statistic is approximately normally distributed with mean $E(T)$ and standard deviation $\sigma_T$ where

$$E(T) = \frac{n_1(n_1 + n_2 + 1)}{2}$$

and

$$\sigma_T = \sqrt{\frac{n_1 n_2(n_1 + n_2 + 1)}{12}}$$

Thus, the standardized test statistic is

$$z = \frac{T - E(T)}{\sigma_T}$$

## EXAMPLE 19.2 Comparing Pharmaceutical Painkillers

DATA Xm19-02

A pharmaceutical company is planning to introduce a new painkiller. In a preliminary experiment to determine its effectiveness, 30 people were randomly selected, of whom 15 were given the new painkiller and 15 were given aspirin. All 30 were told to use the drug when headaches or other minor pains occurred and to indicate which of the following statements most accurately represented the effectiveness of the drug they took:

5 = The drug was extremely effective.
4 = The drug was quite effective.
3 = The drug was somewhat effective.
2 = The drug was slightly effective.
1 = The drug was not at all effective.

The responses are listed here using the codes. Can we conclude at the 5% significance level that the new painkiller is perceived to be more effective?

New painkiller: 3, 5, 4, 3, 2, 5, 1, 4, 5, 3, 3, 5, 5, 5, 4
Aspirin: 4, 1, 3, 2, 4, 1, 3, 4, 2, 2, 2, 4, 3, 4, 5

SOLUTION:

### IDENTIFY

The objective is to compare two populations: the perceived effectiveness of the new painkiller and of aspirin. We recognize that the data are ordinal; except for the order of the codes, the numbers used to record the results are arbitrary. Finally, the samples are independent. These factors tell us that the appropriate technique is the Wilcoxon Rank Sum Test. We denote the effectiveness scores of the new painkiller as sample 1 and the effectiveness scores of aspirin as sample 2. Because we want to know whether the new painkiller is better than aspirin, the alternative hypothesis is

$H_1$: The location of population 1 is to the right of the location of population 2.

We specify the null hypothesis as

$H_0$: The two population locations are the same.

### COMPUTE

MANUALLY:

If the alternative hypothesis is true, the location of population 1 will be located to the right of the location of population 2. It follows that $T$ and $z$ would be large. Our job is to determine whether $z$ is large enough to reject the null hypothesis in favor of the alternative hypothesis. Thus, the rejection region is

$$z > z_\alpha = z_{.05} = 1.645$$

We compute the test statistic by ranking all the observations.

| New Painkiller | Rank | Aspirin | Rank |
|---|---|---|---|
| 3 | 12 | 4 | 19.5 |
| 5 | 27 | 1 | 2 |
| 4 | 19.5 | 3 | 12 |
| 3 | 12 | 2 | 6 |
| 2 | 6 | 4 | 19.5 |
| 5 | 27 | 1 | 2 |
| 1 | 2 | 3 | 12 |
| 4 | 19.5 | 4 | 19.5 |
| 5 | 27 | 2 | 6 |
| 3 | 12 | 2 | 6 |
| 3 | 12 | 2 | 6 |
| 5 | 27 | 4 | 19.5 |
| 5 | 27 | 3 | 12 |
| 5 | 27 | 4 | 19.5 |
| 4 | 19.5 | 5 | 27 |
| | $T_1 = 276.5$ | | $T_2 = 188.5$ |

Notice that three "ones" occupy ranks 1, 2, and 3. The average is 2. Thus, each "one" is assigned a rank of 2. There are five "twos" whose ranks are 4, 5, 6, 7, and 8, the average of which is 6. We continue until all the observations have been similarly ranked. The rank sums are computed with $T_1 = 276.5$ and $T_2 = 188.5$. The unstandardized test statistic is $T = T_1 = 276.5$. To standardize, we determine $E(T)$ and $\sigma_T$ as follows.

$$E(T) = \frac{n_1(n_1 + n_2 + 1)}{2} = \frac{15(31)}{2} = 232.5$$

$$\sigma_T = \sqrt{\frac{n_1 n_2(n_1 + n_2 + 1)}{12}} = \sqrt{\frac{(15)(15)(31)}{12}} = 24.1$$

The standardized test statistic is calculated next:

$$z = \frac{T - E(T)}{\sigma_T} = \frac{276.5 - 232.5}{24.1} = 1.83$$

The $p$-value of the test is

$$p\text{-value} = P(Z > 1.83) = 1 - .9664 = .0336$$

Excel does not perform any of the nonparametric tests covered in this book. We will use XLSTAT for all techniques.

XLSTAT performs the Mann–Whitney test, which has the same result as the Wilcoxon rank sum test. The Mann–Whitney test statistic is defined as

$$\text{U} = T_1 - \frac{n_1(n_1 + 1)}{2}$$

For large samples, we use the normal approximation

$$Z = \frac{U - E(U)}{\sigma_U}$$

where

$$E(U) = \frac{n_1 n_2}{2}$$

and

$$\sigma_U = \sqrt{\frac{n_1 n_2 (n_1 + n_2 + 1)}{12}}$$

It should be noted that when there are tied values, there is an adjustment to the standard deviation. The resulting test statistic is only slightly altered.

## XLSTAT

| | A | B |
|---|---|---|
| 1 | Mann-Whitney test / Upper-tailed test: | |
| 2 | | |
| 3 | U | 156.500 |
| 4 | Expected value | 112.500 |
| 5 | Variance (U) | 552.802 |
| 6 | p-value (one-tailed) | 0.0306 |
| 7 | alpha | 0.05 |
| 8 | An approximation has been used to compute the p-value. | |
| 9 | Ties have been detected in the data and the appropriate corrections have been applied. | |

*INSTRUCTIONS*

1. Click **XLSTAT**, **Nonparametric tests**, and **Comparison of two samples (Wilcoxon, Mann-Whitney, . . .)**
2. Check **One column per sample**. Specify the ranges of the two samples (**A1:A16**) (**B1:B16**). Check the **Mann-Whitney Test**.
3. Click **Options** and specify the **Alternative hypothesis** (**Sample 1-Sample 2 > D**) and specify D (**0**). Check **Asymptotic *p*-value**. Do not check **Continuity correction**. Click **OK**.

## INTERPRET

The data provide sufficient evidence to infer that the new painkiller is perceived to be more effective than aspirin. We note that the data were generated from a controlled experiment; that is, the subjects were assigned to take either the new painkiller or aspirin. (When subjects decide for themselves which medication to take, the data are observational.) This factor helps support the claim that the new painkiller is indeed more effective than aspirin. Factors that weaken the argument are small sample sizes and the inexactness of the responses. There may be methods to measure the effectiveness less subjectively. In addition, a double-blind experiment should have been conducted.

As we pointed out in the introduction to this chapter, the Wilcoxon Rank Sum Test is used to compare two populations when the data are either ordinal or interval. Example 19.2 illustrated the use of the Wilcoxon Rank Sum Test when the data are ordinal. In the next example we demonstrate its use when the data are interval.

## EXAMPLE 19.3 Retaining Workers

DATA Xm19-03

Because of the high cost of hiring and training new employees, employers would like to ensure that they retain highly qualified workers. To help develop a hiring program, the human resources manager of a large company wanted to compare how long business and nonbusiness university graduates worked for the company before quitting to accept a position elsewhere. The manager selected a random sample of 25 business and 20 nonbusiness graduates who had been hired 5 years ago. The number of months each had worked for the company was recorded. (Those who had not quit were recorded as having worked for 60 months.) The data are listed below. Can the human resources manager conclude at the 5% significance level that a difference in duration of employment exists between business and nonbusiness graduates?

**Duration of Employment (Months)**

| Business Graduates | Nonbusiness Graduates |
|---|---|
| 60 11 18 19 5 25 60 7 8 17 37 4 8 | 25 60 22 24 23 36 39 15 35 16 28 |
| 28 27 11 60 25 5 13 22 11 17 9 4 | 9 60 29 16 22 60 17 60 32 |

SOLUTION:

### IDENTIFY

The problem objective is to compare two populations whose data are interval. The samples are independent. Thus, the appropriate parametric technique is the $t$-test of $\mu_1 - \mu_2$, which requires that the populations be normally distributed. However, when the histograms are drawn (see Figures 19.5 and 19.6), it becomes clear that this requirement is unsatisfied. It follows that the correct statistical procedure is the Wilcoxon Rank Sum Test. The null and alternative hypotheses are

$H_0$: The two population locations are the same.

$H_1$: The location of population 1 (business graduates) is different from the location of population 2 (nonbusiness graduates).

FIGURE **19.5** **Histogram of Length of Employment of Business Graduates in Retaining Workers Example**

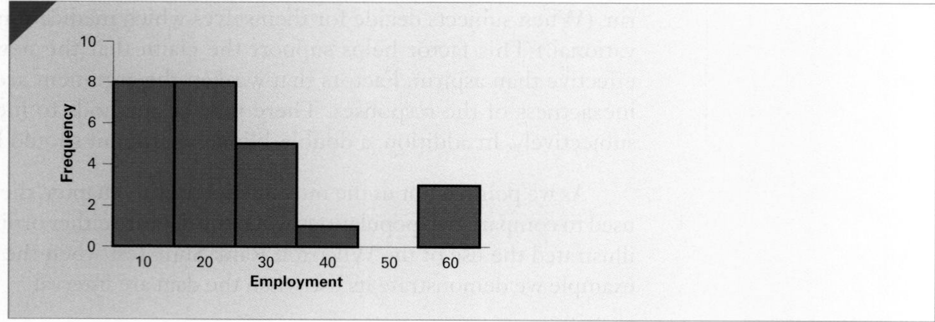

FIGURE **19.6** **Histogram of Length of Employment of Nonbusiness Graduates in Retaining Workers Example**

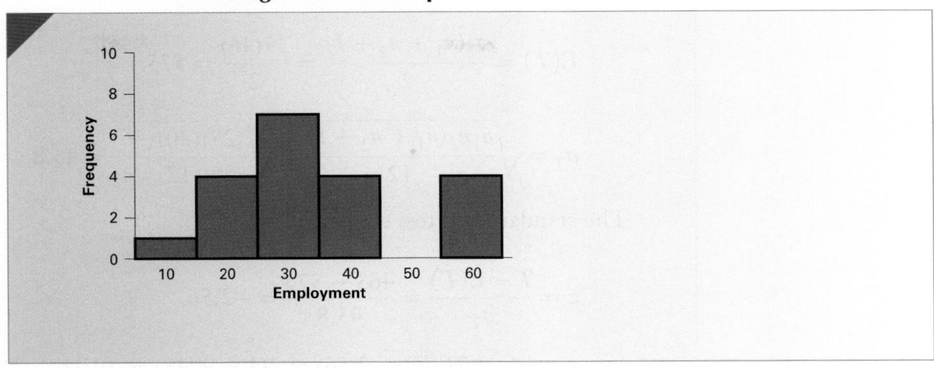


COMPUTE

MANUALLY:

The rejection region is

$$z < -z_{\alpha/2} = -z_{.025} = -1.96 \quad \text{or} \quad z > z_{\alpha/2} = z_{.025} = 1.96$$

We calculate the value of the test statistic in the following way.

| Business | Rank | Nonbusiness | Rank |
|---|---|---|---|
| 60 | 42 | 25 | 28 |
| 11 | 11 | 60 | 42 |
| 18 | 20 | 22 | 23 |
| 19 | 21 | 24 | 26 |
| 5 | 3.5 | 23 | 25 |
| 25 | 28 | 36 | 36 |
| 60 | 42 | 39 | 38 |
| 7 | 5 | 15 | 14 |
| 8 | 6.5 | 35 | 35 |
| 17 | 18 | 16 | 15.5 |
| 37 | 37 | 28 | 31.5 |
| 4 | 1.5 | 9 | 8.5 |
| 8 | 6.5 | 60 | 42 |
| 28 | 31.5 | 29 | 33 |
| 27 | 30 | 16 | 15.5 |
| 11 | 11 | 22 | 23 |
| 60 | 42 | 60 | 42 |
| 25 | 28 | 17 | 18 |
| 5 | 3.5 | 60 | 42 |
| 13 | 13 | 32 | 34 |
| 22 | 23 | | $T_2 = 572$ |
| 11 | 11 | | |
| 17 | 18 | | |
| 9 | 8.5 | | |
| 4 | 1.5 | | |
| | $T_1 = 463$ | | |

The unstandardized test statistic is $T = T_1 = 463$. To calculate $z$, we first determine the mean and standard deviation of $T$. Note that $n_1 = 25$ and $n_2 = 20$.

$$E(T) = \frac{n_1(n_1 + n_2 + 1)}{2} = \frac{25(46)}{2} = 575$$

$$\sigma_T = \sqrt{\frac{n_1 n_2(n_1 + n_2 + 1)}{12}} = \sqrt{\frac{(25)(20)(46)}{12}} = 43.8$$

The standardized test statistic is

$$z = \frac{T - E(T)}{\sigma_T} = \frac{463 - 575}{43.8} = -2.56$$

$$p\text{-value} = 2P(Z < -2.56) = 2(1 - .9948) = .0104$$

**XLSTAT**

| | A | B |
|---|---|---|
| 1 | Mann-Whitney test / Two-tailed test: | |
| 2 | | |
| 3 | U | 138.000 |
| 4 | Expected value | 250.000 |
| 5 | Variance (U) | 1906.818 |
| 6 | p-value (Two-tailed) | 0.0103 |
| 7 | alpha | 0.05 |
| 8 | An approximation has been used to compute the p-value. | |
| 9 | Ties have been detected in the data and the appropriate corrections have been applied. | |

**INTERPRET**

There is strong evidence to infer that the duration of employment is different for business and nonbusiness graduates. The data cannot tell us the cause of this conclusion. For example, we don't know whether business graduates are in greater demand, making it more likely that such employees will leave for better jobs, or whether nonbusiness graduates are more satisfied with their jobs and thus remain longer. Moreover, we don't know what the results would have been had we surveyed employees 10 years after they were employed.

## 19-1a Required Conditions

The Wilcoxon Rank Sum Test (like the other nonparametric tests presented in this chapter) actually tests to determine whether the population *distributions* are identical. This means that it tests not only for identical locations but also for identical spreads (variances) and shapes (distributions). Unfortunately, this means that the rejection of the null hypothesis may not necessarily signify a difference in population locations. The rejection of the null hypothesis may result instead from a difference in distribution shapes or spreads. To avoid this problem, we will require that the two probability distributions be identical except with respect to location, which then becomes the sole focus of the test. This requirement is made for the tests introduced in the next two sections (sign test, Wilcoxon Signed Rank Sum Test, Kruskal–Wallis Test, and Friedman Test).

Both histograms (Figures 19.5 and 19.6) are approximately bimodal. Although there are differences between them, it would appear that the required condition for the use of the Wilcoxon Rank Sum Test is roughly satisfied in the example about retaining workers.

## 19-1b Developing an Understanding of Statistical Concepts

When applying nonparametric techniques, we do not perform any calculations using the original data. Instead, we perform computations only on the ranks. (We determine the rank sums and use them to make our decision.) As a result, we do not care about the actual distribution of the data (hence the name *distribution-free techniques*), and we do not specify parameters in the hypotheses (hence the name *nonparametric techniques*). Although there are other techniques that do not specify parameters in the hypotheses, we use the term *nonparametric* for procedures that feature these concepts.

Here is a summary of how to identify the Wilcoxon Rank Sum Test.

**Factors That Identify the Wilcoxon Rank Sum**

1. **Problem objective**: Compare two populations
2. **Data type**: Ordinal or interval but nonnormal
3. **Experimental design**: Independent samples

## Exercises

### Developing an Understanding of Statistical Concepts

*Exercises 19.1 and 19.2 are "what-if" analyses designed to determine what happens to the test statistics and p-values when elements of the statistical inference change. These problems can be solved manually or by creating an Excel spreadsheet.*

**19.1** a. Given the following statistics calculate the value of the test statistic to determine whether the population locations differ.

$T_1 = 250$ $\quad n_1 = 15$
$T_2 = 215$ $\quad n_2 = 15$

b. Repeat part (a) with $T_1 = 275$ and $T_2 = 190$.

c. Describe the effect on the test statistic of increasing $T_1$ to 275.

**19.2** a. From the following statistics, test (with $\alpha = .05$) to determine whether the location of population 1 is to the right of the location of population 2.

$T_1 = 1{,}205$ $\quad n_1 = 30$
$T_2 = 1{,}280$ $\quad n_2 = 40$

b. Repeat part (a) with $T_1 = 1{,}065$.

c. Discuss the effect on the test statistic and $p$-value of decreasing $T_1$ to 1,065.

**19.3** Xr19-03 Use the Wilcoxon Rank Sum Test on the following data to determine whether the location of population 1 is to the left of the location of population 2. (Use $\alpha = .05$.)

| Sample 1: | 75 | 60 | 73 | 66 | 81 |
|---|---|---|---|---|---|
| Sample 2: | 90 | 72 | 103 | 82 | 78 |

**19.4** Xr19-04 Use the Wilcoxon Rank Sum Test on the following data to determine whether the two population locations differ. (Use a 10% significance level.)

| Sample 1: | 15 | 7 | 22 | 20 | 32 | 18 | 26 | 17 | 23 | 30 |
|---|---|---|---|---|---|---|---|---|---|---|
| Sample 2: | 8 | 27 | 17 | 25 | 20 | 16 | 21 | 17 | 10 | 18 |

*Exercises 19.5 to 19.24 require the use of a computer and software.* ***Conduct tests of hypotheses at the 5% significance level.***

**19.5** a. Xr19-05a In a taste test of a new beer, 25 people rated the new beer and another 25 rated the leading brand on the market. The possible ratings were Poor, Fair, Good, Very Good, and Excellent. The responses for the new beer and the leading beer were stored using a 1-2-3-4-5 coding system. Can we infer that the new beer is less highly rated than the leading brand?

b. Xr19-05b The responses were recoded so that 3 = Poor, 8 = Fair, 22 = Good, 37 = Very Good, and 55 = Excellent. Can we infer that the new beer is less highly rated than the leading brand?

c. What does this exercise tell you about ordinal data?

**19.6** a. Xr19-06a To determine whether the satisfaction rating of an airline differs between business class and economy class, a survey was performed. Random samples of both groups were asked to rate their satisfaction with the quality of service using the following responses:

Very satisfied
Quite satisfied
Somewhat satisfied
Neither satisfied nor dissatisfied
Somewhat dissatisfied
Quite dissatisfied
Very dissatisfied

Using a 7-6-5-4-3-2-1 coding system, the results were recorded. Can we infer that business and economy class differ in their degree of satisfaction with the service?

b. Xr19-06b The responses were recoded using the values 88-67-39-36-25-21-18. Can we infer that business and economy class differ in their degree of satisfaction with the service?

c. What is the effect of changing the codes? Why was this expected?

**19.7** a. Xr19-07 Refer to Example 19.2. Suppose that the responses were coded as follows:

100 = The drug was extremely effective.
60 = The drug was quite effective.
40 = The drug was somewhat effective.
35 = The drug was slightly effective.
10 = The drug was not at all effective.

Determine whether we can infer that the new painkiller is more effective than aspirin.

b. Why are the results of Example 19.2 and part (a) identical?

## Applications

*Exercises 19.8 to 19.16 may be solved manually. See Appendix A for the sample statistics.*

**19.8** Xr19-08 A survey of statistics professors asked them to rate the importance of teaching nonparametric techniques. The possible responses are

Very important
Quite important
Somewhat important
Not too important
Not important at all

The professors were classified as either a member of the Mathematics Department or a member of some other department. The responses were coded (codes 5, 4, 3, 2, and 1, respectively) and recorded. Can we infer that members of the Mathematics Department rate nonparametric techniques as more important than do members of other departments?

**19.9** Xr19-09 In recent years, insurance companies offering medical coverage have given discounts to companies that are committed to improving the health of their employees. To help determine whether this policy is reasonable, the general manager of one large insurance company organized a study of a random sample of 30 workers who regularly participate in their company's lunchtime exercise program and 30 workers who do not. Over a 2-year period he observed the total dollar amount of medical expenses for each individual. Can the manager conclude that companies that provide exercise programs should be given discounts?

**19.10** Xr19-10 Feminist organizations often use the issue of who does the housework in two-career families as a gauge of equality. Suppose that a study was undertaken and a random sample of 125 two-career families was taken. The wives were asked to report the number of hours of housework they performed the previous week. The results, together with the responses from a survey performed last year (with a different sample of two-career families), were recorded. Can we conclude that women are doing less housework today than last year?

**19.11** Xr19-11 The American public's support for the space program is important for the program's continuation and for the financial health of the aerospace industry. In a poll conducted by the Gallup organization last year, a random sample of 100 Americans was asked, "Should the amount of money being spent on the space program be increased or kept at current levels (3), decreased (2), or ended altogether (1)?" The survey was conducted again this year. The results were recorded using the codes in parentheses. Can we conclude that public support decreased between this year and last year?

**19.12** Xr19-12 Certain drugs differ in their side effects depending on the gender of the patient. In a study to determine whether men or women suffer more serious side effects when taking a powerful penicillin substitute, 50 men and 50 women were given the drug. Each was asked to evaluate the level of stomach upset on a 4-point scale, where 4 = extremely upset, 3 = somewhat upset, 2 = not too upset, and 1 = not upset at all. Can we conclude that men and women experience different levels of stomach upset from the drug?

**19.13** Xr19-13 The president of Tastee Inc., a baby-food producer, claims that her company's product is superior to that of her leading competitor because babies gain weight faster with her product. As an experiment, 40 healthy newborn infants are randomly selected. For two months, 15 of the babies are fed Tastee baby food and the other 25 are fed the competitor's product. Each baby's weight gain (in ounces) was recorded. If we use weight gain as our criterion, can we conclude that Tastee baby food is indeed superior? (This exercise is identical to Exercise 13.17 except for the data.)

**19.14** Xr19-14 Do the ways that women dress influence the ways that other women judge them? This question was addressed by a researcher at Ohio State University (*Working Mother*, April 1992). The experiment consisted of asking women to rate how professional two women looked. One woman wore a size 6 dress and the other wore a size 14. Suppose that the researcher asked 20 women to rate the woman wearing the size 6 dress and another 20 to rate the woman wearing the size 14 dress. The ratings were as follows:

4 = Highly professional
3 = Somewhat professional
2 = Not very professional
1 = Not at all professional

Do these data provide sufficient evidence to infer that women perceive another woman wearing a size 6 dress as more professional than one wearing a size 14 dress?

**19.15** Xr19-15 The image of the lowly prune is not very good. It is perceived as a product used by seniors to help avoid constipation. However, in reality it is a nutritious and (for many) a tasty treat. To help improve the image of the prune, a company that produces the product decided to see the effect of changing its name to dried plums (which is what a prune is). To gauge the effect, a random sample of shoppers was asked how likely it was that they would purchase the product. Half the sample was shown a package that identified its contents as prunes. The other half was shown packages labeled dried plums. The responses are

Highly unlikely (1)
Somewhat unlikely (2)
Somewhat likely (3)
Highly likely (4)

a. Can we infer from these data that changing the name of prunes to dried plums increases the likelihood that shoppers will buy the product?
b. Write a report to the marketing manager of the company and describe your findings.

**19.16** Xr19-16 Burger King Restaurants regularly survey customers to determine how well they are doing. Suppose that a survey asked customers to rate (among other things) the speed of service. The responses are

1 = Poor
2 = Good
3 = Very good
4 = Excellent

The responses for the day shift and night shift were recorded. Can we infer that night shift customers rate the service differently than the day shift?

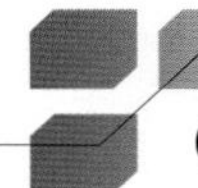

## General Social Survey Exercises

*Exercises 19.17 to 19.23 refer to the following questions. Please look at the list below and specify which one you would most prefer in a job. Which comes second? Which comes third? Which comes fourth? Which comes fifth? (1 = First, 2 = Second, 3 = Third, 4 = Fourth, 5 = Fifth)*

High income (JOBINC)
No danger of being fired (JOPBSEC)
Working hours are short, lots of free time (JOBHOUR)
Chances for advancement (JOBPROMO)
Work is important and gives a feeling of accomplishment (JOBMEANS)

**19.17** GSS2014* Do men (SEX: 1 = Male, 2 = Female) prefer jobs with higher incomes more than do women? Conduct a statistical test to answer the question.

**19.18** GSS2014* There appear to be many attractive features of government jobs, the most attractive being job security. But is this actually the case? Conduct a test to determine whether government workers (WRKGOVT: 1 = Government, 2 = Private) show a greater preference for job security.

**19.19** GSS2014* Working for one's self generally means that the amount of time devoted to work is up to the individual. Is there sufficient evidence to conclude that people who work for themselves (WRKSLF: 1 = Self, 2 = Someone else) prefer shorter work hours with lots of free time?

19.20 GSS2014* Can we infer that men and women (SEX: 1 = Male, 2 = Female) differ in their preference for work that is important and gives a feeling of accomplishment?

19.21 GSS2014* Almost everyone dreams of being rich enough to quit working. Respondents were asked, If you were to get enough money to live as comfortably as you would like for the rest of your life, would you continue to work, or would you stop working (RICHWORK: 1 = Continue working, 2 = Stop working)? Is there enough evidence to conclude that those who would continue working and those who would stop working differ in their preference for high income?

19.22 GSS2014* Refer to Exercise 19.21. For those who would continue working is it because they consider the work important? Test to determine whether those who would continue working have a higher preference for work they consider important and gives them a feeling of accomplishment.

19.23 GSS2014* Can we infer that men and women (SEX: 1 = Male, 2 = Female) differ in their preference for jobs where there is a chance for advancement?

19.24 GSS2014* Do Democrats and Republicans (PARTYID3:1 = Democrat, 3 = Republican) differ in their views about the federal income tax that they have to pay (TAX: Do you consider the amount of federal income tax which you have to pay as too high, about right, or too low: 1 = Too high, 2 = About right, 3 = Too low)?

19.25 GSS2014* Refer to Exercise 19.24. Is there sufficient evidence to infer that people who work for themselves (WRKSLF: 1 = Self-employed, 2 = Work for someone else) differ from those who work for someone else with respect to how they describe the federal income tax they have to pay?

19.26 GSS2014* Can we infer that women are more likely than men to lose their jobs in the next 12 months (JOBLOSE: In the next 12 months how likely is it that you will lose your job or be laid off: 1 = Very likely, 2 = Fairly likely, 3 = Not too likely, 4 = Not likely)?

19.27 GSS2014* It is well known that on average women live about four years longer than men. However, are they healthier? Conduct a test to determine if women (SEX: 1 = Male, 2 = Female) consider themselves to be healthier than men (HEALTH: 1 = Excellent, 2 = Good, 3 = Fair, 4 = Poor).

*Exercises 19.28 to 19.31 compare various aspects of 2012 and 2014.*

19.28 GSS2012*, GSS2014* Is there sufficient evidence to infer that Americans were healthier (HEALTH: 1 = Excellent, 2 = Good, 3 = Fair, 4 = Poor) in 2012 than in 2014?

19.29 GSS2012*, GSS2014* Were Americans more worried about their chances of losing their jobs (JOBLOSE: 1 = Very likely, 2 = Fairly likely, 3 = Not too likely, 4 = Not likely) in 2012 than in 2014?

19.30 GSS2012*, GSS2014* Were Americans more optimistic about their children's standard of living (KIDSSOL: When your children are at the age you are now, do you think their standard of living will be 1 = Much better, 2 = Somewhat better, 3 = About the same, 4 = Somewhat worse, or 5 = Much worse than your standard of living is now?) in 2014 than they were in 2012?

## Survey of Consumer Finances Exercises

19.31 SCF2013:\MC* Refer to Exercise 13.79, which asked whether there is enough evidence to conclude that heads of households with college degrees (EDCL: 3 = some college, 4 = college degree) have more assets than those who have some college (ASSET).

a. The appropriate technique in Chapter 13 was the $t$-test of the difference between two means. What is the required condition for this test?

b. Is the required condition satisfied? If not, what technique should be used?

c. Use the technique you chose in part (b) to answer the question about debt.

19.32 SCF2013:\MC* Exercise 13.70 asked, "Is there sufficient evidence that middle-class heads of households who work for someone else (OCCAT1: 1 = Someone else, 2 = Self-employed/partnership) have higher incomes that heads of households who are self-employed (INCOME)?"

a. What is the required condition for a $t$-test of the difference between two means? Is it satisfied? If not, what technique should be used?
b. Use the appropriate method to answer the question about employment and income.

**19.33** SCF2013:\MC* Refer to Exercise 13.77.

a. What is the required condition to apply the $t$-test of two means to determine whether there is enough evidence to conclude that male heads of households (HHSEX: 1 = Male, 2 = Female) have higher incomes than do female heads of households (INCOME)?
b. Is the required condition satisfied? If not, what technique should be used?
c. Use the technique you chose in part (b) to answer the question about male and female incomes.

**19.34** SCF2013:\MC* Exercise 13.80 asked whether there is enough evidence to conclude that households whose heads have some college (EDCL: 3 = some college, 4 = college degree) have less debt (DEBT) than households whose heads completed a college degree.

a. In order to use the $t$-test of the difference between two means what condition must be satisfied? Is it satisfied? If not, what is the appropriate technique?
b. Use the technique you chose in part (a) to answer the question.

## 19-2 Sign Test and Wilcoxon Signed Rank Sum Test

In the preceding section, we discussed the nonparametric technique for comparing two populations of data that are either ordinal or interval (nonnormal) and where the data are independently drawn. In this section, the problem objective and data type remain as they were in Section 19-1, but we will be working with data generated from a matched pairs experiment. We have dealt with this type of experiment before. In Section 13-3, we dealt with the mean of the paired differences represented by the parameter $\mu_D$. In this section, we introduce two nonparametric techniques that test hypotheses in problems with the following characteristics:

1. The problem objective is to compare two populations.
2. The data are either ordinal or interval (where the normality requirement necessary to perform the parametric test is unsatisfied).
3. The samples are matched pairs.

To extract all the potential information from a matched pairs experiment, we must create the matched pair differences. Recall that we did so when conducting the $t$-test and estimate of $\mu_D$. We then calculated the mean and standard deviation of these differences and determined the test statistic and confidence interval estimator. The first step in both nonparametric methods presented here is the same: Compute the differences for each pair of observations. However, if the data are ordinal, we cannot perform any calculations on those differences because differences between ordinal values have no meaning.

To understand this point, consider comparing two populations of responses of people rating a product or service. The responses are "excellent," "good," "fair," and "poor." Recall that we can assign any numbering system as long as the order is maintained. The simplest system is 4-3-2-1. However, any other system such as 66-38-25-11 (or another set of numbers of decreasing order) is equally valid. Now suppose that in one matched pair the sample 1 response was "excellent" and the sample 2 response was "good." Calculating the matched pairs difference under the 4-3-2-1 system gives a difference of 4 – 3 = 1. Using the 66-38-25-11 system gives a difference of 66 – 38 = 28.

If we treat this and other differences as real numbers, we are likely to produce different results depending on which numbering system we used. Thus, we cannot use any method that uses the actual differences. However, we can use the sign of the differences. In fact, when the data are ordinal that is the only method that is valid. In other words, no matter what numbering system is used we know that "excellent" is better than "good." In the 4-3-2-1 system the difference between "excellent" and "good" is +1. In the 66-38-25-11 system the difference is +28. If we ignore the magnitude of the number and record only the sign, the two numbering systems (and all other systems where the rank order is maintained) will produce exactly the same result.

As you will shortly discover, the sign test uses only the sign of the differences. That's why it's called the *sign test*.

When the data are interval, however, differences have real meaning. Although we can use the sign test when the data are interval, doing so results in a loss of potentially useful information. For example, knowing that the difference in sales between two matched used-car salespeople is 25 cars is much more informative than simply knowing that the first salesperson sold more cars than the second salesperson. As a result, when the data are interval, but not normal, we will use the *Wilcoxon Signed Rank Sum Test*, which incorporates not only the sign of the difference (hence the name) but also the magnitude.

## 19-2a Sign Test

The **sign test** is employed in the following situations:

1. The problem objective is to compare two populations.
2. The data are ordinal.
3. The experimental design is matched pairs.

## 19-2b Test Statistic and Sampling Distribution

The sign test is quite simple. For each matched pair, we calculate the difference between the observation in sample 1 and the related observation in sample 2. We then count the number of positive differences and the number of negative differences. If the null hypothesis is true, we expect the number of positive differences to be approximately equal to the number of negative differences. Expressed another way, we expect the number of positive differences and the number of negative differences each to be approximately equal to half the total sample size. If either number is too large or too small, we reject the null hypothesis. By now you know that the determination of what is too large or too small comes from the sampling distribution of the test statistic. We will arbitrarily choose the test statistic to be the number of positive differences, which we denote $x$. The test statistic $x$ is a binomial random variable, and under the null hypothesis, the binomial proportion is $p = .5$. Thus, the sign test is none other than the $z$-test of $p$ introduced in Section 12-3.

Recall from Sections 7-4 and 9-2 that $x$ is binomially distributed and that, for sufficiently large $n$, $x$ is approximately normally distributed with mean $\mu = np$ and standard deviation $\sqrt{np(1-p)}$. Thus, the standardized test statistic is

$$z = \frac{x - np}{\sqrt{np(1-p)}}$$

The null hypothesis

$H_0$: The two population locations are the same

is equivalent to testing

$H_0$: $p = .5$

Therefore, the test statistic, assuming that the null hypothesis is true, becomes

$$z = \frac{x - np}{\sqrt{np(1-p)}} = \frac{x - .5n}{\sqrt{n(.5)(.5)}} = \frac{x - .5n}{.5\sqrt{n}}$$

The normal approximation of the binomial distribution is valid when $np \geq 5$ and $n(1 - p) \geq 5$. When $p = .5$,

$$np = n(.5) \geq 5$$

and

$$n(1 - p) = n(1 - .5) = n(.5) \geq 5$$

implies that $n$ must be greater than or equal to 10. Thus, this is one of the required conditions of the sign test. However, the quality of the inference with very small sample size is poor. Larger sample sizes are recommended and will be used in the examples and exercises that follow.

It is common practice in this type of test to eliminate the matched pairs of observations when the differences equal 0. Consequently, $n$ equals the number of nonzero differences in the sample.

EXAMPLE 19.4

## Comparing the Comfort of Two Midsize Cars

DATA Xm19-04

In an experiment to determine which of two cars is perceived to have the more comfortable ride, 25 people rode (separately) in the back seat of an expensive European model and also in the back seat of a North American midsize car. Each of the 25 people was asked to rate the ride on the following 5-point scale:

1 = Ride is very uncomfortable.
2 = Ride is quite uncomfortable.
3 = Ride is neither uncomfortable nor comfortable.
4 = Ride is quite comfortable.
5 = Ride is very comfortable.

The results are shown here. Do these data allow us to conclude at the 5% significance level that the European car is perceived to be more comfortable than the North American car?

| | Comfort Ratings | |
|---|---|---|
| **Respondent** | **European Car** | **North American Car** |
| 1 | 3 | 4 |
| 2 | 2 | 1 |
| 3 | 5 | 4 |
| 4 | 3 | 2 |

| Respondent | Comfort Ratings | |
|---|---|---|
| | European Car | North American Car |
| 5 | 2 | 1 |
| 6 | 5 | 3 |
| 7 | 2 | 3 |
| 8 | 4 | 2 |
| 9 | 4 | 2 |
| 10 | 2 | 2 |
| 11 | 2 | 1 |
| 12 | 3 | 4 |
| 13 | 2 | 1 |
| 14 | 3 | 4 |
| 15 | 2 | 1 |
| 16 | 4 | 3 |
| 17 | 5 | 4 |
| 18 | 2 | 3 |
| 19 | 5 | 4 |
| 20 | 3 | 1 |
| 21 | 4 | 2 |
| 22 | 3 | 3 |
| 23 | 3 | 4 |
| 24 | 5 | 2 |
| 25 | 5 | 3 |

SOLUTION:

## IDENTIFY

The problem objective is to compare two populations of ordinal data. Because the same 25 people rated both cars, we recognize the experimental design as matched pairs. The sign test is applied, with the following hypotheses:

$H_0$: The two population locations are the same.

$H_1$: The location of population 1 (European car rating) is to the right of the location of population 2 (North American car rating).

## COMPUTE

MANUALLY:

The rejection region is

$$z > z_\alpha = z_{.05} = 1.645$$

To calculate the value of the test statistic, we calculate the paired differences and count the number of positive, negative, and zero differences. The matched pairs differences are

| | | | | | | | | | | | | |
|---|---|---|---|---|---|---|---|---|---|---|---|---|
| −1 | 1 | 1 | 1 | 1 | 2 | −1 | 2 | 2 | 0 | 1 | −1 | 1 |
| −1 | 1 | 1 | 1 | −1 | 1 | 2 | 2 | 0 | −1 | 3 | 2 | |

There are 17 positive, 6 negative, and 2 zero differences. Thus, $x = 17$ and $n = 23$. The value of the test statistic is

$$z = \frac{x - .5n}{.5\sqrt{n}} = \frac{17 - .5(23)}{.5\sqrt{23}} = 2.29$$

Because the test statistic is normally distributed, we can calculate the $p$-value of the test:

$$p\text{-value} = P(Z > 2.29) = 1 - .9890 = .0110.$$

## XLSTAT

| | A | B |
|---|---|---|
| 1 | Sign test / Lower-tailed test: | |
| 2 | | |
| 3 | N+ | 6 |
| 4 | Expected value | 11.500 |
| 5 | Variance (N+) | 5.750 |
| 6 | p-value (one-tailed) | 0.0173 |
| 7 | alpha | 0.05 |
| 8 | The p-value is computed using an exact method. | |
| 9 | Ties have been detected in the data and the appropriate corrections have been applied. | |

XLSTAT calculates the $p$-value using the binomial distribution (exact distribution). In this example X is binomial with $n = 23$ and $p = .5$. Hence (using Excel),

$$p\text{-value} = P(X \le 6) = .0173$$

### *INSTRUCTIONS*

Use the same instructions for the Mann–Whitney test. Click **Sign test** and **Paired samples**.

## INTERPRET

There is relatively strong evidence to indicate that people perceive the European car as providing a more comfortable ride than the North American car. There are, however, two aspects of the experiment that may detract from that conclusion. First, did the respondents know in which car they were riding? If so, they may have answered on their preconceived bias that European cars are more expensive and therefore better. If the subjects were blindfolded, we would be more secure in our conclusion. Second, was the order in which each subject rode the two cars varied? If all the subjects rode in the North American car first and the European car second, that may have influenced their ratings. The experiment should have been conducted so that the car each subject rode in first was randomly determined.

## 19-2c Checking the Required Conditions

As we noted in Section 19-1, the sign test requires that the populations be identical in shape and spread. The histogram of the ratings for the European car (Figure 19.7) suggests that the ratings may be uniformly distributed between 2 and 5. The histogram of the ratings for the North American car (Figure 19.8) seems to indicate that the ratings are uniformly distributed between 1 and 4. Thus, both sets of ratings have the same shape and spread but their locations differ. The other condition is that the sample size exceeds 10.

FIGURE **19.7** **Histogram of Ratings of European Car in Example 19.4**

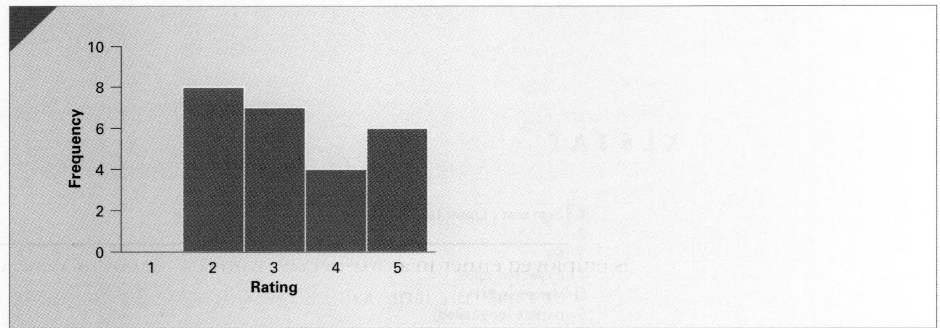


FIGURE **19.8** **Histogram of Ratings of North American Car in Example 19.4**

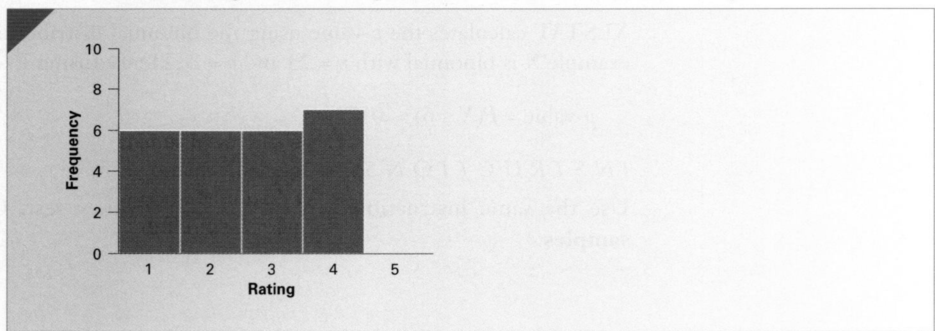


## 19-2d Wilcoxon Signed Rank Sum Test

The **Wilcoxon Signed Rank Sum Test** is used under the following circumstances:

1. The problem objective is to compare two populations.
2. The data (matched pairs differences) are interval, but not normally distributed.
3. The samples are matched pairs.

The Wilcoxon Signed Rank Sum Test is the nonparametric counterpart of the $t$-test of $\mu_D$. Because the data are interval, we can refer to the Wilcoxon Signed Rank Sum Test as a test of $\mu_D$. However, to be consistent with the other nonparametric techniques and to avoid confusion, we will express the hypotheses to be tested in the same way as we did in Section 19-1.

## 19-2e Test Statistic and Sampling Distribution

We begin by computing the paired differences. As we did in the sign test, we eliminate all differences that are equal to 0. Next, we rank the absolute values of the nonzero differences where 1 = smallest value and $n$ = largest value, with $n$ = number of nonzero differences. (We average the ranks of tied observations.) The sum of the ranks of the positive differences (denoted $T^+$) and the sum of the ranks of the negative differences (denoted $T^-$) are then calculated. We arbitrarily select $T^+$, which we label $T$, as our test statistic.

For relatively small samples, which we define as $n \le 30$, the critical values of $T$ can be determined from Table 10 in Appendix B (reproduced here as Table 19.4). This table lists values of $T_L$ and $T_U$ for sample sizes between 6 and 30. The values of $T_L$ and $T_U$ in part (a) of the table are such that

$$P(T \le T_L) = P(T \ge T_U) = .025$$

The values of $T_L$ and $T_U$ in part (b) of the table are such that

$$P(T \le T_L) = P(T \ge T_U) = .05$$

Part (a) is used either in a two-tail test with $\alpha = .05$ or in a one-tail test with $\alpha = .025$. Part (b) is employed either in a two-tail test with $\alpha = .10$ or in a one-tail test with $\alpha = .05$.

For relatively large sample sizes (we will define this to mean $n > 30$), $T$ is approximately normally distributed with mean

$$E(T) = \frac{n(n+1)}{4}$$

and standard deviation

$$\sigma_T = \sqrt{\frac{n(n+1)(2n+1)}{24}}$$

Thus, the standardized test statistic is

$$z = \frac{T - E(T)}{\sigma_T}$$

TABLE **19.4** **Critical Values of the Wilcoxon Signed Rank Sum Test**

| | (a) $\alpha = .025$ One-Tail $\alpha = .05$ Two-Tail | | (b) $\alpha = .05$ One-Tail $\alpha = .10$ Two-Tail | |
|---|---|---|---|---|
| $n$ | $T_L$ | $T_U$ | $T_L$ | $T_U$ |
| 6 | 1 | 20 | 2 | 19 |
| 7 | 2 | 26 | 4 | 24 |
| 8 | 4 | 32 | 6 | 30 |
| 9 | 6 | 39 | 8 | 37 |
| 10 | 8 | 47 | 11 | 44 |
| 11 | 11 | 55 | 14 | 52 |
| 12 | 14 | 64 | 17 | 61 |
| 13 | 17 | 74 | 21 | 70 |
| 14 | 21 | 84 | 26 | 79 |
| 15 | 25 | 95 | 30 | 90 |

TABLE **19.4** ***(Continued)***

| | (a) $\alpha = .025$ One-Tail $\alpha = .05$ Two-Tail | | (b) $\alpha = .05$ One-Tail $\alpha = .10$ Two-Tail | |
|---|---|---|---|---|
| $n$ | $T_L$ | $T_U$ | $T_L$ | $T_U$ |
| 16 | 30 | 106 | 36 | 100 |
| 17 | 35 | 118 | 41 | 112 |
| 18 | 40 | 131 | 47 | 124 |
| 19 | 46 | 144 | 54 | 136 |
| 20 | 52 | 158 | 60 | 150 |
| 21 | 59 | 172 | 68 | 163 |
| 22 | 66 | 187 | 75 | 178 |
| 23 | 73 | 203 | 83 | 193 |
| 24 | 81 | 219 | 92 | 208 |
| 25 | 90 | 235 | 101 | 224 |
| 26 | 98 | 253 | 110 | 241 |
| 27 | 107 | 271 | 120 | 258 |
| 28 | 117 | 289 | 130 | 276 |
| 29 | 127 | 308 | 141 | 294 |
| 30 | 137 | 328 | 152 | 313 |

**EXAMPLE 19.5**

DATA
Xm19-05

## Comparing Flextime and Fixed Time Schedules

Traffic congestion on roads and highways costs industry billions of dollars annually as workers struggle to get to and from work. Several suggestions have been made about how to improve this situation, one of which is called *flextime*—workers are allowed to determine their own schedules (provided they work a full shift). Such workers will likely choose an arrival and departure time to avoid rush-hour traffic. In a preliminary experiment designed to investigate such a program, the general manager of a large company wanted to compare the times it took workers to travel from their homes to work at 8 A.M. with travel time under the flextime program. A random sample of 32 workers was selected. The employees recorded the time (in minutes) it took to arrive at work at 8 A.M. on Wednesday of one week. The following week, the same employees arrived at work at times of their own choosing. The travel time on Wednesday of that week was recorded. These results are listed in the following table. Can we conclude at the 5% significance level that travel times under the flextime program are different from travel times to arrive at work at 8 A.M.?

| | Travel Time | |
|---|---|---|
| **Worker** | **Arrival at 8:00 A.M.** | **Flextime Program** |
| 1 | 34 | 31 |
| 2 | 35 | 31 |
| 3 | 43 | 44 |
| 4 | 46 | 44 |
| 5 | 16 | 15 |
| 6 | 26 | 28 |
| 7 | 68 | 63 |

*(Continued)*

| Worker | Travel Time | |
| --- | --- | --- |
| | Arrival at 8:00 A.M. | Flextime Program |
| 8 | 38 | 39 |
| 9 | 61 | 63 |
| 10 | 52 | 54 |
| 11 | 68 | 65 |
| 12 | 13 | 12 |
| 13 | 69 | 71 |
| 14 | 18 | 13 |
| 15 | 53 | 55 |
| 16 | 18 | 19 |
| 17 | 41 | 38 |
| 18 | 25 | 23 |
| 19 | 17 | 14 |
| 20 | 26 | 21 |
| 21 | 44 | 40 |
| 22 | 30 | 33 |
| 23 | 19 | 18 |
| 24 | 48 | 51 |
| 25 | 29 | 33 |
| 26 | 24 | 21 |
| 27 | 51 | 50 |
| 28 | 40 | 38 |
| 29 | 26 | 22 |
| 30 | 20 | 19 |
| 31 | 19 | 21 |
| 32 | 42 | 38 |

SOLUTION:

IDENTIFY

The objective is to compare two populations; the data are interval and were produced from a matched pairs experiment. If matched pairs differences are normally distributed, we should apply the $t$-test of $\mu_D$. To judge whether the data are normal, we computed the paired differences and drew the histogram (actually Excel did). Figure 19.9 depicts this histogram. Apparently, the normality requirement is not satisfied, indicating that we should employ the Wilcoxon Signed Rank Sum Test.

FIGURE **19.9** **Histogram of the Differences for Example 19.5**

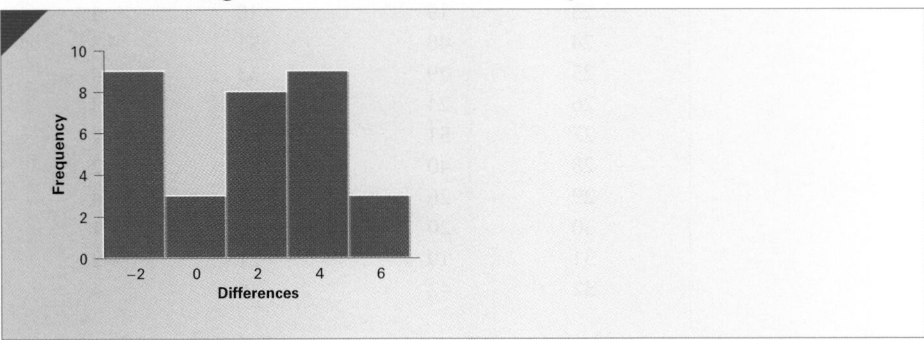

Because we want to know whether the two groups of times differ, we perform a two-tail test whose hypotheses are

$H_0$: The two population locations are the same.
$H_1$: The location of population 1 (travel times for current work schedule) is different from the location of population 2 (travel times for flextime program).

## COMPUTE

### MANUALLY:

For each worker, we compute the difference between travel time with arrival at 8 A.M. and travel time under flextime.

| | Travel Time | | | | | |
|---|---|---|---|---|---|---|
| **Worker** | **Arrival at 8:00 A.M.** | **Flextime Program** | **Difference** | **\|Difference\|** | **Rank** | **\|Rank\|** |
| 1 | 34 | 31 | 3 | 3 | 21.0 | |
| 2 | 35 | 31 | 4 | 4 | 27.0 | |
| 3 | 43 | 44 | −1 | 1 | | 4.5 |
| 4 | 46 | 44 | 2 | 2 | 13.0 | |
| 5 | 16 | 15 | 1 | 1 | 4.5 | |
| 6 | 26 | 28 | −2 | 2 | | 13.0 |
| 7 | 68 | 63 | 5 | 5 | 31.0 | |
| 8 | 38 | 39 | −1 | 1 | | 4.5 |
| 9 | 61 | 63 | −2 | 2 | | 13.0 |
| 10 | 52 | 54 | −2 | 2 | | 13.0 |
| 11 | 68 | 65 | 3 | 3 | 21.0 | |
| 12 | 13 | 12 | 1 | 1 | 4.5 | |
| 13 | 69 | 71 | −2 | 2 | | 13.0 |
| 14 | 18 | 13 | 5 | 5 | 31.0 | |
| 15 | 53 | 55 | −2 | 2 | | 13.0 |
| 16 | 18 | 19 | −1 | 1 | | 4.5 |
| 17 | 41 | 38 | 3 | 3 | 21.0 | |
| 18 | 25 | 23 | 2 | 2 | 13.0 | |
| 19 | 17 | 14 | 3 | 3 | 21.0 | |
| 20 | 26 | 21 | 5 | 5 | 31.0 | |
| 21 | 44 | 40 | 4 | 4 | 27.0 | |
| 22 | 30 | 33 | −3 | 3 | | 21.0 |
| 23 | 19 | 18 | 1 | 1 | 4.5 | |
| 24 | 48 | 51 | −3 | 3 | | 21.0 |
| 25 | 29 | 33 | −4 | 4 | | 27.0 |
| 26 | 24 | 21 | 3 | 3 | 21.0 | |
| 27 | 51 | 50 | 1 | 1 | 4.5 | |
| 28 | 40 | 38 | 2 | 2 | 13.0 | |
| 29 | 26 | 22 | 4 | 4 | 27.0 | |
| 30 | 20 | 19 | 1 | 1 | 4.5 | |
| 31 | 19 | 21 | −2 | 2 | | 13.0 |
| 32 | 42 | 38 | 4 | 4 | 27.0 | |
| | | | | | $T^+ = 367.5$ | $T^- = 160.5$ |

The differences and the absolute values of the differences are calculated. We rank the absolute differences. (If there were any zero differences, we would eliminate them before ranking the absolute differences.) Ties are resolved by calculating the averages. The ranks of the negative differences are offset to facilitate the summing of the ranks. The rank sums of the positive and negative differences are

$$T^+ = 367.5 \quad \text{and} \quad T^- = 160.5$$

The test statistic is

$$z = \frac{T - E(T)}{\sigma_T}$$

where

$$T = T^+ = 367.5$$

$$E(T) = \frac{n(n+1)}{4} = \frac{32(33)}{4} = 264$$

$$\sigma_T = \sqrt{\frac{n(n+1)(2n+1)}{24}} = \sqrt{\frac{32(33)(65)}{24}} = 53.48$$

Thus,

$$z = \frac{T - E(T)}{\sigma_T} = \frac{367.5 - 264}{53.48} = 1.94$$

The rejection region is

$$z < -z_{\alpha/2} = -z_{.025} = -1.96 \quad \text{or} \quad z > z_{\alpha/2} = z_{.025} = 1.96$$

The $p$-value is $2P(Z > 1.94) = 2(1 - .9738) = .0524$

## XLSTAT

| | A | B |
|---|---|---|
| 1 | Wilcoxon signed-rank test / Two-tailed test: | |
| 2 | | |
| 3 | V | 367.500 |
| 4 | Expected value | 264.000 |
| 5 | Variance (V) | 2824.500 |
| 6 | p-value (Two-tailed) | 0.0515 |
| 7 | alpha | 0.05 |
| 8 | An approximation has been used to compute the p-value. | |
| 9 | Ties have been detected in the data and the appropriate corrections have been applied. | |

Note that the manually calculated variance is 2860. XLSTAT uses a correction when there are ties as is the case here. This accounts for the different $p$-values.

*INSTRUCTIONS*

1. Click **Wilcoxon signed rank test** and **Paired samples.**

## INTERPRET

There is not enough evidence to infer that flextime commutes are different from the commuting times under the current schedule. This conclusion may be due primarily to the way in which this experiment was performed. All of the drivers recorded their travel time with 8 A.M. arrival on the first Wednesday and their flextime travel time on the second Wednesday. If the second day's traffic was heavier than usual, that may account for the conclusion reached. As we pointed out in Example 19.4, the order of schedules should have been randomly determined for each employee. In this way, the effect of varying traffic conditions could have been minimized.

Here is how we recognize when to use the two techniques introduced in this section.

**Factors That Identify the Sign Test**

1. **Problem objective**: Compare two populations
2. **Data type**: Ordinal
3. **Experimental design**: Matched pairs

**Factors That Identify the Wilcoxon Signed Rank Sum Test**

1. **Problem objective**: Compare two populations
2. **Data type**: Interval
3. **Distribution of differences**: Nonnormal
4. **Experimental design**: Matched pairs

## EXERCISES

**19.35** In a matched pairs experiment, if we find 30 negative, 5 zero, and 15 positive differences, perform the sign test to determine whether the two population locations differ. (Use a 5% significance level.)

**19.36** Suppose that in a matched pairs experiment we find 28 positive differences, 7 zero differences, and 41 negative differences. Can we infer at the 10% significance level that the location of population 1 is to the left of the location of population 2?

**19.37** A matched pairs experiment yielded the following results:

Positive differences: 18

Zero differences: 0

Negative differences: 12

Can we infer at the 5% significance level that the location of population 1 is to the right of the location of population 2?

**19.38** Xr19-38 Use the sign test on the following data to determine whether the location of population 1 is to the right of the location of population 2. (Use $\alpha = .05$.)

| **Pair:** | 1 | 2 | 3 | 4 | 5 | 6 | 7 | 8 | 9 | 10 | 11 | 12 | 13 | 14 | 15 | 16 |
|---|---|---|---|---|---|---|---|---|---|---|---|---|---|---|---|---|
| **Sample 1** | 5 | 3 | 4 | 2 | 3 | 4 | 3 | 5 | 4 | 3 | 4 | 5 | 4 | 5 | 3 | 2 |
| **Sample 2** | 3 | 2 | 4 | 3 | 3 | 1 | 3 | 4 | 2 | 5 | 1 | 2 | 2 | 3 | 1 | 2 |

**19.39** Given the following statistics from a matched pairs experiment, perform the Wilcoxon signed rank sum test to determine whether we can infer at the

5% significance level that the two population locations differ.

$T^+ = 660 \quad T^- = 880 \quad n = 55$

**19.40** A matched pairs experiment produced the following statistics. Conduct a Wilcoxon signed rank sum test to determine whether the location of population 1 is to the right of the location of population 2. (Use $\alpha = .01$.)

$T^+ = 3{,}457 \quad T^- = 2{,}429 \quad n = 108$

**19.41** Perform the Wilcoxon signed rank sum test for the following matched pairs to determine whether the two population locations differ. (Use $\alpha = .10$.)

| **Pair** | 1 | 2 | 3 | 4 | 5 | 6 |
|---|---|---|---|---|---|---|
| **Sample 1** | 9 | 12 | 13 | 8 | 7 | 10 |
| **Sample 2** | 5 | 10 | 11 | 9 | 3 | 9 |

**19.42** Xr19-42 Perform the Wilcoxon signed rank sum test to determine whether the location of population 1 differs from the location of population 2 given the data shown here. (Use $\alpha = .05$.)

| **Pair** | 1 | 2 | 3 | 4 | 5 | 6 | 7 | 8 | 9 | 10 | 11 | 12 |
|---|---|---|---|---|---|---|---|---|---|---|---|---|
| **Sample 1** | 18.2 | 14.1 | 24.5 | 11.9 | 9.5 | 12.1 | 10.9 | 16.7 | 19.6 | 8.4 | 21.7 | 23.4 |
| **Sample 2** | 18.2 | 14.1 | 23.6 | 12.1 | 9.5 | 11.3 | 9.7 | 17.6 | 19.4 | 8.1 | 21.9 | 21.6 |

*Exercises 19.43 to 19.57 require the use of a computer and software.* ***Use a 5% significance level, unless specified otherwise.***

### Developing an Understanding of Statistical Concepts

**19.43** a. Xr19-43a In a taste test of a new beer 100 people rated the new beer and the leading brand on the market. The possible ratings were Poor, Fair, Good, Very good, and Excellent. The responses for the new beer and the leading beer were recorded using a 1-2-3-4-5 coding system. Can we infer that the new beer is more highly rated than the leading brand?

b. Xr19-43b The responses were recoded so that 3 = Poor, 8 = Fair, 22 = Good, 37 = Very good, and 55 = Excellent. Can we infer that the new beer is more highly rated than the leading brand?

c. Why are the answers to Parts (a) and (b) identical?

**19.44** a. Xr19-44a A random sample of 50 people was asked to rate two brands of ice cream using the following responses:

Delicious
OK
Not bad
Terrible

The responses were converted to codes 4, 3, 2, and 1, respectively. Can we infer that Brand A is preferred?

b. Xr19-44b The responses were recoded using the values 28-25-16-3. Can we infer that Brand A is preferred?

c. Compare your answers for Parts (a) and (b). Are they identical? Explain why?

**19.45** Xr19-45 Refer to Example 19.4. Suppose that the responses have been recorded in the following way:

6 = Ride is very uncomfortable.
24 = Ride is quite uncomfortable.
28 = Ride is neither uncomfortable nor comfortable.
53 = Ride is quite comfortable.
95 = Ride is very comfortable.

a. Do these data allow us to conclude that the European car is perceived to be more comfortable than the North American car?

b. Compare your answer with that obtained in Example 19.4. Explain why the results are identical.

**19.46** a. Xr19-46 Data from a matched pairs experiment were recorded. Use the sign test to determine whether the population locations differ.

b. Repeat Part (a) using the Wilcoxon signed rank sum test.

c. Why do the answers to Parts (a) and (b) differ?

**19.47** a. Xr19-47 Data from a matched pairs experiment were recorded. Use the sign test to determine whether the population locations differ.

b. Repeat Part (a) using the Wilcoxon signed rank sum test.

c. Why do the results of Parts (a) and (b) differ?

### Applications

*Exercises 19.48 to 19.57 may be solved manually. See Appendix A for the sample statistics.*

**19.48** Xr19-48 Research scientists at a pharmaceutical company have recently developed a new nonprescription sleeping pill. They decide to test its effectiveness by measuring the time it takes for people to fall asleep after taking the pill. Preliminary analysis indicates that the time to fall asleep varies considerably from one person to another. Consequently, they organize the experiment in the following way. A random sample of 100 volunteers who regularly suffer from insomnia is chosen. Each person is given one pill containing the newly developed drug and one placebo. (A placebo is a pill that contains absolutely no medication.) Participants are told to take one pill one night and the second pill one night a week later. (They do not know whether the pill they are taking is the placebo or the new drug, and the order of use is random.) Each participant is fitted with a device that measures the time until sleep occurs. Can we conclude that the new drug is effective? (This exercise is identical to Exercise 13.198, except for the data.)

**19.49** Xr19-49 Suppose that the housework study referred to in Exercise 19.10 was repeated with some changes. In the revised experiment, 60 women were asked last year and again this year how many hours of housework they perform weekly. Can we conclude at the 1% significance level that women as a group are doing less housework now than last year?

**19.50** Xr19-50 At the height of the energy shortage during the 1970s, governments were actively seeking ways to persuade consumers to reduce their energy consumption. Among other efforts undertaken, several advertising campaigns were launched. To provide input on how to design effective advertising messages, a poll was taken in which people were asked how concerned they were about shortages of gasoline and electricity. There were four possible responses to the questions:

Not concerned at all (1)
Not too concerned (2)
Somewhat concerned (3)
Very concerned (4)

A poll of 150 individuals was undertaken. Do these data provide enough evidence to allow us to infer that concern about a gasoline shortage exceeded concern about an electricity shortage?

**19.51** Xr19-51 A locksmith is in the process of selecting a new key-cutting machine. If there is a difference in key-cutting speed between the two machines under consideration, he will purchase the faster one. If there is no difference, he will purchase the cheaper machine. The times (in seconds) required to cut each of the 35 most common types of keys were recorded. What should he do?

**19.52** Xr19-52 A large sporting-goods store located in Florida is planning a renovation that will result in an increase in the floor space for one department. The manager of the store has narrowed her choice about which department's floor space to increase to two possibilities: the tennis-equipment department or the swimming-accessories department. The manager would like to enlarge the tennis-equipment department because she believes that this department improves the overall image of the store. She decides, however, that if the swimming-accessories department can be shown to have higher gross sales, she will choose that department. She has collected each of the two departments' weekly gross sales data for the past 32 weeks. Which department should be enlarged?

**19.53** Xr19-53 Does the brand name of an ice cream affect consumers' perceptions of it? The marketing manager of a major dairy pondered this question. She decided to ask 60 randomly selected people to taste the same flavor of ice cream in two different dishes. The dishes contained exactly the same ice cream but were labeled differently. One was given a name that suggested that its maker was European and sophisticated; the other was given a name that implied that the product was domestic and inexpensive. The tasters were asked to rate each ice cream on a 5-point scale, where 1 = Poor, 2 = Fair, 3 = Good, 4 = Very good, and 5 = Excellent. Do the results allow the manager to conclude at the 10% significance level that the European brand is preferred?

**19.54** Xr19-54 Do children feel less pain than adults? That question was addressed by nursing professors at the University of Alberta and the University of Saskatchewan. Suppose that in a preliminary study, 50 8-year-old children and their mothers were subjected to moderately painful pressure on their hands. Each was asked to rate the level of pain as Very severe (4), Severe (3), Moderate (2), or Weak (1). The data were recorded using the codes in parentheses. Can we conclude at the 1% significance level that children feel less pain than adults?

**19.55** Xr19-55 In a study to determine whether gender affects salary offers for graduating MBA students, 45 pairs of students were selected. Each pair consisted of a male and a female student who had almost identical grade-point averages, courses taken, ages, and previous work experience. The highest salary offered to each student upon graduation was recorded. Is there sufficient evidence to allow us to conclude that the salary offers differ between men and women? (This exercise is identical to Exercise 13.203, except for the data.)

**19.56** Xr19-56 Admissions officers at universities and colleges face the problem of comparing grades achieved at different high schools. As a step toward developing a more informed interpretation of such grades, an admissions officer at a large state university conducts the following experiment. The records of 100 students from the same local high school (high school 1) who just completed their first year at the university were selected. Each of these students was paired (according to average grade in the last year of high school) with a student from another local high school (high school 2) who also just completed the first year at the university. For each matched pair, the average letter grades (4 = A, 3 = B, 2 = C, 1 = D, or 0 = F) in the first year of university study were recorded. Do these results allow us to conclude that, in comparing two students with the same high-school average (one from high school 1 and the other from high school 2), preference in admissions should be given to the student from high school 1?

**19.57** Xr19-57 Some movie studios believe that by adding sexually explicit scenes to the home video version of a movie, they can increase the movie's appeal and profitability. A studio executive decided to test this belief. She organized a study that involved 40 movies that were rated PG-13. Versions of each movie were created by adding scenes that changed the rating to R. The two versions of the movies were then made available to rental shops. For each of the 40 pairs of movies, the total number of rentals in one major city during a 1-week period was recorded.

a. Do these data provide enough evidence to support the belief?
b. As an analyst for a movie studio write a report detailing the statistical analysis.

## General Social Survey Exercises

**19.58** GSS2014* The survey asked these two questions.

1. Compared to your parents at your age is your standard of living . . . (PARSOL: 1 = Much better, 2 = Somewhat better, 3 = About the same, 4 = Somewhat worse, 5= Much worse)?
2. When your children are at your age will their standard of living be. . . (KIDSSOL 1 = Much better, 2 = Somewhat better, 3 = About the same, 4 = Somewhat worse, 5 = Much worse)?

Is there enough evidence to infer that Americans are more optimistic about their children than themselves?

**19.59** GSS2014* Do married couples typically have the same completed degrees? Conduct a test to determine whether there is enough evidence to conclude that married couples do not have the same degrees (DEGREE, SPDEG, Highest degree completed of respondent and spouse: 0 = Left high school, 1 = High school, 2 = Junior college, 3 = Bachelor's degree, 4 = Graduate).

# 19-3 Kruskal–Wallis Test and Friedman Test

In this section we introduce two statistical procedures designed to compare two or more populations. The first test is the **Kruskal–Wallis Test**, which is applied to problems with the following characteristics:

1. The problem objective is to compare two or more populations.
2. The data are either ordinal or interval, but nonnormal.
3. The samples are independent.

When the data are interval and normal, we use the one-way analysis of variance $F$-test presented in Section 14-1 to determine whether differences exist. When the data are not normal, we will treat the data as if they were ordinal and employ the Kruskal–Wallis Test.

The second procedure is the **Friedman Test**, which is applied to problems with the following characteristics:

1. The problem objective is to compare two or more populations.

2. The data are either ordinal or interval, but not normal.

3. The data are generated from a randomized block experiment.

The parametric counterpart is the two-way analysis of variance, which we use when the data are interval and normal.

## 19-3a Hypotheses

The null and alternative hypotheses for both tests are similar to those we specified in the analysis of variance. Because the data are ordinal or are treated as ordinal, we test population locations instead of population means. In all applications of the Kruskal–Wallis Test and the Friedman Test, the null and alternative hypotheses are

$H_0$: The locations of all $k$ populations are the same.
$H_1$: At least two population locations differ.

Here, $k$ represents the number of populations to be compared.

## 19-3b Kruskal–Wallis Test

**Test Statistic** The test statistic is calculated in a way that closely resembles the way in which the Wilcoxon Rank Sum Test was calculated. The first step is to rank all the observations. As before, 1 = smallest observation and $n$ = largest observation, where $n = n_1 + n_2 + \cdots + n_k$. In case of ties, average the ranks.

If the null hypothesis is true, the ranks should be evenly distributed among the $k$ samples. The degree to which this is true is judged by calculating the rank sums (labeled $T_1, T_2, \ldots, T_k$). The last step is to calculate the test statistic, which is denoted $H$.

**Test Statistic for Kruskal–Wallis Test**

$$H = \left[\frac{12}{n(n+1)}\sum_{j=1}^{k}\frac{T_j^2}{n_j}\right] - 3(n+1)$$

Although it is impossible to see from this formula, if the rank sums are similar, the test statistic will be small. As a result, a small value of $H$ supports the null hypothesis. Conversely, if considerable differences exist between the rank sums, the test statistic will be large. To judge the value of $H$, we need to know its sampling distribution.

**Sampling Distribution** The distribution of the test statistic can be derived in the same way we derived the sampling distribution of the test statistic in the Wilcoxon

Rank Sum Test. In other words, we can list all possible combinations of ranks and their probabilities to yield the sampling distribution. A table of critical values can then be determined. However, this is necessary only for small sample sizes. For sample sizes greater than or equal to 5, the test statistic $H$ is approximately chi-squared distributed with $k - 1$ degrees of freedom. Recall that we introduced the chi-squared distribution in Section 8-4.

**Rejection Region and *p*-Value** As we noted previously, large values of $H$ are associated with different population locations. Consequently, we want to reject the null hypothesis if $H$ is sufficiently large. Thus, the rejection region is

$$H > \chi^2_{\alpha,k-1}$$

and the $p$-value is

$$P(\chi^2 > H)$$

Figure 19.10 describes this sampling distribution and the $p$-value.

FIGURE **19.10** **Sampling Distribution of *H***

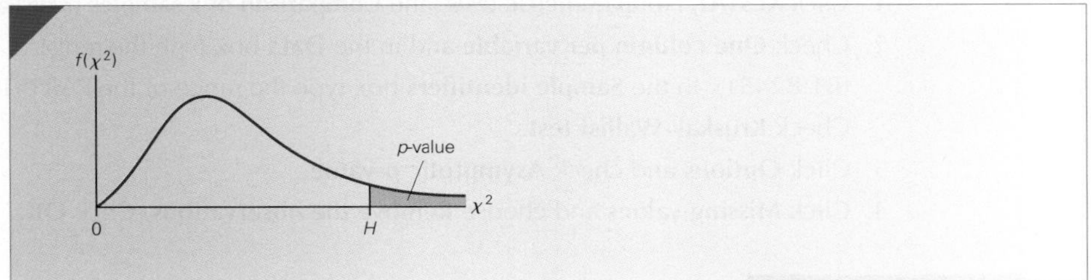


## General Social Survey

### Do Democrats, Independents, and Republicans Differ in the Number of Times per Week That They Read Newspapers?

Kiyoshi Ota/Getty Images

SOLUTION:

**IDENTIFY**

The problem objective is to compare three populations (Democrats, Independents, and Republicans). The data are ordinal and the samples are independent. These factors are sufficient to justify the use of the Kruskal–Wallis test. The null and alternative hypotheses are:

$H_0$: The locations of all three populations are the same.
$H_1$: At least two population locations differ.

*(Continued)*

COMPUTE

XLSTAT

| | | |
|---|---|---|
| 11 | Kruskal-Wallis test (NEWS): | |
| 12 | K (Observed value) | 20.86 |
| 13 | K (Critical value) | 5.99 |
| 14 | DF | 2 |
| 15 | p-value (Two-tailed) | < 0.0001 |
| 16 | alpha | 0.05 |
| 17 | An approximation has been used to compute the p-value. | |
| 18 | Ties have been detected in the data and the appropriate corrections have been applied. | |

Note that when there are ties, the manually calculated test statistic will differ from the one computed by XLSTAT.

*INSTRUCTIONS*

We copied PARTYID3 and NEWS from the GSS2014 file into two columns (Columns A and B). The rows with blanks in column A were deleted.

1. Click **XLSTAT, Nonparametric tests**, and **Comparison of k samples (Kruskal–Wallis, Friedman, . . .)**
2. Check **One column per variable** and in the **Data** box type the range of the observations (B1:B2451). In the **Sample identifiers** box type the range of the PARTYID3 data (A1:A2451). Check **Kruskal–Wallist test**.
3. Click **Options** and check **Asymptotic *p*-value**.
4. Click **Missing values** and choose **Remove the observations**. Click **OK**.

INTERPRET

There is enough evidence to infer that a difference in frequency of newspaper reading differs between the three political affiliations.

## 19-3c Kruskal–Wallis Test and the Wilcoxon Rank Sum Test

When the Kruskal–Wallis Test is used to test for a difference between two populations, it will produce the same outcome as the two-tail Wilcoxon Rank Sum Test. However, the Kruskal–Wallis Test can determine only whether a difference exists. To determine, for example, if one population is located to the right of another, we must apply the Wilcoxon Rank Sum Test.

## 19-3d Friedman Test

**Test Statistic** To calculate the test statistic, we first rank each observation within each block, where 1 = smallest observation and $k$ = largest observation, averaging the ranks of ties. Then we compute the rank sums, which we label $T_1, T_2, \ldots, T_k$. The test statistic is defined as follows. (Recall that $b$ = number of blocks.)

**Test Statistic for the Friedman Test**

$$F_r = \left[\frac{12}{b(k)(k+1)}\sum_{j=1}^{k} T_j^2\right] - 3b(k+1)$$

**Sampling Distribution of the Test Statistic** The test statistic is approximately chi-squared distributed with $k - 1$ degrees of freedom, provided that either $k$ or $b$ is greater than or equal to 5. As was the case with the Kruskal–Wallis Test, we reject the null hypothesis when the test statistic is large. Hence, the rejection region is

$$F_r > \chi^2_{\alpha,k-1}$$

and the $p$-value is

$$P(\chi^2 > F_r)$$

Figure 19.11 depicts the sampling distribution and $p$-value.

FIGURE **19.11** **Sampling Distribution of $F_r$**

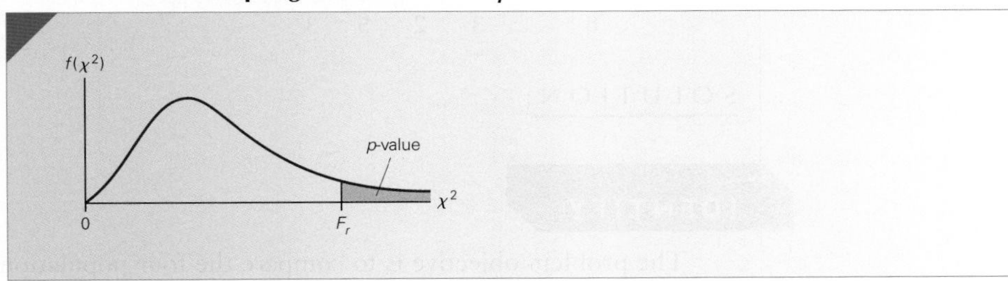


This test, like all the other nonparametric tests, requires that the populations being compared be identical in shape and spread.

EXAMPLE 19.6

DATA Xm19-06

## Comparing Managers' Evaluations of Job Applicants

The personnel manager of a national accounting firm has been receiving complaints from senior managers about the quality of recent hirings. All new accountants are hired through a process in which four managers interview the candidate and rate her or him on several dimensions, including academic credentials, previous work experience, and personal suitability. Each manager then summarizes the results and produces an evaluation of the candidate. There are five possibilities:

1. The candidate is in the top 5% of applicants.
2. The candidate is in the top 10% of applicants, but not in the top 5%.

3. The candidate is in the top 25% of applicants, but not in the top 10%.
4. The candidate is in the top 50% of applicants, but not in the top 25%.
5. The candidate is in the bottom 50% of applicants.

The evaluations are then combined in making the final decision. The personnel manager believes that the quality problem is caused by the evaluation system. However, she needs to know whether there is general agreement or disagreement between the interviewing managers in their evaluations. To test for differences between the managers, she takes a random sample of the evaluations of eight applicants. The results are shown below. What conclusions can the personnel manager draw from these data? Employ a 5% significance level.

| | **Manager** | | | |
|---|---|---|---|---|
| **Applicant** | **1** | **2** | **3** | **4** |
| 1 | 2 | 1 | 2 | 2 |
| 2 | 4 | 2 | 3 | 2 |
| 3 | 2 | 2 | 2 | 3 |
| 4 | 3 | 1 | 3 | 2 |
| 5 | 3 | 2 | 3 | 5 |
| 6 | 2 | 2 | 3 | 4 |
| 7 | 4 | 1 | 5 | 5 |
| 8 | 3 | 2 | 5 | 3 |

SOLUTION:

IDENTIFY

The problem objective is to compare the four populations of managers' evaluations, which we can see are ordinal data. This experiment is identified as a randomized block design because the eight applicants were evaluated by all four managers. (The treatments are the managers, and the blocks are the applicants.) The appropriate statistical technique is the Friedman Test. The null and alternative hypotheses are as follows:

$H_0$: The locations of all four populations are the same.
$H_1$: At least two population locations differ.

COMPUTE

MANUALLY:

The rejection region is

$$F_r > \chi^2_{\alpha,k-1} = \chi^2_{.05,3} = 7.81$$

The following table demonstrates how the ranks are assigned and the rank sums calculated. Notice how the ranks are assigned by moving across the rows (blocks) and the rank sums computed by adding down the columns (treatments).

| | Manager | | | |
|---|---|---|---|---|
| **Applicant** | **1 (Rank)** | **2 (Rank)** | **3 (Rank)** | **4 (Rank)** |
| 1 | 2(3) | 1(1) | 2(3) | 2(3) |
| 2 | 4(4) | 2(1.5) | 3(3) | 2(1.5) |
| 3 | 2(2) | 2(2) | 2(2) | 3(4) |
| 4 | 3(3.5) | 1(1) | 3(3.5) | 2(2) |
| 5 | 3(2.5) | 2(1) | 3(2.5) | 5(4) |
| 6 | 2(1.5) | 2(1.5) | 3(3) | 4(4) |
| 7 | 4(2) | 1(1) | 5(3.5) | 5(3.5) |
| 8 | 3(2.5) | 2(1) | 5(4) | 3(2.5) |
| | $T_1 = 21$ | $T_2 = 10$ | $T_3 = 24.5$ | $T_4 = 24.5$ |

The value of the test statistic is

$$F_r = \left[\frac{12}{b(k)(k+1)}\sum_{j=1}^{k} T_j^2\right] - 3b(k+1)$$

$$= \left[\frac{12}{(8)(4)(5)}(21^2 + 10^2 + 24.5^2 + 24.5^2\right] - 3(8)(5)$$

$$= 10.61$$

**XLSTAT**

| | | |
|---|---|---|
| 9 | Friedman's test: | |
| 10 | Q (Observed value) | 12.86 |
| 11 | Q (Critical value) | 7.81 |
| 12 | DF | 3 |
| 13 | p-value (Two-tailed) | 0.0049 |
| 14 | alpha | 0.05 |
| 15 | Ties have been detected in the data and the appropriate corrections have been applied. | |

Note that because of tied values the manually calculated test statistic and $p$-value will differ from those computed by XLSTAT.

*INSTRUCTIONS*

1. Click **XLSTAT**, **Nonparametric tests**, and **Comparison of k samples (Kruskal–Wallis, Friedman, . . .)**
2. Check, **Paired samples** and **Friedman's test**. In the **Samples** box type the range of the observations (**A1:D9**).
3. Click **Options** and check **Asymptotic *p*-value**. Click **OK**.

INTERPRET

There appears to be sufficient evidence to indicate that the managers' evaluations differ. The personnel manager should attempt to determine why the evaluations differ. Is there a problem with the way in which the assessments are conducted, or are some managers using different criteria? If it is the latter, those managers may need additional training.

## 19-3e The Friedman Test and the Sign Test

The relationship between the Friedman and sign tests is the same as the relationship between the Kruskal–Wallis and Wilcoxon Rank Sum Tests; that is, we can use the Friedman Test to determine whether two populations differ. The conclusion will be the same as that produced from the sign test. However, we can use the Friedman Test to determine only whether a difference exists. If we want to determine whether one population is, for example, to the left of another population, we must use the sign test.

Here is a list of the factors that tell us when to use the Kruskal Wallis Test and the Friedman Test.

**Factors That Identify the Kruskal–Wallis Test**

1. **Problem objective**: Compare two or more populations
2. **Data type**: Ordinal or interval but not normal
3. **Experimental design**: Independent samples

**Factors That Identify the Friedman Test**

1. **Problem objective**: Compare two or more populations
2. **Data type**: Ordinal or interval but not normal
3. **Experimental design**: Randomized blocks

## Exercises

**19.60** Conduct the Kruskal–Wallis test on the following statistics. Use a 5% significance level.

$T_1 = 984$ $n_1 = 23$
$T_2 = 1{,}502$ $n_2 = 36$
$T_3 = 1{,}430$ $n_3 = 29$

**19.61** From the following statistics, use the Kruskal–Wallis test (with $\alpha = .01$) to determine whether the population locations differ.

$T_1 = 1{,}207$ $n_1 = 25$
$T_2 = 1{,}088$ $n_2 = 25$
$T_3 = 1{,}310$ $n_3 = 25$
$T_4 = 1{,}445$ $n_4 = 25$

**19.62** Apply the Kruskal–Wallis test and the following statistics to determine whether there is enough statistical evidence at the 10% significance level to infer that the population locations differ.

$T_1 = 3{,}741$ $n_1 = 47$
$T_2 = 1{,}610$ $n_2 = 29$
$T_3 = 4{,}945$ $n_3 = 67$

**19.63** Xr19-63 Use the Kruskal–Wallis test on the following data to determine whether the population locations differ. (Use $\alpha = .05$.)

| | | | | | | | |
|---|---|---|---|---|---|---|---|
| Sample 1: | 27 | 33 | 18 | 29 | 41 | 52 | 75 |
| Sample 2: | 37 | 12 | 17 | 22 | 30 | | |
| Sample 3: | 19 | 12 | 33 | 41 | 28 | 18 | |

**19.64** Xr19-64 Using the Kruskal–Wallis test, determine whether there is enough evidence provided by the accompanying data to enable us to infer that at least two population locations differ. (Use $\alpha = .05$.)

| | | | | | |
|---|---|---|---|---|---|
| Sample 1: | 25 | 15 | 20 | 22 | 23 |
| Sample 2: | 19 | 21 | 23 | 22 | 28 |
| Sample 3: | 27 | 25 | 22 | 29 | 28 |

## Developing an Understanding of Statistical Concepts

*Exercise 19.65 requires the use of a computer and software.*

**19.65** a. Xr19-65a Four random samples of 50 people each were asked to rate four different computer printers in terms of their ease of use. The responses are:

Very easy to use
Easy to use
Difficult to use
Very difficult to use

The responses were coded using a 4-3-2-1 system. Do these data yield enough evidence at the 5% significance level to infer that differences in ratings exist among the four printers?

b. Xr19-65b The responses were recoded using a 25-22-5-2 system. Do these data yield enough evidence to infer that differences in ratings exist between the four printers?

c. Why are the results of Parts (a) and (b) identical?

**19.66** Xr19-66 Apply the Friedman test to the accompanying table of data to determine whether we can conclude that at least two population locations differ. (Use $\alpha = .10$.)

| | Treatment | | | |
|---|---|---|---|---|
| Block | 1 | 2 | 3 | 4 |
| 1 | 10 | 12 | 15 | 9 |
| 2 | 8 | 10 | 11 | 6 |
| 3 | 13 | 14 | 16 | 11 |
| 4 | 9 | 9 | 12 | 13 |
| 5 | 7 | 8 | 14 | 10 |

**19.67** Xr19-67 The following data were generated from a blocked experiment. Conduct a Friedman test to determine whether at least two population locations differ. (Use $\alpha = .05$.)

| | Treatment | | |
|---|---|---|---|
| Block | 1 | 2 | 3 |
| 1 | 7.3 | 6.9 | 8.4 |
| 2 | 8.2 | 7.0 | 7.3 |
| 3 | 5.7 | 6.0 | 8.1 |
| 4 | 6.1 | 6.5 | 9.1 |
| 5 | 5.9 | 6.1 | 8.0 |

## Developing an Understanding of Statistical Concepts

*Exercises 19.68 to 19.93 require the use of a computer and software.* ***Use a 5% significance level.***

**19.68** a. Xr19-68a A random sample of 30 people was asked to rate each of four different premium brands of coffee. The ratings are:

Excellent
Good
Fair
Poor

The responses were assigned numbers 1 through 4, respectively. Can we infer that differences exist between the ratings of the four brands of coffee?

b. Xr19-68b Suppose that the codes were 12, 31, 66, and 72, respectively. Can we infer that differences exist between the ratings of the four brands of coffee?

c. Compare your answers in Parts (a) and (b). Why are they identical?

**19.69** a. Xr19-69 Refer to Example 19.6. Suppose that the responses were recoded so that the numbers equaled the midpoint of the range of percentiles. That is:

97.5 = The candidate is in the top 5% of applicants
92.5 = The candidate is in the top 10% of applicants, but not in the top 5%
82.5 = The candidate is in the top 25% of applicants, but not in the top 10%
62.5 = The candidate is in the top 50% of applicants, but not in the top 25%
25 = The candidate is in the bottom 50% of applicants

Can we conclude that differences exist between the ratings assigned by the four professors?

b. Compare your answer in Part (a) with the one obtained in Example 19.6. Are they the same? Explain why.

**Applications (*Unless specified otherwise, use a 5% significance level.*)**

*Exercises 19.70 to 19.84 can be solved manually. See Appendix A for the sample statistics.*

**19.70** Xr19-70 In an effort to determine whether differences exist between three methods of teaching statistics, a professor of business taught his course differently in each of three large sections. In the first section, he taught by lecturing; in the second, he taught by the case method; and in the third, he used a computer software package extensively. At the end of the semester, each student was asked to evaluate the course on a 7-point scale, where 1 = Atrocious, 2 = Poor, 3 = Fair, 4 = Average, 5 = Good, 6 = Very good, and 7 = Excellent. From each section, the professor chose 25 evaluations at random. Is there evidence that differences in student satisfaction exist with respect to at least two of the three teaching methods?

**19.71** Xr19-71 Applicants to MBA programs must take the Graduate Management Admission Test (GMAT). There are several companies that offer assistance in preparing for the test. To determine whether they work, and if so, which one is best, an experiment was conducted. Several hundred MBA applicants were surveyed and asked to report their GMAT score and which, if any, GMAT preparation course they took. The responses are course A, course B, course C, or no preparatory course. Do these data allow us to infer that there are differences between the four groups of GMAT scores?

**19.72** Xr19-72 Ten judges were asked to test the quality of four different brands of orange juice. The judges assigned scores using a 5-point scale where 1 = Bad, 2 = Poor, 3 = Average, 4 = Good, and 5 = Excellent. The results are shown here. Can we conclude at the 5% significance level that there are differences in sensory quality between the four brands of orange juice?

| | Orange Juice Brand | | | |
|---|---|---|---|---|
| **Judge** | **1** | **2** | **3** | **4** |
| 1 | 3 | 5 | 4 | 3 |
| 2 | 2 | 3 | 5 | 4 |
| 3 | 4 | 4 | 3 | 4 |
| 4 | 3 | 4 | 5 | 2 |
| 5 | 2 | 4 | 4 | 3 |
| 6 | 4 | 5 | 5 | 3 |
| 7 | 3 | 3 | 4 | 4 |
| 8 | 2 | 3 | 3 | 3 |
| 9 | 4 | 3 | 5 | 4 |
| 10 | 2 | 4 | 5 | 3 |

**19.73** Xr19-73 The manager of a chain of electronic-products retailers is trying to decide on a location for its newest store. After a thorough analysis, the choice has been narrowed to three possibilities. An important factor in the decision is the number of people passing each location. The number of people passing each location per day was counted during 30 days.

a. Which techniques should be considered to determine whether the locations differ? What are the required conditions? How do you select a technique?

b. Can management conclude that there are differences in the numbers of people passing the three locations if the number of people passing each location is not normally distributed?

**19.74** Xr19-74 In recent years, lack of confidence in the U.S. Postal Service has led many companies to send all of their correspondence by private courier. A large company is in the process of selecting one of three possible couriers to act as its sole delivery method. To help make the decision, an experiment was performed whereby letters were sent using each of the three couriers at 12 different times of the day to a delivery point across town. The number of minutes required for delivery was recorded. Can we conclude that there are differences in delivery times between the three couriers? (This exercise is identical to Exercise 14.91, except for the data.)

**19.75** Xr19-75 The manager of a personnel company is in the process of examining her company's advertising programs. Currently, the company advertises in each of the three local newspapers for a wide variety of positions, including computer programmers, secretaries, and receptionists. The manager has decided that only one newspaper will be used if it can be determined that there are differences between the newspapers in the number of inquiries. The following experiment was performed. For 1 week (6 days), six different jobs were advertised in each of the three newspapers. The number of inquiries was counted, and the results appear in the accompanying table.

| | Newspaper | | |
|---|---|---|---|
| **Job Advertised** | **1** | **2** | **3** |
| Receptionist | 14 | 17 | 12 |
| Systems analyst | 8 | 9 | 6 |
| Junior secretary | 25 | 20 | 23 |
| Computer programmer | 12 | 15 | 10 |
| Legal secretary | 7 | 10 | 5 |
| Office manager | 5 | 9 | 4 |

a. What techniques should be considered to apply in reaching a decision? What are the required conditions? How do we determine whether the conditions are satisfied?

b. Assuming that the data are not normally distributed, can we conclude at the 5% significance level that differences exist between the newspapers' abilities to attract potential employees?

**19.76** Xr19-76 Because there are no national or regional standards, it is difficult for university admission committees to compare graduates of different high schools. University administrators have noted that an 80% average at a high school with low standards may be equivalent to a 70% average at another school with higher standards of grading. In an effort to more equitably compare applications, a pilot study was initiated. Random samples of students who were admitted the previous year from four local high schools were drawn. All the students entered the business program with averages between 70% and 80%. Their average grades in the first year at the university were computed. Can the university admissions officer conclude that there are differences in grading standards between the four high schools? (This exercise is identical to Exercise 14.9, except for the data.)

**19.77** Xr19-77 Many North Americans suffer from high levels of cholesterol, which can lead to heart attacks. For those with very high levels (over 280), doctors prescribe drugs to reduce cholesterol levels. A pharmaceutical company has recently developed three such drugs. To determine whether any differences exist in their benefits, an experiment was organized. The company selected 25 groups of four men, each of whom had cholesterol levels in excess of 280. In each group, the men were matched according to age and weight. The drugs were administered over a 2-month period, and the reduction in cholesterol was recorded. Do these results allow the company to conclude differences exist between the four new drugs? (This exercise is identical to Example 14.3, except for the data.)

**19.78** Xr19-78 A well-known soft-drink manufacturer has used the same secret recipe for its product since its introduction over 100 years ago. In response to a decreasing market share, however, the president of the company is contemplating changing the recipe. He has developed two alternative recipes. In a preliminary study, he asked 20 people to taste the original recipe and the two new recipes. He asked each to evaluate the taste of the product on a 5-point scale, where 1 = Awful, 2 = Poor, 3 = Fair, 4 = Good, and 5 = Wonderful. The president decides that unless significant differences exist between evaluations of the products, he will not make any changes. Can we conclude that there are differences in the ratings of the three recipes?

**19.79** Xr19-79 The management of fast-food restaurants is extremely interested in knowing how their customers rate the quality of food and service and the cleanliness of the restaurants. Customers are given the opportunity to fill out customer comment cards. Suppose that one franchise wanted to compare how customers rate the three shifts (4:00 P.M. to midnight, midnight to 8:00 A.M., and 8:00 A.M. to 4:00 P.M.). In a preliminary study, 100 customer cards were randomly selected from each shift. The responses to the question concerning speed of service were recorded, where 4 = Excellent, 3 = Good, 2 = Fair, and 1 = Poor, and are listed here. Do these data provide sufficient evidence at the 5% significance level to indicate whether customers perceive the speed of service to be different between the three shifts?

**19.80** Xr19-80 A consumer testing service compared the effectiveness of four different brands of drain cleaner. The experiment consisted of using each product on 50 different clogged sinks and measuring the amount of time that elapsed until each drain became unclogged. The recorded times were measured in minutes.

a. Which techniques should be considered as possible procedures to apply to determine whether differences exist? What are the required conditions? How do you decide?

b. If a statistical analysis has shown that the times are not normally distributed, can the service conclude that differences exist between the speeds at which the four brands perform?

**19.81** Xr19-81 During the last presidential campaign, the Gallup organization surveyed a random sample of 30 registered Democrats in January, another 30 in February, and yet another 30 in March. All 90 Democrats were asked to "rate the chances of the Democrats winning the presidential race in your state." The responses and their numerical codes were Excellent (4), Good (3), Fair (2), and Poor (1). Do these data allow us to infer that Democrats' ratings of their chances of winning the presidency changed over the 3-month period?

**19.82** Xr19-82 It is common practice in the advertising business to create several different advertisements and then ask a random sample of potential customers to rate the ads on several different dimensions. Suppose that an advertising firm developed four different ads for a new breakfast cereal and asked a sample of 400 shoppers to rate the believability of the advertisements. One hundred people viewed ad 1, another 100 viewed ad 2, another 100 saw ad 3, and another 100 saw ad 4. The ratings were Very believable (4), Quite believable (3), Somewhat believable (2), and Not believable at all (1). Can the firm's management conclude that differences exist in believability between the four ads?

**19.83** Xr19-83 Do university students become more supportive of their varsity teams as they progress through their 4-year stint? To help answer this question, a sample of students was drawn. Each was asked their class standing (freshman, sophomore, junior, or senior) and to what extent they supported the university's football team, the Hawks. The responses to the latter question are:

Wildly fanatic
Support the Hawks wholeheartedly
Support the Hawks, but not that enthusiastically
Who are the Hawks?

The responses were coded using a 4-3-2-1 numbering system. Can we conclude that the four levels of students differ in their support for the Hawks?

**19.84** Xr19-84 In anticipation of buying a new scanner, a student turned to a website that reported the results of surveys of users of the different scanners. A sample of 133 responses was listed showing the ease of use of five different brands. The survey responses were:

Very easy
Easy
Not easy
Difficult
Very difficult

The responses were assigned numbers from 1 to 5. Can we infer that there are differences in perceived ease of use between the five brands of scanners?

## General Social Survey Exercises

**19.85** GSS2014* Do more educated people derive more satisfaction from their jobs? Test to determine whether there are differences in job satisfaction (SATJOB: 1 = Very satisfied, 2 = Moderately satisfied, 3 = A little dissatisfied, 4 = Very dissatisfied) between the degree holders (DEGREE: 0 = Left high school, 1 = Finished high school, 2 = Junior college, 3 = Bachelor's degree, 4 = Graduate degree).

**19.86** GSS2014* Respondents were asked the following question, Compared to your parents at your age is your standard of living (PARSOL: 1 = Much better, 2 = Somewhat better, 3 = About the same, 4 = Somewhat worse, 5 = Much worse)? Test to determine whether we can infer that differences in perception exist between the three races (RACE).

**19.87** GSS2014* Are there differences between the five categories of marital status (MARITAL) with respect to health (HEALTH: 1 = Excellent, 2 = Good, 3 = Fair, 4 = Poor)? Conduct a statistical test to answer the question.

**19.88** GSS2014* Do less-educated people believe that they have a higher probability of losing their job? Test to determine whether there is enough evidence to conclude that there are differences in perceived likelihood of losing their jobs (JOBLOSE: 1 = Very likely, 2 = Fairly likely, 3 = Not too likely, 4 = Not likely) between the degree holders (DEGREE: 0 = Left high school, 1 = Finished high school, 2 = Junior college, 3 = Bachelor's degree, 4 Graduate degree).

**19.89** GSS2014* Is there enough statistical evidence to infer that there are differences between the three race categories (RACE) with respect to how likely they are to lose their jobs (JOBLOSE: 1 = Very likely, 2 = Fairly likely, 3 = Not too likely, 4 = Not likely)?

**19.90** GSS2014* Is there enough statistical evidence to conclude that Democrats, Republicans, and Independents (PARTYID3: 1 = Democrat, 2 = Independent, 3 = Republican) differ in their views about the federal income tax that they have to pay (TAX: Do you consider the amount of federal income tax that you have to pay as too high, about right, or too low: 1 = Too high, 2 = About right, 3 = Too low)?

**19.91** GSS2014* Can we infer from the data that liberals, moderates, and conservatives (POLVIEWS3: 1 = Liberal, 2 = Moderate, 3 = Conservative) differ in their views about the federal income tax that they have to pay (TAX: Do you consider the amount of federal income tax that you have to pay as too high, about right, or too low: 1 = Too high, 2 = About right, 3 = Too low)?

**19.92** GSS2014* Are there differences between the races with respect to their perceptions of their health (HEALTH: Would you say your own health, in general, is . . . 1. Excellent, 2. Good, 3. Fair, 4. Poor)? Use an appropriate statistical technique to determine whether there is enough evidence to infer that there are differences between the races (RACE: 1. White, 2. Black, 3.Other).

**19.93** GSS2014* How does educational attainment affect newspaper readership? Is there enough evidence to conclude that there are differences between the five educational attainment groups (DEGREE: Highest degree completed of respondent, spouse, father, mother: 0 = Left high school, 1 = High school, 2 = Junior college, 3 = Bachelor's degree, 4 = Graduate) with respect to how frequently they read newspapers (NEWS: 1 = Every day, 2 = Few times per week, 3 = Once per week, 4 = Less than once per week, 5 = Never)?

## 19-4 Spearman Rank Correlation Coefficient

In Section 17-4, we introduced the test of the coefficient of correlation, which allows us to determine whether there is evidence of a linear relationship between two interval variables. Recall that the required condition for the $t$-test of $\rho$ is that the variables are bivariate normally distributed. In many situations, however, one or both variables may be ordinal; or if both variables are interval, the normality requirement may not be satisfied. In such cases, we measure and test to determine whether a relationship exists by employing a nonparametric technique, the **Spearman rank correlation coefficient**.

The Spearman rank correlation coefficient is calculated like all of the other previously introduced nonparametric methods by first ranking the data. We then calculate the *Pearson correlation coefficient* of the ranks.

The population Spearman correlation coefficient is labeled $\rho_s$, and the sample statistic used to estimate its value is labeled $r_s$.

**Sample Spearman Rank Correlation Coefficient**

$$r_s = \frac{s_{ab}}{s_a s_b}$$

where $a$ and $b$ are the ranks of $x$ and $y$, respectively, $s_{ab}$ is the covariance of the values of $a$ and $b$, $s_a$ is the standard deviation of the values of $a$, and $s_b$ is the standard deviation of the values of $b$.

We can test to determine whether a relationship exists between the two variables. The hypotheses to be tested are

$H_0$: $\rho_s = 0$

$H_1$: $\rho_s \neq 0$

(We also can conduct one-tail tests.) The test statistic is the absolute value of $r_s$. To determine whether the value of $r_s$ is large enough to reject the null hypothesis, we refer to Table 11 in Appendix B, reproduced here as Table 19.5, which lists the critical values of the test statistic for one-tail tests. To conduct a two-tail test, the value of $\alpha$ must be doubled. The table lists critical values for $\alpha = .01, .025$, and $.05$ and for $n = 5$ to 30. When $n$ is greater than 30, $r_s$ is approximately normally distributed with mean 0 and standard deviation $1/\sqrt{n-1}$. Thus, for $n > 30$, the test statistic is as shown in the box.

**Test Statistic for Testing $\rho_s = 0$ When $n > 30$**

$$z = \frac{r_s - 0}{1/\sqrt{n-1}} = r_s\sqrt{n-1}$$

which is standard normally distributed

TABLE **19.5** **Critical Values for the Spearman Rank Correlation Coefficient**

The $\alpha$ values correspond to a one-tail test of $H_0$: $\rho_s = 0$. The value should be doubled for two-tail tests.

| $n$ | $\alpha = .05$ | $\alpha = .025$ | $\alpha = .01$ |
|---|---|---|---|
| 5 | .900 | — | — |
| 6 | .829 | .886 | .943 |
| 7 | .714 | .786 | .893 |
| 8 | .643 | .738 | .833 |
| 9 | .600 | .683 | .783 |
| 10 | .564 | .648 | .745 |
| 11 | .523 | .623 | .736 |
| 12 | .497 | .591 | .703 |
| 13 | .475 | .566 | .673 |
| 14 | .457 | .545 | .646 |
| 15 | .441 | .525 | .623 |
| 16 | .425 | .507 | .601 |
| 17 | .412 | .490 | .582 |
| 18 | .399 | .476 | .564 |
| 19 | .388 | .462 | .549 |
| 20 | .377 | .450 | .534 |
| 21 | .368 | .438 | .521 |
| 22 | .359 | .428 | .508 |
| 23 | .351 | .418 | .496 |
| 24 | .343 | .409 | .485 |
| 25 | .336 | .400 | .475 |
| 26 | .329 | .392 | .465 |
| 27 | .323 | .385 | .456 |
| 28 | .317 | .377 | .448 |
| 29 | .311 | .370 | .440 |
| 30 | .305 | .364 | .432 |

EXAMPLE 19.7

## Testing the Relationship between Aptitude Tests and Performance

DATA Xm19-07

The production manager of a firm wants to examine the relationship between aptitude test scores given before hiring production-line workers and performance ratings received by the employees 3 months after starting work. The results of the study would allow the firm to decide how much weight to give to these aptitude tests relative to other work-history information obtained, including references. The aptitude test results range from 0 to 100. The performance ratings are as follows:

1 = Employee has performed well below average.
2 = Employee has performed somewhat below average.
3 = Employee has performed at the average level.
4 = Employee has performed somewhat above average.
5 = Employee has performed well above average.

A random sample of 40 production workers yielded the results listed here. Can the firm's manager infer at the 5% significance level that aptitude test scores are correlated with performance rating?

| Employee | Aptitude | Performance |
|---|---|---|
| 1 | 59 | 3 |
| 2 | 47 | 2 |
| 3 | 58 | 4 |
| 4 | 66 | 3 |
| 5 | 77 | 2 |
| 6 | 57 | 4 |
| 7 | 62 | 3 |
| 8 | 68 | 3 |
| 9 | 69 | 5 |
| 10 | 36 | 1 |
| 11 | 48 | 3 |
| 12 | 65 | 3 |
| 13 | 51 | 2 |
| 14 | 61 | 3 |
| 15 | 40 | 3 |
| 16 | 67 | 4 |
| 17 | 60 | 2 |
| 18 | 56 | 3 |
| 19 | 76 | 3 |
| 20 | 71 | 2 |
| 21 | 52 | 3 |
| 22 | 62 | 5 |
| 23 | 54 | 2 |
| 24 | 50 | 3 |
| 25 | 57 | 1 |
| 26 | 59 | 5 |
| 27 | 66 | 4 |
| 28 | 84 | 5 |
| 29 | 56 | 2 |

(*Continued*)

| Employee | Aptitude | Performance |
|---|---|---|
| 30 | 61 | 1 |
| 31 | 53 | 4 |
| 32 | 76 | 3 |
| 33 | 42 | 4 |
| 34 | 59 | 4 |
| 35 | 58 | 2 |
| 36 | 66 | 4 |
| 37 | 58 | 2 |
| 38 | 53 | 1 |
| 39 | 63 | 5 |
| 40 | 85 | 3 |

SOLUTION:

## IDENTIFY

The problem objective is to analyze the relationship between two variables. The aptitude test score is interval, but the performance rating is ordinal. We will treat the aptitude test score as if it were ordinal and calculate the Spearman rank correlation coefficient. To answer the question, we specify the hypotheses as

$H_0$: $\rho_s = 0$

$H_1$: $\rho_s \neq 0$

## COMPUTE

MANUALLY:

We rank each of the variables separately, averaging any ties that we encounter. The original data and ranks are as follows.

| Employee | Aptitude | Rank *a* | Performance | Rank *b* |
|---|---|---|---|---|
| 1 | 59 | 20 | 3 | 20.5 |
| 2 | 47 | 4 | 2 | 9 |
| 3 | 58 | 17 | 4 | 31.5 |
| 4 | 66 | 30 | 3 | 20.5 |
| 5 | 77 | 38 | 2 | 9 |
| 6 | 57 | 14.5 | 4 | 31.5 |
| 7 | 62 | 25.5 | 3 | 20.5 |
| 8 | 68 | 33 | 3 | 20.5 |
| 9 | 69 | 34 | 5 | 38 |
| 10 | 36 | 1 | 1 | 2.5 |
| 11 | 48 | 5 | 3 | 20.5 |
| 12 | 65 | 28 | 3 | 20.5 |

| Employee | Aptitude | Rank *a* | Performance | Rank *b* |
|---|---|---|---|---|
| 13 | 51 | 7 | 2 | 9 |
| 14 | 61 | 23.5 | 3 | 20.5 |
| 15 | 40 | 2 | 3 | 20.5 |
| 16 | 67 | 32 | 4 | 31.5 |
| 17 | 60 | 22 | 2 | 9 |
| 18 | 56 | 12.5 | 3 | 20.5 |
| 19 | 76 | 36 | 3 | 20.5 |
| 20 | 71 | 35 | 2 | 9 |
| 21 | 52 | 8 | 3 | 20.5 |
| 22 | 62 | 25.5 | 5 | 38 |
| 23 | 54 | 11 | 2 | 9 |
| 24 | 50 | 6 | 3 | 20.5 |
| 25 | 57 | 14.5 | 1 | 2.5 |
| 26 | 59 | 20 | 5 | 38 |
| 27 | 66 | 30 | 4 | 31.5 |
| 28 | 84 | 39 | 5 | 38 |
| 29 | 56 | 12.5 | 2 | 9 |
| 30 | 61 | 23.5 | 1 | 2.5 |
| 31 | 53 | 9.5 | 4 | 31.5 |
| 32 | 76 | 37 | 3 | 20.5 |
| 33 | 42 | 3 | 4 | 31.5 |
| 34 | 59 | 20 | 4 | 31.5 |
| 35 | 58 | 17 | 2 | 9 |
| 36 | 66 | 30 | 4 | 31.5 |
| 37 | 58 | 17 | 2 | 9 |
| 38 | 53 | 9.5 | 1 | 2.5 |
| 39 | 63 | 27 | 5 | 38 |
| 40 | 85 | 40 | 3 | 20.5 |

The next step is to calculate the following sums:

$$\sum a_i b_i = 18{,}319$$

$$\sum a_i = 820 \quad \sum b_i = 820$$

$$\sum a_i^2 = 22{,}131.5$$

$$\sum b_i^2 = 21{,}795.5$$

Using the shortcut calculation on page 110, we determine that the covariance of the ranks is

$$s_{ab} = \frac{1}{n-1}\left(\sum a_i b_i - \frac{\sum a_i \sum b_i}{n}\right) = \frac{1}{40-1}\left[18{,}319 - \frac{(820)(820)}{40}\right] = 38.69$$

The sample variances of the ranks (using the short-cut formula on page 98) are

$$s_a^2 = \frac{1}{n-1}\left[\sum a_i^2 - \frac{\left(\sum a_i\right)^2}{n}\right] = \frac{1}{40-1}\left[22{,}131.5 - \frac{(820)^2}{40}\right] = 136.45$$

$$s_b^2 = \frac{1}{n-1}\left[\sum b_i^2 - \frac{\left(\sum ab_i\right)^2}{n}\right] = \frac{1}{40-1}\left[21{,}795.5 - \frac{(820)^2}{40}\right] = 127.83$$

The standard deviations are

$$s_a = \sqrt{s_a^2} = \sqrt{136.45} = 11.68$$

$$s_b = \sqrt{s_b^2} = \sqrt{127.83} = 11.31$$

Thus,

$$r_s = \frac{s_{ab}}{s_a s_b} = \frac{38.69}{(11.68)(11.31)} = .2929$$

The value of the test statistic is

$$z = r_s\sqrt{n-1} = .2929\sqrt{40-1} = 1.83$$

$$p\text{-value} = 2P(Z > 1.83) = 2(1 - .9664) = .0672$$

## XLSTAT

| | A | B | C |
|---|---|---|---|
| 1 | Correlation matrix (Spearman): | | |
| 2 | | | |
| 3 | Variables | Aptitude | Performance |
| 4 | Aptitude | 1 | 0.2930 |
| 5 | Performance | 0.2930 | 1 |
| 6 | | | |
| 7 | p-values: | | |
| 8 | | | |
| 9 | Variables | Aptitude | Performance |
| 10 | Aptitude | 0 | 0.0668 |
| 11 | Performance | 0.0668 | 0 |

*INSTRUCTIONS*

1. Click **XLSTAT**, **Correlation/Association test**, and **Correlation test**.
2. Specify the input range (A1:B41) and check **Spearman**.
3. Click **Outputs** and check **Correlations** and ***p*-values**.

## INTERPRET

There is not enough evidence to believe that the aptitude test scores and performance ratings are related. This conclusion suggests that the aptitude test should be improved to better measure the knowledge and skill required by a production-line worker. If this proves impossible, the aptitude test should be discarded.

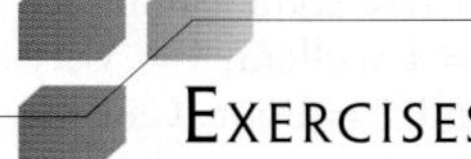

## EXERCISES

**19.94** Test the following hypotheses:

$H_0$: $\rho_s = 0$

$H_1$: $\rho_s \neq 0$

$n = 50$ $r_s = .23$ $\alpha = .05$

**19.95** Is there sufficient evidence at the 5% significance level to infer that there is a positive relationship between two ordinal variables given that $r_s = .15$ and $n = 12$?

**19.96** Xr19-96 A statistics student asked seven first-year economics students to report their grades in the required mathematics and economics courses. The results (where 1 = F, 2 = D, 3 = C, 4 = B, 5 = A) are as follows:

| **Mathematics** | 4 | 2 | 5 | 4 | 2 | 2 | 1 |
|---|---|---|---|---|---|---|---|
| **Economics** | 5 | 2 | 3 | 5 | 3 | 3 | 2 |

Calculate the Spearman rank correlation coefficient, and test to determine whether we can infer that a relationship exists between the grades in the two courses. (Use $\alpha = .05$.)

**19.97** Xr19-97 Does the number of commercials shown during a half-hour television program affect how viewers rate the show? In a preliminary study eight people were asked to watch a pilot for a situation comedy and rate the show (1 = Terrible, 2 = Bad, 3 = OK, 4 = Good, 5 = Very good). Each person was shown a different number of 30-second commercials. The data are shown here. Calculate the Spearman rank correlation coefficient and test with a 10% significance level to determine whether there is a relationship between the two variables.

| **Number of commercials** | 1 | 2 | 3 | 4 | 5 | 6 | 7 | 8 |
|---|---|---|---|---|---|---|---|---|
| **Rating** | 4 | 5 | 3 | 3 | 3 | 2 | 3 | 1 |

**19.98** Xr19-98 The weekly returns of two stocks for a 13-week period were recorded and are listed here. Assuming that the returns are not normally distributed, can we infer at the 5% significance level that the stock returns are correlated?

| **Stock 1** | −7 | −4 | −7 | −3 | 2 | −10 | −10 |
|---|---|---|---|---|---|---|---|
| **Stock 2** | 6 | 6 | −4 | 9 | 3 | −3 | 7 |
| **Stock 1** | 5 | 1 | −4 | 2 | 6 | −13 | |
| **Stock 2** | −3 | 4 | 7 | 9 | 5 | −7 | |

**19.99** Xr19-99 The general manager of an engineering firm wants to know whether a draftsman's experience influences the quality of his work. She selects 24 draftsmen at random and records their years of work experience and their quality rating (as assessed by their supervisors, where 5 = Excellent, 4 = Very good, 3 = Average, 2 = Fair, and 1 = Poor). The data are listed here. Can we infer from these data that years of work experience is a factor in determining the quality of work performed? (Use $\alpha = .05$.)

| Draftsman | Experience | Rating | Draftsman | Experience | Rating |
|---|---|---|---|---|---|
| 1 | 1 | 1 | 13 | 8 | 2 |
| 2 | 17 | 4 | 14 | 20 | 5 |
| 3 | 20 | 4 | 15 | 21 | 3 |
| 4 | 9 | 5 | 16 | 19 | 2 |
| 5 | 2 | 2 | 17 | 1 | 1 |
| 6 | 13 | 4 | 18 | 22 | 3 |
| 7 | 9 | 3 | 19 | 20 | 4 |
| 8 | 23 | 5 | 20 | 11 | 3 |
| 9 | 7 | 2 | 21 | 18 | 5 |
| 10 | 10 | 5 | 22 | 14 | 4 |
| 11 | 12 | 5 | 23 | 21 | 3 |
| 12 | 24 | 2 | 24 | 21 | 1 |

*The following exercises require the use of a computer and software.* ***Use a 5% significance level.***

**19.100** Xm16-02 Refer to Example 16.2. If the required condition is not satisfied conduct another more appropriate test to determine whether odometer reading and price are related.

**19.101** Xr19-101 At the completion of most courses in universities and colleges, a course evaluation is undertaken. Some professors believe that the way in which students fill out the evaluations is based on how well the student is doing in the course. To test this theory, a random sample of course evaluations was selected. Two answers were recorded. The questions and answers are:

a. How would you rate the course?

1. Poor 2. Fair 3. Good 4. Very good 5. Excellent

b. What grade do you expect in this course?

1. F 2. D 3. C 4. B 5. A

Is there enough evidence to conclude that the theory is correct?

**19.102** Xr19-102 Many people suffer from heartburn. It appears, however, that the problem may increase with age. A researcher for a pharmaceutical company wanted to determine whether age and the incidence and extent of heartburn are related. A random sample of 325 adults was drawn. Each person was asked to give his or her age and to rate the severity of heartburn (1 = Low, 2 = Moderate, 3 = High,

4 = Very high). Do these data provide sufficient evidence to indicate that older people suffer more severe heartburn?

**19.103** Xr16-06 Assume that the conditions for the test conducted in Exercise 16.6 are not met. Do the data allow us to conclude that the longer the commercial, the higher the memory test score will be?

**19.104** Xr16-07 Assume that the normality requirement in Exercise 16.7 is not met. Test to determine whether the price of a condominium and floor number are positively related.

**19.105** Xr19-105 Many people who quit smoking gain weight. Many explain that after they quit smoking food tastes better. To examine the relationship between smoking and taste, a researcher randomly sampled 280 smokers. Each was asked how many cigarettes they smoked on an average day. In addition, each person was asked to taste and rate some vanilla ice cream. The responses are 5 = Excellent, 4 = Very good, 3 = Good, 2 = Fair, and 1 = Poor. Can the researcher infer that the more a person smokes the less taste sensation he or she has?

**19.106** Xr19-106 Gambling on sports is big business in the United States and Canada. A television executive wants to know whether the amount of money wagered on a professional football game affects the enjoyment of viewers. A random sample of 200 men who regularly watch football Sunday afternoons and wager on the outcomes was drawn. Each was asked to report the amount wagered on the game they watched and to rate the enjoyment (where 1 = Not enjoyable, 2 = Somewhat enjoyable, 3 = Moderately, enjoyable, and 4 = Very enjoyable). Do these data provide enough evidence to conclude that the greater the wager the more enjoyable the game is for the viewer?

## General Social Survey Exercises

**19.107** GSS2014* Do older Americans have a greater fear of losing their jobs? Test to determine whether there is enough evidence to conclude that as one gets older (AGE) the probability of losing one's job (JOBLOSE: 1 = Very likely, 2 = Fairly likely, 3 = Not too likely, 4 = Not likely) decreases.

**19.108** GSS2014* Is there sufficient evidence to infer that more educated (EDUC) people read newspapers more often (NEWS: 1 = Every day, 2 = A few times per week, 3 = Once a week, 4 = Less than once a week, 5 = Never)?

**19.109** GSS2014* Do the most satisfying jobs also produce the highest income? Test to determine whether there is enough evidence to infer that more satisfying jobs (SATJOB: 1 = Very satisfied, 2 = Moderately satisfied, 3 = A little dissatisfied, 4 = Very dissatisfied) have higher incomes (RINCOME).

**19.110** GSS2014* Can we infer from the data that jobs that are most secure (JOBLOSE: 1 =Very likely, 2 = Fairly likely, 3 = Not too likely, 4 = Not likely) are also the most satisfying (SATJOB: 1 = Very satisfied, 2 = Moderately satisfied, 3 = A little dissatisfied, 4 = Very dissatisfied)?

**19.111** GSS2014* Can we conclude from the data that more educated (EDUC) people are more likely to perceive themselves as healthier (HEALTH: 1 = Excellent, 2 = Good, 3 = Fair, 4 = Poor)?

**19.112** GSS2014* Are more educated people (EDUC) more likely to believe that that compared to their parents at their age their standard of living is better (PARSOL: 1 = Much better, 2 = Somewhat better, 3 = About the same, 4 = Somewhat worse, 5 = Much worse)? Perform an appropriate test to answer the question.

**19.113** GSS2014* Is it a myth that younger Americans do not read newspapers, choosing instead to get their news from the Internet or television (or not at all)? Conduct a test to determine whether there is sufficient statistical evidence to conclude that younger people (AGE) read newspapers (NEWS: 1 = Every day, 2 = A few times per week, 3 = Once a week, 4 = Less than once a week, 5 = Never) less frequently than older people.

**19.114** GSS2014* If one works longer hours (HRS1) does the chances of losing one's job (JOBLOSE: 1 = Very likely, 2 = Fairly likely, 3 = Not too likely, 4 = Not likely) become less likely? Conduct a test to answer the question.

**19.115** GSS2014* Does age (AGE) affect one's belief concerning the federal income tax that one has to pay (TAX: Do you consider the amount of federal income tax that you have to pay as too high, about right, or too low: 1 = Too high, 2 = About right, 3 = Too low)?

**19.116** GSS2014* Are richer people healthier? Conduct a test to determine whether there is enough evidence to infer that higher income (RINCOME) individuals are healthier (HEALTH: Would you say your own health, in general, is . . . 1. Excellent, 2. Good, 3. Fair, 4. Poor)?

**19.117** GSS2014* Are richer (RINCOME) Americans pessimistic about their children's chances of having a higher standard of living (KIDSSOL: When your children are at your age will their standard of living be. . . 1. Much better, 2. Somewhat better, 3. About the same, 4. Somewhat worse, 5. Much worse)? Conduct a statistical test to answer the question.

## Chapter Summary

Nonparametric statistical tests are applied to problems where the data are either ordinal or interval but not normal. The Wilcoxon Rank Sum Test is used to compare two populations of ordinal or interval data when the data are generated from independent samples. The sign test is used to compare two populations of ordinal data drawn from a matched pairs experiment. The Wilcoxon Signed Rank Sum Test is employed to compare two populations of nonnormal interval data taken from a matched pairs experiment. When the objective is to compare two or more populations of independently sampled ordinal or interval nonnormal data the Kruskal–Wallis Test is employed. The Friedman Test is used instead of the Kruskal–Wallis Test when the samples are blocked. To determine whether two variables are related, we employ the test of the Spearman rank correlation coefficient.

### IMPORTANT TERMS:

Nonparametric techniques 763
Distribution-free statistics 763
Wilcoxon Rank Sum Test 765
Sign test 780
Wilcoxon Signed Rank Sum Test 784
Kruskal–Wallis Test 793
Friedman Test 793
Spearman rank correlation coefficient 805

### SYMBOLS:

| Symbol | Pronounced | Represents |
|---|---|---|
| $T_i$ | *T* sub *i* or *T i* | Rank sum of sample $i\ (i = 1, 2, \ldots, k)$ |
| $T^+$ | *T* plus | Rank sum of positive differences |
| $T^-$ | *T* minus | Rank sum of negative differences |
| $\sigma_T$ | Sigma sub *T* or sigma *T* | Standard deviation of the sampling distribution of *T* |
| $\rho_s$ | Rho sub *s* or rho *s* | Spearman rank correlation coefficient |

### FORMULAS:

Wilcoxon Rank Sum Test

$$T = T_1$$

$$E(T) = \frac{n_1(n_1 + n_2 + 1)}{2}$$

$$\sigma_T = \sqrt{\frac{n_1 n_2(n_1 + n_2 + 1)}{12}}$$

$$z = \frac{T - E(T)}{\sigma_T}$$

Sign test

$$x = \text{number of positive differences}$$

$$z = \frac{x - .5n}{.5\sqrt{n}}$$

Wilcoxon Signed Rank Sum Test

$$T = T^+$$

$$E(T) = \frac{n(n + 1)}{4}$$

$$\sigma_T = \sqrt{\frac{n(n+1)(2n+1)}{24}}$$

$$z = \frac{T - E(T)}{\sigma_T}$$

Kruskal–Wallis Test

$$H = \left[\frac{12}{n(n+1)} \sum_{j=1}^{k} \frac{T_j^2}{n_j}\right] - 3(n+1)$$

Friedman Test

$$F_r = \left[\frac{12}{b(k)(k+1)} \sum_{j=1}^{k} T_j^2\right] - 3b(k+1)$$

Spearman rank correlation coefficient

$$r_s = \frac{s_{ab}}{s_a s_b}$$

Spearman test statistic for $n > 30$

$$z = r_s\sqrt{n-1}$$

## COMPUTER OUTPUT AND INSTRUCTIONS:

| Technique | XLSTAT |
|---|---|
| Wilcoxon Rank Sum Test | 771 |
| Sign test | 783 |
| Wilcoxon Signed Rank Sum Test | 789 |
| Kruskal–Wallis Test | 796 |
| Friedman Test | 799 |
| Spearman rank correlation coefficient | 810 |

## CHAPTER EXERCISES

*The following exercises require the use of a computer and software.* ***Use a 5% significance level.***

**19.118** Xr19-118 Are education and income related? To answer this question, a random sample of people was selected and each was asked to indicate into which of the following categories of education they belonged:

1. Less than high school
2. High school graduate
3. Some college or university but no degree
4. University degree
5. Postgraduate degree

Additionally, respondents were asked for their annual income group from the following choices:

1. Under $25,000
2. $25,000 up to but not including $40,000
3. $40,000 up to but not including $60,000
4. $60,000 up to $100,000
5. Greater than $100,000

Conduct a test to determine whether more education and higher incomes are linked.

**19.119** Xr19-119 In a study to determine which of two teaching methods is perceived to be better, two sections of an introductory marketing course were taught in different ways by the same professor. At the course's completion, each student rated the course on a boring/stimulating spectrum, with 1 = Very boring, 2 = Somewhat boring, 3 = A little boring, 4 = Neither boring nor stimulating, 5 = A little stimulating, 6 = Somewhat stimulating, and 7 = Very stimulating. Can we conclude that the ratings of the two teaching methods differ?

**19.120** Xr19-120 The researchers at a large carpet manufacturer have been experimenting with a new dyeing process in hopes of reducing the streakiness that frequently occurs with the current process. As an experiment, 15 carpets are dyed using the new process, and another 15 are dyed using the existing method. Each carpet is rated on a 5-point scale of streakiness, where 5 is Extremely streaky, 4 is Quite streaky, 3 is Somewhat streaky, 2 is A little streaky, and 1 is Not streaky at all. Is there enough evidence to infer that the new method is better?

**19.121** Xr19-121 The editor of the student newspaper was in the process of making some major changes in the newspaper's layout. He was also contemplating changing the typeface of the print used. To help make a decision, he set up an experiment in which 20 individuals were asked to read four newspaper pages, with each page printed in a different typeface. If the reading speed differed, the typeface that was read fastest would be used. However, if there was not enough evidence to allow the editor to conclude that such differences exist, the current typeface would be continued. The times (in seconds) to completely read one page were recorded. We have determined that the times are not normally distributed. Determine the course of action the editor should follow. (This exercise is identical to Exercise 14.116, except in this exercise, the data are not normally distributed.)

**19.122** Xr19-122 Large potential profits for pharmaceutical companies exist in the area of hair growth drugs. The head chemist for a large pharmaceutical company is conducting experiments to determine which of two new drugs is more effective in growing hair among balding men. One experiment was conducted as follows. A total of 30 pairs of men—each pair of which was matched according to their degree of baldness—was selected. One man used drug A, and the other used drug B. After 10 weeks, the men's new hair growth was examined, and the new growth was judged using the following ratings:

0 = No growth
1 = Some growth
2 = Moderate growth

Do these data provide sufficient evidence that drug B is more effective?

**19.123** Xr19-123 Suppose that a precise measuring device for new hair growth has been developed and is used in the experiment described in Exercise 19.122. The percentages of new hair growth for the 30 pairs of men involved in the experiment were recorded. Do these data allow the chemist to conclude that drug B is more effective?

**19.124** Xr19-124 The printing department of a publishing company wants to determine whether there are differences in durability between three types of book bindings. Twenty-five books with each type of binding were selected and placed in machines that continually opened and closed them. The numbers of openings and closings until the pages separated from the binding were recorded.

a. What techniques should be considered to determine whether differences exist between the types of bindings? What are the required conditions? How do you decide which technique to use?
b. If we know that the number of openings and closings is not normally distributed, test to determine whether differences exist between the types of bindings.

**19.125** Xr19-125 In recent years, consumers have become more safety conscious, particularly about children's products. A manufacturer of children's pajamas is looking for material that is as nonflammable as possible. In an experiment to compare a new fabric with the kind now being used, 50 pieces of each kind were exposed to an open flame, and the number of seconds until the fabric burst into flames was recorded. Because the new material is much more expensive than the current material, the manufacturer will switch only if the new material can be shown to be better. On the basis of these data, what should the manufacturer do?

**19.126** Xr19-126 Samuel's is a chain of family restaurants. Like many other service companies, Samuel's surveys its customers on a regular basis to monitor their opinions. Two questions (among others) asked in the survey are as follows:

a. While you were at Samuel's, did you find the service Slow (1), Moderate (2), or Fast (3)?
b. What day was your visit to Samuel's?

The responses of a random sample of 269 customers were recorded. Can the manager infer that there are differences in customer perceptions of the speed of service between the days of the week?

**19.127** Xr19-127 An advertising firm wants to determine the relative effectiveness of two recently produced commercials for a car dealership. An important attribute of such commercials is their believability. To judge this aspect of the commercials, 60 people were randomly selected. Each watched both commercials and then rated them on a 5-point scale (where 1 = Not believable, 2 = Somewhat believable, 3 = Moderately believable, 4 = Quite believable, and 5 = Very believable). Do these data provide sufficient evidence to indicate that there are differences in believability between the two commercials?

**19.128** Xr19-128 Researchers at the U.S. National Institute of Aging in Bethesda, Maryland, have been studying hearing loss. They have hypothesized that as men age they will lose their hearing faster than comparably aged women because many more men than women have worked at jobs where noise levels have been excessive. To test their beliefs, the researchers randomly selected one man and one woman aged 45, 46, 47, . . . , 78, 79, 80 and measured the percentage hearing loss for each person. What conclusions can be drawn from these data?

**19.129** Xr19-129 In a Gallup poll this year, 200 people were asked, "Do you feel that the newspaper you read most does a good job of presenting the news?" The same question was asked of another 200 people 10 years ago. The possible responses were as follows:

3 = Good job
2 = Fair job
1 = Not a good job

Do these data provide enough evidence to infer that people perceive newspapers as doing a better job 10 years ago than today?

**19.130** Xr10-130 It is common practice in many MBA programs to require applicants to arrange for a letter of reference. Some universities have their own forms in which referees assess the applicant using the following categories:

5: The candidate is in the top 5% of applicants.
4: The candidate is in the top 10% of applicants, but not in the top 5%.
3: The candidate is in the top 25% of applicants, but not in the top 10%.
2: The candidate is in the top 50% of applicants, but not in the top 25%.
1: The candidate is in the bottom 50% of applicants.

However, the question arises, Are the referees' ratings related to how well the applicant performs in the MBA program? To answer the question, a random sample of recently graduated MBAs was drawn. For each, the rating of the referee and the MBA grade-point average (GPA) were recorded. Do these data present sufficient evidence to infer that the letter of reference and the MBA GPA are related?

**19.131** Xr19-131 The increasing number of traveling businesswomen represents a large potential clientele for the hotel industry. Many hotel chains have made changes designed to attract more women. To help direct these changes, a hotel chain commissioned a study to determine whether major differences exist between male and female business travelers. A total of 100 male and 100 female executives were questioned on a variety of topics, one of which was the number of trips they had taken in the previous 12 months. We would like to know whether these data provide enough evidence to allow us to conclude that businesswomen and businessmen differ in the number of business trips taken per year.

**19.132** Xr19-132 To examine the effect that a tough midterm test has on student evaluations of professors, a statistics professor had her class evaluate her teaching effectiveness before the midterm test. The questionnaire asked for opinions on a number of dimensions, but the last question is considered the most important. It is, "How would you rate the overall performance of the instructor?" The possible responses are 1 = poor, 2 = fair, 3 = good, and 4 = excellent. After a difficult test, the evaluation was redone. The evaluation scores before and after the test for each of the 40 students in the class were recorded. Do the data allow the professor to conclude that the results of the midterm negatively influence student opinion?

**19.133** Xr19-133 The town of Stratford, Ontario, is very much dependent on the Shakespearean Festival it holds every summer for its financial well-being. Thousands of people visit Stratford to attend one or more Shakespearean plays and spend money in hotels, restaurants, and gift shops. As a consequence, any sign that the number of visitors will decrease in the future is cause for concern. Two years ago, a survey of 100 visitors asked how likely it was that they would return within the next 2 years. This year the survey was repeated with another 100 visitors. The likelihood of returning within 2 years was measured as:

4 = Very likely
3 = Somewhat likely
2 = Somewhat unlikely
1 = Very unlikely

Conduct whichever statistical procedures you deem necessary to determine whether the citizens of Stratford should be concerned about the results of the two surveys.

**19.134** Xr19-134 Scientists have been studying the effects of lead in children's blood, bones, and tissue for a number of years. It is known that lead reduces intelligence and can cause a variety of other problems. A study directed by Dr. Herman Needleman, a psychiatrist at the University of Pittsburgh Medical Center, examined some of these problems. Two hundred boys attending public schools in Pittsburgh were recruited. Each boy was categorized as having low or high levels of lead in their bones. Each boy was then assessed by his teachers on a 4-point scale (where 1 = low, 2 = moderate, 3 = high, and 4 = extreme) on degrees of aggression. Is there evidence to infer that boys with high levels of lead are more aggressive than boys with low levels of lead?

**19.135** Xr19-135 How does gender affect teaching evaluations? Several researchers addressed this question during the past decade. In one study several female and male professors in the same department with similar backgrounds were selected. A random sample of 100 female students was drawn. Each student evaluated a female professor and a male professor. A sample of 100 male students was drawn and each also evaluated a female professor and a male professor. The ratings were based on a 4-point scale (where 1 = Poor, 2 = Fair, 3 = Good, and 4 = Excellent). The evaluations were recorded in the following way:

Column 1 = Female student
Column 2 = Female professor rating
Column 3 = Male professor rating
Column 4 = Male student
Column 5 = Female professor rating
Column 6 = Male professor rating

a. Can we infer that female students rate female professors higher than they rate male professors?
b. Can we infer that male students rate male professors higher than they rate female professors?

**19.136** Xr19-136 It is an unfortunate fact of life that the characteristics that one is born with play a critical role in later life. For example, race is a critical factor in almost all aspects of North American life. Height and weight also determine how friends, teachers, employers, and customers will treat you. And now we may add physical attractiveness to this list. A recent study followed the careers of students from a prestigious U.S. law school. A panel of independent raters examined the graduation yearbook photos of the students and rated their appearance as unattractive, neither attractive nor unattractive, or attractive. The annual incomes in thousands of dollars 5 years after graduation were recorded. Assuming that incomes are not normally distributed, can we infer that incomes of lawyers are affected by physical attractiveness?

**19.137** Xr19-137 According to a CNN news report 9% of full-time workers telecommute. This means that they do not work in their employers' offices but instead perform their work at home using a computer and modem. To ascertain whether such workers are more satisfied than their nontelecommuting counterparts, a study was undertaken. A random sample of telecommuters and regular office workers was taken. Each was asked how satisfied they were with their current employment. The responses are 1 = Very unsatisfied, 2 = Somewhat unsatisfied, 3 = Somewhat satisfied, and 4 = Very satisfied. What conclusions can we draw from these data?

**19.138** Xr19-138 How does alcohol affect judgment? To provide some insight, an experiment was conducted. A random sample of customers of an Ohio club was selected. Each respondent was asked to assess the attractiveness of members of the opposite sex who were in the club at the time. The assessment was to be made on a 5-point scale (where 1 = Very unattractive, 2 = Unattractive, 3 = Neither attractive nor unattractive, 4 = Attractive, and 5 = Very attractive). The survey was conducted 3 hours before closing and again just before closing using another group of respondents. Can we conclude that the assessments made just before closing are higher than those made 3 hours earlier? If so, what does this imply about the effects of alcohol on judgment?

**19.139** Xr19-139 Can you become addicted to exercise? In a study conducted at the University of Wisconsin at Madison, a random sample of dedicated exercisers who usually work out every day was drawn. Each completed a questionnaire that gauged their mood on a 5-point scale (where 5 = Very relaxed and happy, 4 = Somewhat relaxed and happy, 3 = Neutral feeling, 2 = Tense and anxious, and 1 = Very tense and anxious). The group was then instructed to abstain from all workouts for the next 3 days. Moreover, they were told to be as physically inactive as possible. Each day their mood was measured using the same questionnaire. Column 1 stores the code identifying the respondent and columns 2 through 5 store the measures of mood for the day before the experiment began and for the 3 days of the experiment, respectively.

a. Can we infer that for each day the exercisers abstained from physical activity they were less happy than when they were exercising?
b. Do the data indicate that by the third day moods were improving?
c. Draw two possible conclusions from your findings.

## CASE 19.1 Customer Ratings of an Automobile Service Center

Dmitry Kalinovsky/Shutterstock.com

DATA CA19-01

A number of retailers regularly survey their customers to determine among other things, whether they were happy with their purchase or service and whether they intended to return. A chain of hardware stores/automobile service centers is one such company. At the completion of repair work customers are asked to fill out the following form:

A random sample of 134 responses was drawn. The responses to questions 1 through 4 (1 = poor, 2 = fair, 3 = good, 4 = very good) are stored in columns 1 through 4, respectively. Responses to question 5 (2 = yes, 1 = no) are stored in column 5. Column 6 stores a 1 if a positive comment was made, 2 if a negative comment was made, and 3 if no comment was made.

a. Can we infer that those who say they will return assess each category higher than those who will not return?

b. Is there sufficient evidence to infer that those who make positive comments, negative comments, and no comments differ in their assessment of each category?

c. Prepare a presentation for the company's executives describing your analysis.

Tell us what you think.

| Are You Satisfied? | Very Good | Good | Fair | Poor |
|---|---|---|---|---|
| 1. Quality of work performed | | | | |
| 2. Fairness of price | | | | |
| 3. Explanation of work and guarantee | | | | |
| 4. Checkout process | | | | |
| 5. Will return in future | | | | |

Comments? YES NO

# APPENDIX 19 REVIEW OF STATISTICAL INFERENCE (CHAPTERS 12 TO 19)

Although there are four more chapters to go in this book, we have completed our presentation of statistical inference. (The remaining techniques—times-series analysis and forecasting, statistical process control, and decision analysis—address different kinds of problems, which tend to be easy to identify.) The list of statistical techniques in Table A19.1 and the flowchart in Figure A19.1 now contain all the statistical inference methods presented in this book. Use them to determine how each of the exercises is to be addressed. Because these exercises were drawn from a wide variety of applications and collectively require the use of all the techniques introduced in this book, they provide the same kind of challenge faced by real statistics practitioners. By attempting to solve these problems, you will be getting realistic exposure to statistical applications. Incidentally, this also provides practice in the approach required to succeed in a statistics course examination.

TABLE **A19.1** **Summary of Statistical Techniques in Chapters 12 to 19**

**Problem objective:** Describe a population.

**Data type:** Interval

**Descriptive measurement:** Central location

Parameter: $\mu$

Test statistic: $t = \dfrac{\bar{x} - \mu}{s/\sqrt{n}}$

Interval estimator: $\bar{x} \pm t_{\alpha/2}\dfrac{s}{\sqrt{n}}$

Required condition: Population is normal.

**Descriptive measurement:** Variability

Parameter: $\sigma^2$

TABLE **A19.1** ***(Continued)***

Test statistic: $\chi^2 = \frac{(n-1)s^2}{\sigma^2}$

Interval estimator: LCL $= \frac{(n-1)s^2}{\chi^2_{\alpha/2}}$ UCL $= \frac{(n-1)s^2}{\chi^2_{1-\alpha/2}}$

Required condition: Population is normal.

**Data type:** Nominal

**Number of categories:** Two

Parameter: $p$

Test statistic: $z = \frac{\hat{p} - p}{\sqrt{p(1-p)/n}}$

Interval estimator: $\hat{p} \pm z_{\alpha/2}\sqrt{\hat{p}(1-\hat{p})/n}$

Required condition: $np \geq 5$ and $n(1-p) \geq 5$ (for test)

$n\hat{p} \geq 5$ and $n(1-\hat{p}) \geq 5$ for estimate

**Number of categories:** Two or more

Parameters: $p_1, p_2, \ldots, p_k$

Statistical technique: Chi-squared goodness-of-fit

Test statistic: $\chi^2 = \sum \frac{(f_i - e_i)^2}{e_i}$

Required condition: $e_i \geq 5$

**Problem objective:** Compare two populations.

**Data type:** Interval

**Descriptive measurement:** Central location

**Experimental design:** Independent samples

**Population variances:** $\sigma_1^2 = \sigma_2^2$

Parameter: $\mu_1 - \mu_2$

Test statistic: $t = \frac{(\bar{x}_1 - \bar{x}_2) - (\mu_1 - \mu_2)}{\sqrt{s_p^2\left(\frac{1}{n_1} + \frac{1}{n_2}\right)}}$

Interval estimator: $(\bar{x}_1 - \bar{x}_2) \pm t_{\alpha/2}\sqrt{s_p^2\left(\frac{1}{n_1} + \frac{1}{n_2}\right)}$

Required condition: Populations are normal.

If populations are nonnormal, apply the Wilcoxon Rank Sum Test.

**Population variances:** $\sigma_1^2 \neq \sigma_2^2$

Parameter: $\mu_1 - \mu_2$

Test statistic: $t = \frac{(\bar{x}_1 - \bar{x}_2) - (\mu_1 - \mu_2)}{\sqrt{\left(\frac{s_1^2}{n_1} + \frac{s_2^2}{n_2}\right)}}$

Interval estimator: $(\bar{x}_1 - \bar{x}_2) \pm t_{\alpha/2}\sqrt{\left(\frac{s_1^2}{n_1} + \frac{s_2^2}{n_2}\right)}$

*(Continued)*

TABLE **A19.1** ***(Continued)***

Required condition: Populations are normal.

**Experimental design:** Matched pairs

Parameter: $\mu_D$

Test statistic: $t = \dfrac{\bar{x}_D - \mu_D}{s_D/\sqrt{n_D}}$

Interval estimator: $\bar{x}_D \pm t_{\alpha/2}\dfrac{s_D}{\sqrt{n_D}}$

Required condition: Differences are normal.

If differences are nonnormal, apply Wilcoxon Signed Rank Sum Test.

Nonparametric technique: Wilcoxon Signed Rank Sum Test

Test statistic: $z = \dfrac{T - E(T)}{\sigma_T}$

Required condition: Populations are identical in shape and spread.

**Descriptive measurement:** Variability

Parameter: $\sigma_1^2/\sigma_2^2$

Test statistic: $F = \dfrac{s_1^2}{s_2^2}$

Interval estimator: LCL $= \left(\dfrac{s_1^2}{s_2^2}\right)\dfrac{1}{F_{\alpha/2,\nu_1,\nu_2}}$ UCL $= \left(\dfrac{s_1^2}{s_2^2}\right)F_{\alpha/2,\nu_2,\nu_1}$

Required condition: Populations are normal.

**Data type:** Ordinal

**Experimental design:** Independent samples

Nonparametric technique: Wilcoxon Rank Sum Test

Test statistic: $z = \dfrac{T - E(T)}{\sigma_T}$

Required condition: Populations are identical in shape and spread.

**Experimental design:** Matched pairs

Nonparametric technique: Sign test

Test statistic: $z = \dfrac{x - .5n}{.5\sqrt{n}}$

Required condition: Populations are identical in shape and spread.

**Data type:** Nominal

**Number of categories:** Two

Parameter: $p_1 - p_2$

Test statistic:

Case 1: $H_0$: $p_1 - p_2 = 0$ $\quad z = \dfrac{(\hat{p}_1 - \hat{p}_2)}{\sqrt{\hat{p}(1-\hat{p})\left(\dfrac{1}{n_1} + \dfrac{1}{n_2}\right)}}$

Case 2: $H_0$: $p_1 - p_2 = D$ $(D \neq 0)$ $z = \dfrac{(\hat{p}_1 - \hat{p}_2) - (p_1 - p_2)}{\sqrt{\dfrac{\hat{p}_1(1-\hat{p}_1)}{n_1} + \dfrac{\hat{p}_2(1-\hat{p}_2)}{n_2}}}$

TABLE **A19.1** ***(Continued)***

Interval estimator: $(\hat{p}_1 - \hat{p}_2) \pm z_{\alpha/2}\sqrt{\frac{\hat{p}_1(1-\hat{p}_1)}{n_1} + \frac{\hat{p}_2(1-\hat{p}_2)}{n_2}}$

Required condition: $n_1\hat{p}_1$, $n_1(1-\hat{p}_1)$, $n_2\hat{p}_2$, and $n_2(1-\hat{p}_2) \geq 5$

**Number of categories:** Two or more

Statistical technique: Chi-squared test of a contingency table

Test statistic: $\chi^2 = \sum \frac{(f_i - e_i)^2}{e_i}$

Required condition: $e_i \geq 5$

**Problem objective:** Compare two or more populations.

**Data type:** Interval

**Experimental design:** Independent samples

**Number of factors:** One

Parameters: $\mu_1, \mu_2, \ldots, \mu_k$

Statistical technique: (One-way analysis of variance)

Test statistic: $F = \frac{\text{MST}}{\text{MSE}}$

Statistical technique: Multiple comparisons:

Fisher and Bonferroni adjustment: $\text{LSD} = t_{\alpha/2}\sqrt{\text{MSE}\left(\frac{1}{n_i} + \frac{1}{n_j}\right)}$

Tukey: $\omega = q_\alpha(k, \nu)\sqrt{\frac{\text{MSE}}{n_g}}$

Required conditions: Populations are normal with equal variances. If populations are nonnormal, apply the Kruskal–Wallis Test.

**Number of factors:** Two

Parameters: $\mu_1, \mu_2, \ldots, \mu_k$

Statistical technique: (Two-factor analysis of variance)

Test statistics: $F = \frac{\text{MS(AB)}}{\text{MSE}}$ $F = \frac{\text{MS(A)}}{\text{MSE}}$ $F = \frac{\text{MS(B)}}{\text{MSE}}$

Required conditions: Populations are normal with equal variances.

**Experimental design:** Randomized blocks

Parameters: $\mu_1, \mu_2, \ldots, \mu_k$

Statistical technique: (Two-way analysis of variance)

Test statistics: $F = \frac{\text{MST}}{\text{MSE}}$ $F = \frac{\text{MSB}}{\text{MSE}}$

Required conditions: Populations are normal with equal variances. If populations are nonnormal, apply the Friedman Test.

**Data type:** Ordinal

**Experimental design:** Independent samples

Nonparametric technique: Kruskal–Wallis Test

Test statistic: $H = \left[\frac{12}{n(n+1)}\sum_{j=1}^{k}\frac{T_j^2}{n_j}\right] - 3(n+1)$

Required condition: Populations are identical in shape and spread and $n_j \geq 5$.

*(Continued)*

TABLE **A19.1** ***(Continued)***

**Experimental design:** Randomized blocks

Nonparametric technique: Friedman Test

Test statistic: $F_r = \left[\frac{12}{b(k)(k+1)}\sum_{j=1}^{k} T_j^2\right] - 3b(k+1)$

Required condition: Populations are identical in shape and spread and $n_j \geq 5$.

**Data type:** Nominal

**Number of categories:** Two or more

Statistical technique: Chi-squared test of a contingency table

Test statistic: $\chi^2 = \sum \frac{(f_i - e_i)^2}{e_i}$

Required condition: $e_i \geq 5$

**Problem objective:** Analyze the relationship between two variables.

**Data type:** Interval

Parameters: $\beta_0, \beta_1, \rho$

Statistical technique: Simple linear regression and correlation

Test statistic: $t = \frac{b_1 - \beta_1}{s_{b_1}}$; $t = r\sqrt{\frac{n-2}{1-r^2}}$

Prediction interval: $\hat{y} \pm t_{\alpha/2,n-2} s_\varepsilon \sqrt{1 + \frac{1}{n} + \frac{(x_g - \bar{x})^2}{(n-1)s_x^2}}$

Interval estimator of expected value: $\hat{y} \pm t_{\alpha/2,n-2} s_\varepsilon \sqrt{\frac{1}{n} + \frac{(x_g - \bar{x})^2}{(n-1)s_x^2}}$

Required conditions: $\varepsilon$ is normally distributed with mean 0 and standard deviation $\sigma_\varepsilon$; $\varepsilon$ values are independent.

To test whether two bivariate normally distributed variables are linearly related:

Parameter: $\rho$

Test statistic: $t = r\sqrt{\frac{n-2}{1-r^2}}$

If $x$ and $y$ are not bivariate normally distributed, apply the Spearman rank correlation coefficient test.

**Data type:** Ordinal

Statistical technique: Spearman rank correlation coefficient test

Parameter: $\rho_s$

Test statistic: $z = r_s\sqrt{n-1}$

Required condition: none

**Data type:** Nominal

Statistical technique: Chi-squared test of a contingency table

Test statistic: $\chi^2 = \sum \frac{(f_i - e_i)^2}{e_i}$

Required condition: $e_i \geq 5$

**Problem objective:** Analyze the relationship among two or more variables.

TABLE **A19.1** ***(Continued)***

**Data type:** Interval

Parameters: $\beta_0, \beta_1, \beta_2, \ldots, \beta_k$

Statistical technique: multiple regression

Test statistics: $t = \dfrac{b_i - \beta_i}{s_{b_i}} (i = 1, 2, \ldots, k); \quad F = \dfrac{\text{MSR}}{\text{MSE}}$

Required conditions: $\varepsilon$ is normally distributed with mean 0 and standard deviation $\sigma_\varepsilon$; $\varepsilon$ values are independent.

FIGURE **A19.1** **Flowchart of All Statistical Inference Techniques**

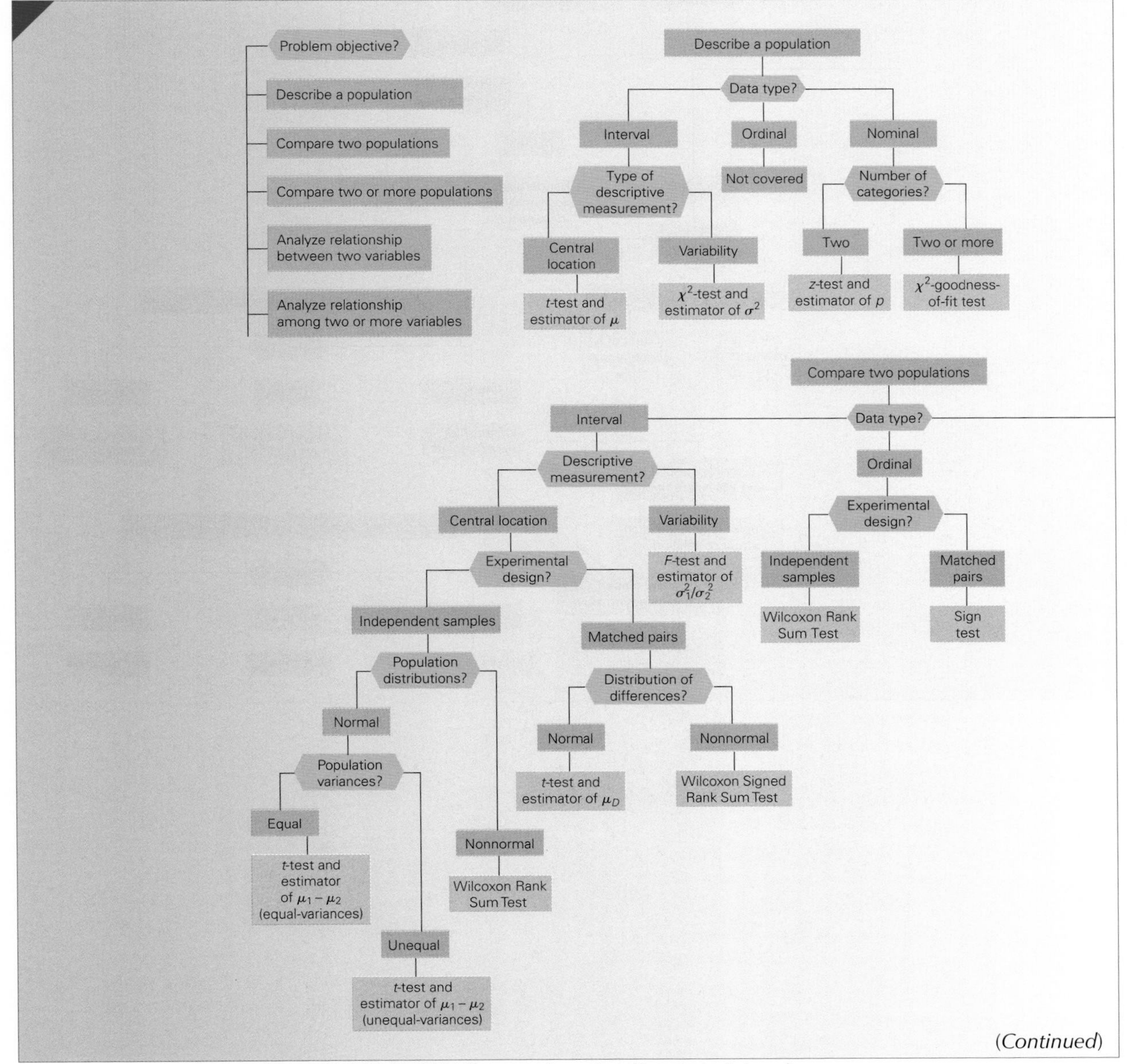


(Continued)

FIGURE **A19.1** ***(Continued)***

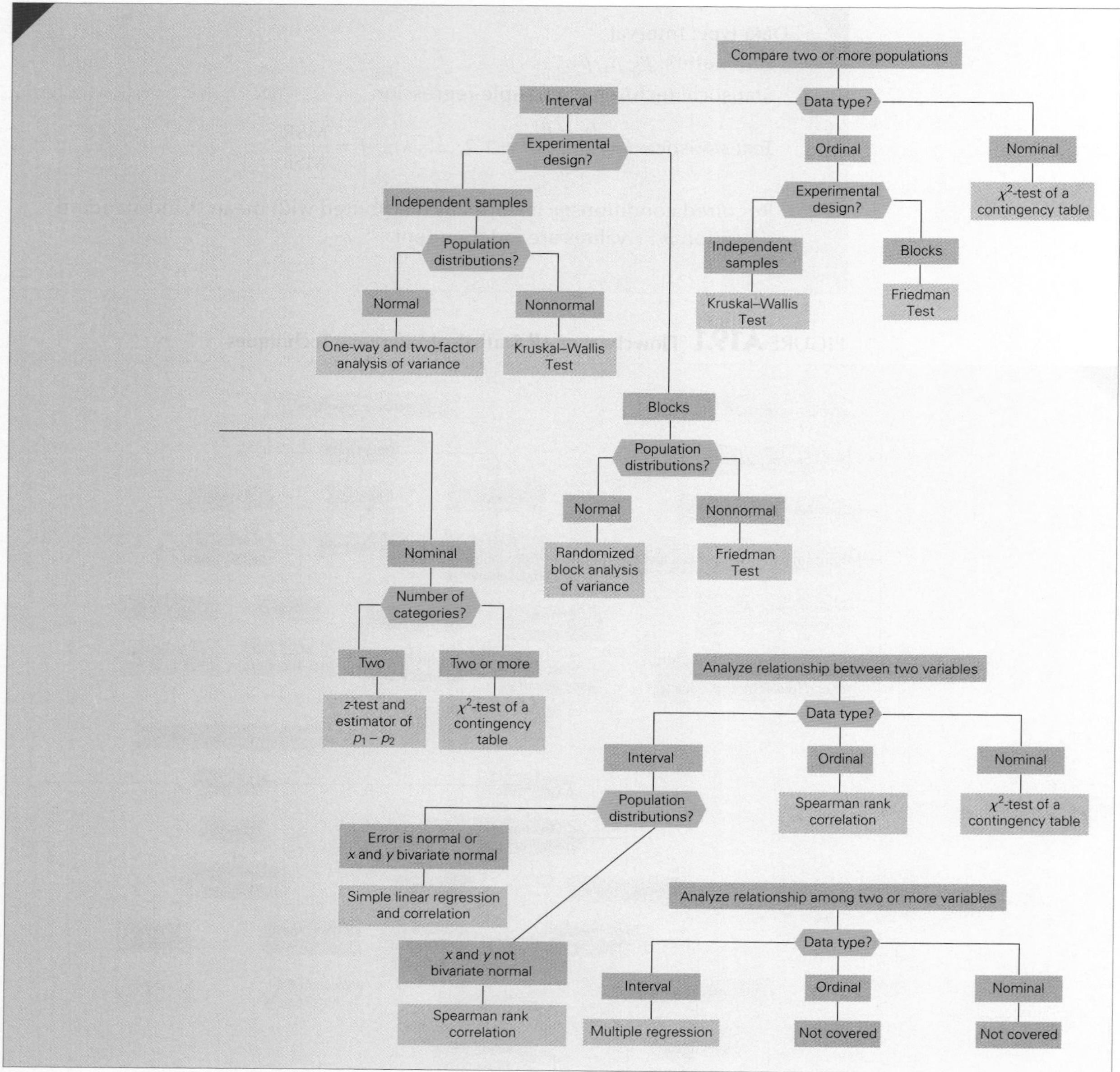

## EXERCISES

**A19.1** XrA19-01 Most supermarkets load groceries into plastic bags. However, plastic bags take many years to decompose in garbage dumps. To determine how big the problem might be, a random sample of American households was each asked to determine the number of plastic bags they use and discard in a week. The last census revealed that there are 112 million households in the United States. Estimate with 95% confidence the total number of plastic bags discarded per week.

*Source:* NBC News May 7, 2007.

**A19.2** XrA19-02 Some customers spend a great deal of time doing research before choosing a particular brand of a product, particularly an expensive product. Does this result in a more satisfied customer? To shed light on this question, a random sample of people who purchased a new car within the last two years was drawn. Each was asked to report the amount of time spent researching (reading newspaper reports and brochures, as well as looking on the Internet) in hours and his or her level of satisfaction measured in the following way:

1. Extremely dissatisfied
2. Somewhat dissatisfied
3. Neither satisfied or dissatisfied
4. Somewhat satisfied
5. Extremely satisfied

Do the data allow us to infer that those who do more research are more satisfied with their choice?

**A19.3** Xr13-36* Refer to Exercise 13.36 where respondents were asked to taste the same wine in two different bottles. The first bottle was capped using a cork, and the second had a metal screw cap. Respondents were also asked to taste the wine and rate it using the following categories.

Poor (1), Fair (2), Good (3), Very good (4), Excellent (5)

Do these data provide sufficient evidence to indicate that wine bottled with a screw cap is perceived to be inferior?

**A19.4** XrA19-04 In an effort to analyze the results of Exercise A15.9, the researcher recorded the total travel length of the course. This variable measures the total distance golfers must walk to play a round of golf. It is the sum of the golf-course playing distance plus the distance golfers must walk from the green to the next tee. What can you conclude from these data?

**A19.5** XrA19-05* In city after city, downtown cores have become less and less populated and poorer because shoppers have taken their money to the suburbs and to shopping malls. One reason often given for the decline in downtown shops is the difficulty in parking. To shed more light on the issue, a random sample of 197 adults was asked to rate the difficulty in parking using the following responses:

Poor (1), Acceptable (2), Good (3), Very good (4), Excellent (5)

These adults were also asked how often they shopped at a downtown store in a typical month. Do these data allow us to infer that the problem of parking is one reason for the decline in downtown shopping?

**A19.6** XrA19-05* Refer to A19.5. To acquire information about who is shopping downtown, the statistics practitioner also recorded the annual household income (in $1,000s) of the respondents. Is there enough evidence to infer that affluent people shop downtown more frequently than poorer people? (The author is grateful to Patricia Gafoor-Darlington and Michael Kirby-MacLean for writing these exercises.)

**A19.7** XrA19-07 Why do some students do well in university while others struggle? To help answer this question, a random sample of first-year students at four universities was selected. Those who had a grade point average of more than 3.0 (group 1) and those who had a grade point average of less than 2.0 (group 2) were surveyed. For each student, researchers recorded the results of tests (scored 0 to 10) that measure the following.

Interpersonal skills (strong social skills, ability to interact effectively)
Stress management (being able to work well under pressure or resist and delay an impulse)

Do these data provide sufficient evidence to infer that students whose GPA is more than 3.0 score higher in interpersonal skills and stress management than students whose GPA is less than 2.0?

*Source: National Post*, August 16, 2004.

**A19.8** XrA19-08 The issue of immigration, legal and illegal, has political and economic ramifications. An important component of the issue is how well immigrants integrate into the American economy. A University of Florida study attempted to answer this question. Researchers randomly surveyed U.S.-born Americans, immigrants who arrived in the United States before 1980, and immigrants who arrived after 1980 in Miami-Dade County, the state of Florida, and the United States. Each respondent was employed full-time and was asked to report his or her annual earnings. Conduct tests to determine whether differences exist between the three groups in each of the three geographic regions.

**A19.9** XrA19-09 The high price of gasoline is likely to lead to less travel. An economist specializing in energy uses wanted to learn more about driving habits, and, in particular, distances traveled by cars, buses, vans, and trucks. In the latest year data were available (2003), there were 136 million cars, 776,000 buses, and 87 million vans, pickups, and SUVs. An economist undertook a survey of each type of vehicle, recording the number of miles driven (in 1,000s). For each type of vehicle, estimate with 95% confidence the mean number of miles driven and the total number of miles driven.

*Source:* U.S. Federal Highway Administration, *Highway Statistics*. Adapted from the *Statistical Abstract of the United States, 2006*, Table 1084.

**A19.10** XrA19-10 Refer to Exercise A19.9. The economist also wanted to know whether there are differences in miles driven between cars, buses, and vans, pickups, and SUVs.

**A19.11** XrA19-11 An important measure of the health of a nation's economy is total debt. A Canadian survey asked a random sample of households how much money (in $1,000s) they owed. This includes mortgages, loans, and credit card debt. Assuming that there are 10 million households in Canada, estimate with 95% confidence the total debt in Canada.

**A19.12** XrA19-12 In Chapter 7, we showed that diversification reduces the risk associated with a portfolio of investments. (Most experts advise their clients that the portfolios should contain between 20 and 30 stocks scattered in different industries.) Do investors understand this concept? To help answer this question, a random sample of investors' portfolios was sampled. This survey was a duplicate of the one done 5 years earlier. The number of stocks in each sampled portfolio was recorded. Do these data allow us to infer that investors' portfolios are becoming more diverse?

*Source:* Adapted from W. Goetzman and A. Kumar, "Equity Portfolio Diversification," NBER Paper 8686.

**A19.13** XrA19-13 The cost of taking an extra year to earn an MBA is quite high. To determine whether it is worthwhile, a BBA graduate surveyed 200 people who had either a BBA or an MBA and recorded their annual salary (in $1,000s) after 5 years of work. The student determined that the added cost of the MBA is warranted only if the mean income of MBAs is more than $5, 000 greater than that of BBAs. Can we conclude that acquiring an MBA is worthwhile?

**A19.14** XrA19-14 Flonase is a nasal allergy treatment; like all drugs, it has side effects. Before approving it, the company (GlaxoSmithKline) performs a number of experiments to determine the drug's side effects. In one such experiment, a random sample of 1,707 volunteers was drawn. Of these, 167 were given a 100-mcg dose once a day (1), 782 were given 200 mcg daily (2), and the remaining 758 were given a placebo spray once a day (3). Each person reported whether he or she had any side effects and, if so, which was the most serious. The following data were recorded.

1. Headache
2. Pharyngitis (sore throat)
3. Epistaxis (nosebleed)
4. Other side effect
5. No side effect

Do these data allow us to infer that there are differences in side effects between the three groups of volunteers?

**A19.15** XrA19-15 Simco Inc. is a manufacturer that purchased a new piece of equipment designed to reduce costs. After several months of operation, the results were quite unsatisfactory. The operations manager believes that the problem lies with the machine's operators, who were unable to master the required skills. It was decided to establish a training program to upgrade the skills of those workers with the greatest likelihood of success. To do so, the company needed to know which skills are most needed to run the machine. Experts identified six such skills: dexterity, attention to detail, teamwork skills, mathematical ability, problem-solving skills, and technical knowledge. To examine the issue, a random sample of workers was drawn. Workers were measured on each of the six skills through a series of paper-and-pencil tests and through supervisor ratings. In addition, each worker received a score on the quality of his or her actual work on the machine. These data are stored in columns 1 through 7. (Column 1 stores the quality-of-work scores, and columns 2 to 7 are the scores on the skill tests. All data are interval.) Identify the skills that affect the quality of work. (We are grateful to Scott Bergen for writing this exercise.)

**A19.16** XrA19-16 Obesity among children in North America is said to be at near-epidemic proportions. Some experts blame television for the problem, citing the statistic that children watch an average of 26 hours per week. During this time, children are not engaged in any physical activity, which results in weight gains. However, the problem may be compounded by a reduction in metabolic rate. In an experiment to address this issue (the study results were published in the February 1993 issue of the medical journal *Pediatrics*), scientists from Memphis State University and the University of Tennessee at Memphis took a random sample of 223 children aged 8 to 12; 41 of them were obese. Each child's metabolic rate (the amount of calories burned per hour) was measured while at rest and also measured while the child watched a television program (*The Wonder Years*). The differences between the two rates were recorded; column 1 contains the numbers representing the decrease in metabolic rate, and column 2 codes the children as 1 = obese and 2 = nonobese.

a. Do these data allow us to conclude that there is a decrease in metabolism when children watch television?
b. Can we conclude that the decrease in metabolism while watching television is greater among obese children?

**A19.17** XrA19-17 Scrabble is one of the oldest and most popular board games. It is played all over the world, and there is even an annual world championship competition. The game is played by forming words and placing them on the board to obtain the maximum number of points. It is generally believed that a large vocabulary is the only skill required to be successful. However, there is a strategic element to the game that suggests that mathematical skills are just as necessary. To determine which skills are most in demand, a statistician recruited a random sample of fourth-year university English and mathematics majors and asked them to play the game. A total of 500 games was played by different pairs of English and mathematics majors. The scores in each game were recorded. (The authors would like to thank Scott Bergen for his assistance in writing this exercise.)

a. Can we conclude that mathematics majors win more frequently than do English majors?
b. Do these data allow us to infer that the average score obtained by English majors is greater than that for mathematics majors?
c. Why are the results of Parts (a) and (b) not the same?

**A19.18** XrA19-18 Ever since the discovery of germs, parents have been telling their children to wash their hands. Common sense tells us that this should help minimize the spread of infectious diseases and lead to better health. A study reported in the *University of California at Berkeley Wellness Letter* (volume 13, issue 6, March 1997) may confirm the advice our parents gave us. A study in Michigan tracked a random sample of children, some of whom washed their hands four or more times during the school day. The number of sick days from colds and flu and the number of sick days from stomach illness were recorded for the past year. Column 1 contains a code representing whether the child washed his or her hands four or more times per school day (1) or not (2). Column 2 stores the number of sick days from cold and flu and column 3 contains the number of sick days from stomach illness.

a. Do these data allow us to infer that a child who washed his or her hands four or more times during the school day will have fewer sick days from cold and flu than other children?
b. Repeat Part (a) for sick days from stomach illness.

**A19.19** XrA19-19 Under the rules of Canada's Employment Insurance (EI) plan, some workers can use EI repeatedly after working only a short time. The amount of time needed to qualify for EI varies by region and by occupation. In a study undertaken by researchers, regular users of EI were surveyed and asked, among other questions, how frequently they used EI and how satisfied they were with their employment situation. The responses are

1. Very unsatisfied
2. Somewhat unsatisfied
3. Neither unsatisfied or satisfied
4. Somewhat satisfied
5. Very satisfied

Do the data allow us to conclude that workers who use EI more often are more satisfied with their employment situation?

*Source: National Post Business,* July 2001.

**A19.20** XrA19-20 Winter is the influenza season in North America. Each winter, thousands of elderly and sick people die from the flu and its attendant complications. Consequently, many elderly people receive flu shots in the fall. It has generally been accepted that young healthy North Americans need not receive flu shots because, although many contract the disease, few die from it. However, there are economic consequences. Sick days cost both employees and employers. A study published in the *New England Journal of Medicine* reported the results of an experiment to determine whether it is useful for young healthy people to take flu shots. A random sample of working adults was selected. Half received a flu shot in November; the other half received a placebo. The numbers of sick days over the next 6-month period were recorded in columns 1 (flu shot) and 2 (placebo). Columns 3 (flu shot) and 4 (placebo) contain the number of visits to the doctor.

a. Can we conclude that those who take flu shots have fewer sick days?
b. Can we conclude that those who take flu shots visit their doctors less frequently?

**A19.21** XrA19-21 The high cost of medical care makes it imperative that hospitals operate efficiently and effectively. As part of a larger study, patients leaving a hospital were surveyed. They were asked how satisfied they were with the treatment they received. The responses were recorded with a measure of the degree of severity of their illness (as determined by the admitting physician) and the length of stay. These data are recorded in the following way:

Column 1: Satisfaction level (1 = very unsatisfied; 2 = somewhat unsatisfied; 3 = neither satisfied nor dissatisfied; 4 = somewhat satisfied; 5 = very satisfied)
Column 2: Severity of illness (1 = least severe and 10 = most severe)
Column 3: Number of days in hospital

a. Is the satisfaction level affected by the severity of illness?
b. Is the satisfaction level higher for patients who stay for shorter periods of time?

**A19.22** XrA19-22 What should be the priority of paramedics who respond to accidents? Should they treat the patients with their limited facilities or should they rush the victims to the nearest hospital (an approach known as "scoop and run")? A research project begun in 1993 may provide the answer. Researchers looked at the care of 1,846 trauma patients—those with life-threatening injuries—in Montreal (1), Toronto (2), and Quebec City (3). Montreal uses physicians to provide advanced life support (ALS) at the scene of the accident. Toronto uses paramedics to provide ALS, and Quebec City uses emergency medical services who apply only basic life support. The outcomes (survived = 1, died = 2) and city were recorded. Determine whether there are differences in the death rate between the three cities. What recommendation would you make?

Source: Adapted from *Annals of Surgery*, 2002. The author is grateful to Jie Hunag for creating this exercise.

**A19.23** XrA19-23 How many golfers are there in the United States? A survey of American adults (age 18 and above) asked whether they had played golf at least once a month during the summer. The responses are 2 = yes and 1 = no. The survey also asked respondents to indicate which of the following household income categories they fell into.

1. Less than $15,000
2. $15,000 to $24,999
3. $25,000 to $34,999
4. $35,000 to $49,999
5. $50,000 to $75, 000
6. More than $75,000

The latest census reveals that the number of American households in each of the income categories is as follows.

1. 75.7 million
2. 36.9 million
3. 28.3 million
4. 27.8 million
5. 21.9 million
6. 17.1 million

a. Estimate with 95% confidence the total number of golfers.
b. For each income category, estimate with 95% confidence the number of golfers who earn at least $75,000.
c. Test to determine whether income is a determinant in who plays golf.

Source: *Statistical Abstract of the United States, 2006*, Tables 685 and 1238.

**A19.24** XrA19-24 One of the arguments put forth by advocates of lower tuition fees is that children of low or moderate income families will not be able to pay for a child's university education. To examine this issue, a random sample of families whose children were at least 20 years old was drawn. Each family was asked to specify which of the following household income categories they fell into and whether at least one child had attended university (2 = yes and 1 = no).

1. Less than $25,000
2. $50,000 to $75,000
3. More than $100,000

Do these data allow researchers to conclude that family income affects whether children attend university?

Source: *Globe and Mail*, Wednesday, October 15, 2003.

**A19.25** XrA19-25 Because of the high cost of hospital stays, anything that can reduce their length and the costs of medication would be appreciated by insurance companies, hospitals, and patients. A physician researcher was searching for ways to reduce costs and decided to investigate the effect of the room the patient stayed in. She gathered data on the length of stay and the amount of pain medication (measured in morphine equivalents). Also recorded was whether the room was sunny or dim. Do these data allow the researcher to conclude that the length of stay and the amount of pain medication is lower in bright rooms than in dim ones?

Source: *USA Today*, Wednesday, March 3, 2004.

## GENERAL SOCIAL SURVEY EXERCISES

***Conduct all tests at the 5% significance level. Use a 95% confidence level for estimates.***

In 2012, there were 221,963,000 Americans aged 21 years or more.

**A19.26** GSS2012* Use an inferential technique to determine whether there is enough evidence to infer that women (SEX: 1 = Male, 2 = Female) are more likely to work for the government (WRKGOVT: 1 = Government, 2 = Private enterprise) than men?

**A19.27** GSS2012* There are some jobs people have for life (university professor comes immediately to mind). But do most people go from one job to another sometimes experiencing unemployment? The General Social survey may have an answer. It asked respondents have they ever experienced unemployment in the 10 years (UNEMP: 1 = Yes). Estimate the total number of people who experienced unemployment in the previous 10 years).

**A19.28** GSS2012* As people age do they believe that government should take no action to reduce income inequality? Conduct a test to determine whether there is enough evidence to infer that older Americans (AGE) are less likely to want government to act (EQWLTH: 1 = Government should reduce differences; 2, 3, 4, 5, 6, 7 = No government action).

**A19.29** GSS2012* Do Americans who want government to improve the standard of living of poor people also want government to help sick people pay doctor and hospital bills? Answer the question by determining whether there is enough evidence to infer that these two variables are positively linearly related: (HELPPOOR: Should government improve standard of living of poor people? 1 = Government act; 2, 3, 4, 5 = People should help themselves) and (HELPSICK: Is it government's responsibility to help pay for doctor and hospital bills? 1 = Government should help; 2, 3, 4, 5 = People should help themselves).

**A19.30** GSS2012* One way of judging the state of the economy is to determine how many hours is the average person working per week. Estimate with 95% confidence the number of hours of work per week for the average person (HRS1).

**A19.31** GSS2012* Who is most educated among the liberals, moderates, and conservatives) (POLVIEWS3: 1 = Liberal, 2 = Moderate, 3 = Conservative)? Conduct a test to determine whether differences in education (EDUC) exist among the three political philosophies.

**A19.32** GSS2012* The survey asked this question. A doctor tells a couple that there is one chance in four that their child will have an inherited disease. Does this mean that if the first child has the illness, the next three will not? (ODDS1: 1 = Yes, 2 = No, 8 = Don't know, 9 = No answer) Estimate the number of Americans who know the correct answer is 2.

**A19.33** GSS2012* The following question was asked. "Is it government's responsibility to help pay for doctor and hospital bills?" (The responses were HELPSICK: 1 = Government should help; 2, 3, 4, 5 = People should help themselves). Can we infer from the data that the responses differ among the three political groups (PARTYID3: 1 = Democrat, 2 = Independent, 3 = Republican)?

**A19.34** GSS2012* Does the amount of education one has affect the number of children (CHILDS)? Conduct a test of the five categories of educational attainment (DEGREE: 0 = Left high school, 1 = High school, 2 = Junior college, 3 = Bachelor's degree, 4 = Graduate) to answer the question.

**A19.35** GSS2012* The survey asked the question, "Do you favor requiring a police permit to buy a gun?" Is there enough evidence to infer that liberals, moderates, and conservatives (POLVIEWS3) differ in their responses to the question (GUNLAW: 1 = Support, 2 = Oppose)?

**A19.36** GSS2012* Do liberals like paying tax and conservative hate it? Or they all the same. Use an appropriate statistical technique to determine whether liberals, moderates, and conservatives (POLVIEWS3) differ in their response to the question, "Federal income tax you pay. . ." (1 = Too high, 2 = About right, 3 = Too low).

**A19.37** GSS2012* Home ownership was always part of the American dream. Estimate the number of Americans who own their own home (DWELOWN: 1 = Own).

**A19.38** GSS2012* Since there are no employers that one needs to impress to get a job we would expect self-employed (WRKSLF: 1 = self-employed, 2 = someone else) people to have less formal education than other workers (EDUC). Is there enough statistical evidence to draw that conclusion?

**A19.39** GSS2012* Can we infer from the data that the majority of Americans support capital punishment for murderers (CAPPUN: 1 = Favor, 2 = Oppose)?

**A19.40** GSS2012* The survey asked respondents :If you were to get enough money to live as comfortably as you would like for the rest of your life, would you continue to work or would you stop working?" Can we infer from the data that more than half would continue working (RICHWORK: 1 = Continue working) ?

**A19.41** GSS2012* Is there a relationship between years of education (EDUC) of people and the years of education of their mothers (MAEDUC)? Use a statistical procedure to answer the question.

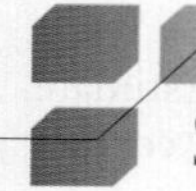

## Survey of Consumer Finances

***Conduct all tests at the 5% significance level. Use a 95% confidence level for estimates.***

**According to the U.S. Census, there were 220,958,853 adults in the United States in 2010.**

**A19.42** SCF2010:\ALL* Is the amount spent of food away from home (FOODAWAY) related to how well educated the head of the household is (EDCL 1 = No high school diploma, 2 = High school diploma, 3 = Some college, 4 = College degree)? Conduct a test to answer the question.

**A19.43** SCF2010:\MC* Do middle-class male heads of households have more invested in the stock market than their female counterparts (HHSEX: 1 = Male, 2 = Female)? Conduct a statistical analysis to determine whether there is enough evidence to infer that males have larger investments in stocks than females (STOCKS).

**A19.44** SCF2010:\ALL* Is the number of people working for themselves a measure of the state of the economy? A large number may mean that a large proportion of the population cannot find a job. Estimate the number of people who are self-employed (OCCAT1: 2 = Self-employed/partnership).

**A19.45** SCF2010:\ALL* Late payments on virtually all loans result in financial penalties. For example, credit card companies often increase their interest rates to around 30% if a customer is late paying their monthly bills. Estimate the number of people who were late in paying their debts in the previous 12 months (LATE: 1).

**A19.46** SCF2010:\UC Students may be surprised to learn that people with high net worth also have large debts. Estimate the mean household debt for members of the upper class (DEBT).

**A19.47** SCF2010:\ALL* One question asked by the survey addressed the issue of whether the household had any debts (DEBT: 1 = Yes). Is there sufficient evidence to infer that male and female heads (HHSEX: 1 = Male, 2 = Female) of households differ?

**A19.48** SCF2010:\ALL* Are there differences between men and women (HHSEX: 1 = Male, 2 = Female) in their choices of employment (OCCAT2 Occupation classification for head of household: 1. Managerial/ professional, 2. Technical/sales/services, 3. other (including production/craft/repair workers, operators. Laborers, farmers, foresters, fishers), 4. Not working)?

**A19.49** SCF2010:\UC* According to the U.S. Census the average family spent $2675 on food away from home (FOODAWAY) eaten at home. Is there enough evidence to infer that the average upper-class household spent more than the average family?

# 20

Nuno Andre/Shutterstock.com

# TIME-SERIES ANALYSIS AND FORECASTING

**CHAPTER OUTLINE**



## Housing Starts

DATA
Xm20-00

iStockphoto.com/stocknroll

**See page 853 for the answer.**

At the end of 2005, a major builder of residential houses in the northeastern United States wanted to predict the number of housing units that would be started in 2006. This information would be extremely useful in determining a variety of variables, including housing demand, availability of labor, and the price of building materials. To help develop an accurate forecasting model, an economist collected data on the number of housing starts (in thousands) for the previous 60 months (2001–2005). Forecast the number of housing starts for the 12 months of 2006. (*Source*: Standard & Poor's Industry Surveys.)*

*We have chosen not to update the housing starts data. In 2008, most of the world's economies were thrown into a recession precipitated by a housing crisis in the United States. As a result, statistical forecasting tools became wildly inaccurate. You can see for yourself how inaccurate by completing Exercise 20.52.

## INTRODUCTION

Any variable that is measured over time in sequential order is called a **time series**. We introduced time series in Chapter 3 and demonstrated how we use a line chart to graphically display the data. Our objective in this chapter is to analyze time series in order to detect patterns that will enable us to forecast future values of the time series. There is an almost unlimited number of such applications in management and economics. Some examples follow.

1. Governments want to know future values of interest rates, unemployment rates, and percentage increases in the cost of living.
2. Housing industry economists must forecast mortgage interest rates, demand for housing, and the cost of building materials.
3. Many companies attempt to predict the demand for their products and their share of the market.
4. Universities and colleges often try to forecast the number of students who will be applying for acceptance at postsecondary-school institutions.

**Forecasting** is a common practice among managers and government decision makers. This chapter focuses on time-series forecasting, which uses historical time-series data to predict future values of variables such as sales or unemployment rates. This entire chapter is an application tool for both economists and managers in all functional areas of business because forecasting is such a vital factor in decision making in these areas.

For example, the starting point for aggregate production planning by operations managers is to forecast the demand for the company's products. These forecasts will make use of economists' forecasts of macroeconomic variables (such as gross domestic product, disposable income, and housing starts) as well as the marketing managers' internal forecasts of their customers' future needs. Not only are these sales forecasts critical to production planning but also they are the key to accurate pro forma (i.e., forecasted) financial statements, which are produced by the accounting and financial managers to assist in their planning for future financial needs such as borrowing. Likewise, the human resources department will find such forecasts of a company's growth prospects to be invaluable in their planning for future worker requirements.

There are many different forecasting techniques. Some are based on developing a model that attempts to analyze the relationship between a dependent variable and one or more independent variables. We presented some of these methods in the chapters on regression analysis (Chapters 16, 17, and 18). The forecasting methods to be discussed in this chapter are all based on time series, which we discuss in the next section. In Sections 20-2 and 20-3, we deal with methods for detecting and measuring which time-series components exist. After we uncover this information, we can develop forecasting tools. We will only scratch the surface of this topic. Our objective is to expose you to the concepts of forecasting and to introduce some of the simpler techniques. The level of this text precludes the investigation of more complicated methods.

## 20-1 Time-Series Components

A time series can consist of four different components as described in the box.

**Time-Series Components**

1. Long-term trend
2. Cyclical variation
3. Seasonal variation
4. Random variation

A **trend** (also known as a **secular trend**) is a long-term, relatively smooth pattern or direction exhibited by a series. Its duration is more than 1 year. For example, the population of the United States exhibited a trend of relatively steady growth from 157 million in 1952 to 314 million in 2012. (The data are stored in Ch20:\Fig20-01.) Figure 20.1 exhibits the line chart.

FIGURE **20.1** **U.S. Population (millions), 1952–2012**

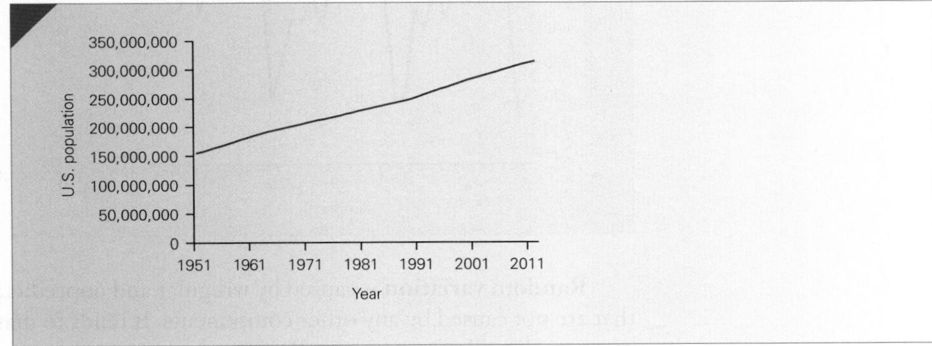


The trend of a time series is not always linear. For example, Figure 20.2 describes U.S annual retail book sales in $millions. As you can see, sales increased from 1992 to 2008 and has decreased since then (data are stored in Ch20:\Fig20-02).

FIGURE **20.2** **U.S. Annual Retail Book Sales ($millions)**

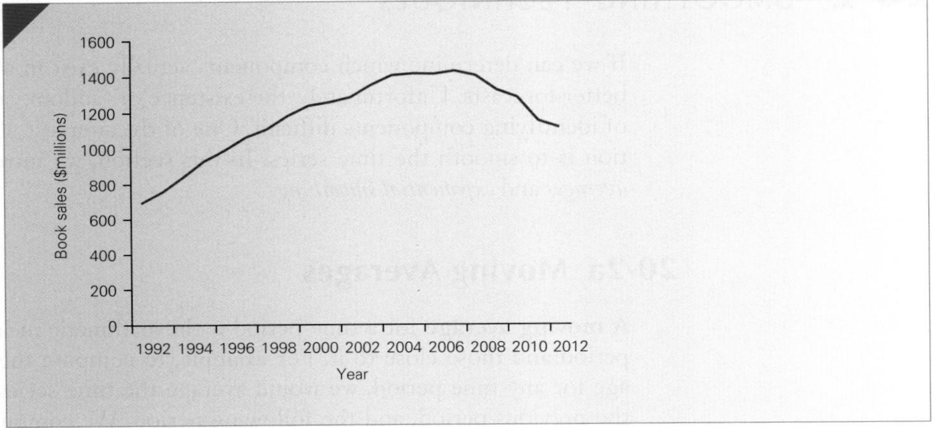

**Cyclical variation** is a wavelike pattern describing a long-term trend that is generally apparent over a number of years, resulting in a cyclical effect. By definition, it has duration of more than 1 year. Examples include business cycles that record periods of economic recession and inflation, long-term product-demand cycles, and cycles in monetary and financial sectors. However, cyclical patterns that are consistent and predictable are quite rare. For practical purposes, we will ignore this type of variation.

**Seasonal variation** refers to cycles that occur over short repetitive calendar periods and, by definition, have a duration of less than 1 year. The term *seasonal variation* may refer to the four traditional seasons or to systematic patterns that occur during a month, a week, or even one day. Demand for restaurants feature "seasonal" variation throughout the day.

An illustration of seasonal variation is provided in Figure 20.3, which graphs monthly U.S. traffic volume (in billions of miles and where period 1 is January). (Data are in Ch20:\Fig20-03.) It is obvious from the graph that Americans drive more during the summer months than during the winter months.

FIGURE **20.3** **Traffic Volume (Billions of Miles)**

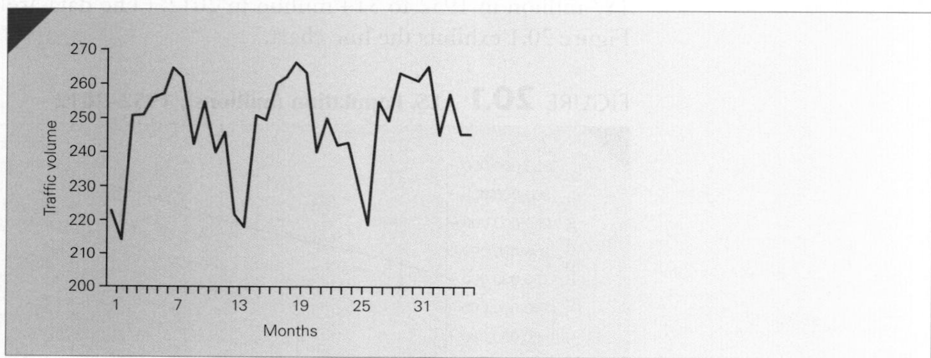


**Random variation** is caused by irregular and unpredictable changes in a time series that are not caused by any other components. It tends to mask the existence of the other more predictable components. Because random variation exists in almost all time series, one of the objectives of this chapter is to introduce ways to reduce the random variation, which will enable statistics practitioners to describe and measure the other components. By doing so, we hope to be able to make accurate predictions of the time series.

## 20-2 Smoothing Techniques

If we can determine which components actually exist in a time series, we can develop better forecasts. Unfortunately, the existence of random variation often makes the task of identifying components difficult. One of the simplest ways to reduce random variation is to smooth the time series. In this section, we introduce two methods: *moving averages* and *exponential smoothing*.

### 20-2a Moving Averages

A **moving average** for a time period is the arithmetic mean of the values in that time period and those close to it. For example, to compute the three-period moving average for any time period, we would average the time-series values in that time period, the previous period, and the following period. We compute the three-period moving averages for all time periods except the first and the last. To calculate the five-period moving average, we average the value in that time period, the values in the two preceding periods, and the values in the two following time periods. We can choose any number of periods with which to calculate the moving averages.

EXAMPLE 20.1

DATA
Xm20-01

## Gasoline Sales, Part 1

As part of an effort to forecast future sales, an operator of five independent gas stations recorded the quarterly gasoline sales (in thousands of gallons) for the past 4 years. These data are shown below. Calculate the three-quarter and five-quarter moving averages. Draw graphs of the time series and the moving averages.

| Time Period | Year | Quarter | Gasoline Sales (Thousands of Gallons) |
|---|---|---|---|
| 1 | 1 | 1 | 39 |
| 2 | | 2 | 37 |
| 3 | | 3 | 61 |
| 4 | | 4 | 58 |
| 5 | 2 | 1 | 18 |
| 6 | | 2 | 56 |
| 7 | | 3 | 82 |
| 8 | | 4 | 27 |
| 9 | 3 | 1 | 41 |
| 10 | | 2 | 69 |
| 11 | | 3 | 49 |
| 12 | | 4 | 66 |
| 13 | 4 | 1 | 54 |
| 14 | | 2 | 42 |
| 15 | | 3 | 90 |
| 16 | | 4 | 66 |

SOLUTION:

COMPUTE

MANUALLY:

To compute the first three-quarter moving average, we group the gasoline sales in periods 1, 2, and 3, and then average them. Thus, the first moving average is

$$\frac{39 + 37 + 61}{3} = \frac{137}{3} = 45.7$$

The second moving average is calculated by dropping the first period's sales (39), adding the fourth period's sales (58), and then computing the new average. Thus, the second moving average is

$$\frac{37 + 61 + 58}{3} = \frac{156}{3} = 52.0$$

The process continues as shown in the following table. Similar calculations are made to produce the five-quarter moving averages (also shown in the table).

| Time Period | Gasoline Sales | Three-Quarter Moving Average | Five-Quarter Moving Average |
|---|---|---|---|
| 1 | 39 | – | – |
| 2 | 37 | 45.7 | – |
| 3 | 61 | 52.0 | 42.6 |
| 4 | 58 | 45.7 | 46.0 |
| 5 | 18 | 44.0 | 55.0 |
| 6 | 56 | 52.0 | 48.2 |
| 7 | 82 | 55.0 | 44.8 |
| 8 | 27 | 50.0 | 55.0 |
| 9 | 41 | 45.7 | 53.6 |
| 10 | 69 | 53.0 | 50.4 |
| 11 | 49 | 61.3 | 55.8 |
| 12 | 66 | 56.3 | 56.0 |
| 13 | 54 | 54.0 | 60.2 |
| 14 | 42 | 62.0 | 63.6 |
| 15 | 90 | 66.0 | – |
| 16 | 66 | – | – |

Notice that we place the moving averages in the center of the group of values being averaged. It is for this reason that we prefer to use an odd number of periods in the moving averages. Later in this section, we discuss how to deal with an even number of periods.

Figure 20.4 displays the line chart for gasoline sales, and Figure 20.5 shows the three-period and five-period moving averages.

FIGURE **20.4** **Quarterly Gasoline Sales**

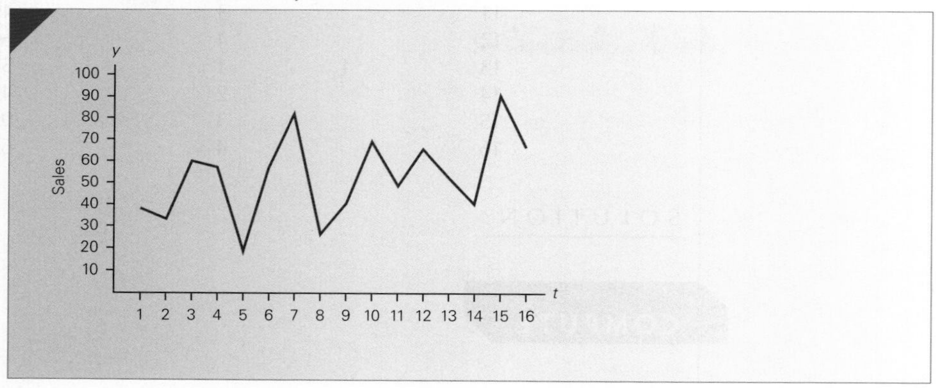


FIGURE **20.5** **Quarterly Gasoline Sales and Three-Quarter and Five-Quarter Moving Averages**

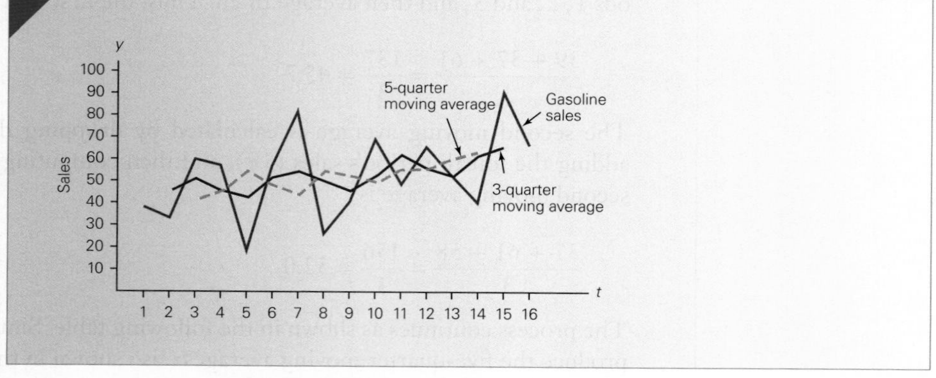

## EXCEL Data Analysis

| | A | B |
|---|---|---|
| 1 | Gas Sales | Moving Average |
| 2 | 39 | |
| 3 | 37 | 45.7 |
| 4 | 61 | 52.0 |
| 5 | 58 | 45.7 |
| 6 | 18 | 44.0 |
| 7 | 56 | 52.0 |
| 8 | 82 | 55.0 |
| 9 | 27 | 50.0 |
| 10 | 41 | 45.7 |
| 11 | 69 | 53.0 |
| 12 | 49 | 61.3 |
| 13 | 66 | 56.3 |
| 14 | 54 | 54.0 |
| 15 | 42 | 62.0 |
| 16 | 90 | 66.0 |
| 17 | 66 | |

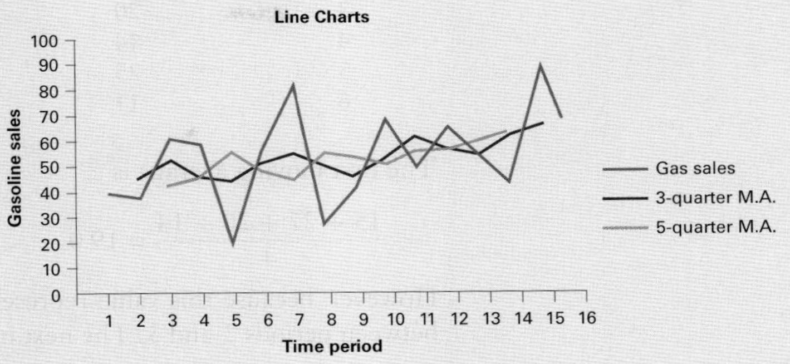

Line Charts
Gasoline sales
100
90
80
70
60
50
40
30
20
10
0
1 2 3 4 5 6 7 8 9 10 11 12 13 14 15 16
Time period
Gas sales
3-quarter M.A.
5-quarter M.A.

*INSTRUCTIONS*

1. Type or import the data into one column. (Open Xm20-01.)
2. Click **Data, Data Analysis,** and **Moving Average**.
3. Specify the **Input Range** (A1:A17). Specify the number of periods (3), and the **Output Range** (B1).
4. Delete the cells containing N/A.
5. To draw the line charts, follow the instructions on page 61.

### INTERPRET

To see how the moving averages remove some of the random variation, examine Figures 20.4 and 20.5. Figure 20.4 depicts the quarterly gasoline sales. Discerning any of the time-series components is difficult because of the large amount of random variation. Now consider the three-quarter moving average in Figure 20.5. You should be able to detect the seasonal pattern that exhibits peaks in the third quarter of each year (periods 3, 7, 11, and 15) and valleys in the first quarter of the year (periods 5, 9, and 13). There is also a small but discernible long-term trend of increasing sales.

Notice also in Figure 20.5 that the five-quarter moving average produces more smoothing than the three-quarter moving average. In general, the longer the time period over which we average, the smoother the series becomes. Unfortunately, in this case we've smoothed too much—the seasonal pattern is no longer apparent in the five-quarter moving average. All we can see is the long-term trend. It is important to realize that our objective is to smooth the time series sufficiently to remove the random variation and to reveal the other components (trend, cycle, or season) present. With too little smoothing, the random variation disguises the real pattern. With too much smoothing, however, some or all of the other effects may be eliminated along with the random variation.

## 20-2b Centered Moving Averages

Using an even number of periods to calculate the moving averages presents a problem about where to place the moving averages in a graph or table. For example, suppose that we calculate the four-period moving average of the following time series:

| Period | Time Series |
|---|---|
| 1 | 15 |
| 2 | 27 |
| 3 | 20 |
| 4 | 14 |
| 5 | 25 |
| 6 | 11 |

The first moving average is

$$\frac{15 + 27 + 20 + 14}{4} = 19.0$$

However, because this value represents time periods 1, 2, 3, and 4, we must place it between periods 2 and 3. The next moving average is

$$\frac{27 + 20 + 14 + 25}{4} = 21.5$$

and it must be placed between periods 3 and 4. The moving average that falls between periods 4 and 5 is

$$\frac{20 + 14 + 25 + 11}{4} = 17.5$$

There are several problems that result from placing the moving averages between time periods, including graphing difficulties. Centering the moving average corrects the problem. We do this by computing the two-period moving average of the four-period moving average. Thus, the centered moving average for period 3 is

$$\frac{19.0 + 21.5}{2} = 20.25$$

The centered moving average for period 4 is

$$\frac{21.5 + 17.5}{2} = 19.50$$

The following table summarizes these results.

| Period | Time Series | Four-Period Moving Average | Four-Period Centered Moving Average |
|---|---|---|---|
| 1 | 15 | — | — |
| 2 | 27 | 19.0 | — |
| 3 | 20 | 21.5 | 20.25 |
| 4 | 14 | 17.5 | 19.50 |
| 5 | 25 | — | — |
| 6 | 11 |  | — |

## 20-2c Exponential Smoothing

Two drawbacks are associated with the moving average method of smoothing time series. First, we do not have moving averages for the first and last sets of time periods. If the time series has few observations, the missing values can represent an important loss of information. Second, the moving average "forgets" most of the previous time-series values. For example, in the five-quarter moving average described in Example 20.1, the average for quarter 4 reflects quarters 2, 3, 4, 5, and 6 but is not affected by quarter 1. Similarly, the moving average for quarter 5 forgets quarters 1 and 2. Both of these problems are addressed by **exponential smoothing**.

**Exponentially Smoothed Time Series**

$$S_t = wy_t + (1 - w)S_{t-1} \text{ for } t \geq 2$$

where

$S_t$ = Exponentially smoothed time series at time period $t$

$y_t$ = Time series at time period $t$

$S_{t-1}$ = Exponentially smoothed time series at time period $t - 1$

$w$ = Smoothing constant, where $0 \leq w \leq 1$

We begin by setting

$$S_1 = y_1$$

Then

$$\begin{aligned} S_2 &= wy_2 + (1 - w)S_1 \\ &= wy_2 + (1 - w)y_1 \\ S_3 &= wy_3 + (1 - w)S_2 \\ &= wy_3 + (1 - w)[wy_2 + (1 - w)y_1] \\ &= wy_3 + w(1 - w)y_2 + (1 - w)^2 y_1 \end{aligned}$$

and so on. In general, we have

$$S_t = wy_t + w(1 - w)y_{t-1} + w(1 - w)^2 y_{t-2} + \cdots + (1 - w)^{t-1} y_1$$

This formula states that the smoothed time series in period $t$ depends on all the previous observations of the time series.

The smoothing constant $w$ is chosen on the basis of how much smoothing is required. A small value of $w$ produces a great deal of smoothing. A large value of $w$ results in very little smoothing. Figure 20.6 depicts a time series and two exponentially smoothed series with $w = .1$ and $w = .5$.

FIGURE **20.6** **Time Series and Two Exponentially Smoothed Series**

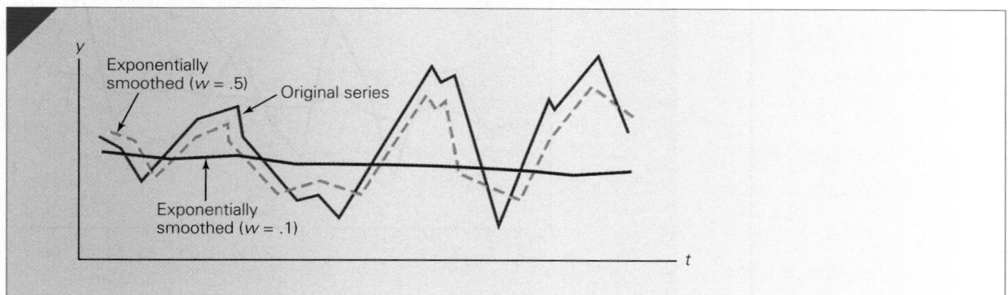

EXAMPLE 20.1

## Gasoline Sales, Part 2

Apply the exponential smoothing technique with $w = .2$ and $w = .7$ to the data in Example 20.1, and graph the results.

SOLUTION:

COMPUTE MANUALLY:

The exponentially smoothed values are calculated from the formula

$$S_t = wy_t + (1 - w)S_{t-1}$$

The results with $w = .2$ and $w = .7$ are shown in the following table.

| Time Period | Gasoline Sales | Exponentially Smoothed with $w = .2$ | Exponentially Smoothed with $w = .7$ |
|---|---|---|---|
| 1 | 39 | 39.0 | 39.0 |
| 2 | 37 | 38.6 | 37.6 |
| 3 | 61 | 43.1 | 54.0 |
| 4 | 58 | 46.1 | 56.8 |
| 5 | 18 | 40.5 | 29.6 |
| 6 | 56 | 43.6 | 48.1 |
| 7 | 82 | 51.2 | 71.8 |
| 8 | 27 | 46.4 | 40.4 |
| 9 | 41 | 45.3 | 40.8 |
| 10 | 69 | 50.1 | 60.6 |
| 11 | 49 | 49.8 | 52.5 |
| 12 | 66 | 53.1 | 61.9 |
| 13 | 54 | 53.3 | 56.4 |
| 14 | 42 | 51.0 | 46.3 |
| 15 | 90 | 58.8 | 76.9 |
| 16 | 66 | 60.2 | 69.3 |

Figure 20.7 shows the exponentially smoothed time series.

FIGURE **20.7** **Quarterly Gasoline Sales and Exponentially Smoothed Sales with $w = .2$ and $w = .7$**

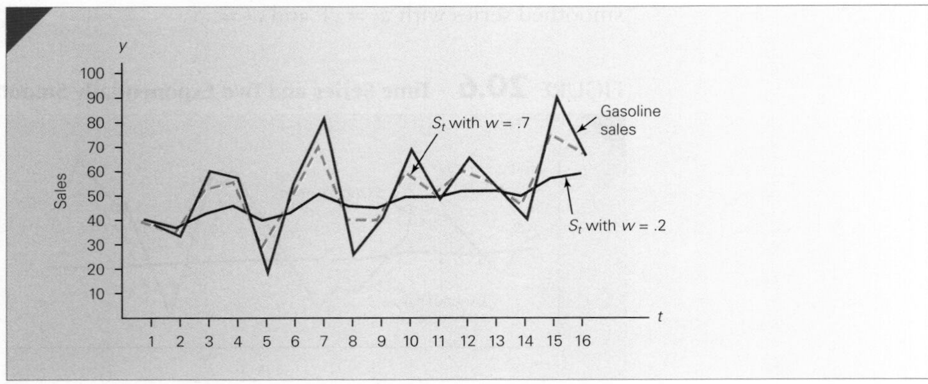

## EXCEL Data Analysis

| | A | B | C |
|---|---|---|---|
| 1 | Gas Sales | Damping factor = .8 | Damping factor = .3 |
| 2 | 39 | 39.0 | 39.0 |
| 3 | 37 | 38.6 | 37.6 |
| 4 | 61 | 43.1 | 54.0 |
| 5 | 58 | 46.1 | 56.8 |
| 6 | 18 | 40.5 | 29.6 |
| 7 | 56 | 43.6 | 48.1 |
| 8 | 82 | 51.2 | 71.8 |
| 9 | 27 | 46.4 | 40.4 |
| 10 | 41 | 45.3 | 40.8 |
| 11 | 69 | 50.1 | 60.6 |
| 12 | 49 | 49.8 | 52.5 |
| 13 | 66 | 53.1 | 61.9 |
| 14 | 54 | 53.3 | 56.4 |
| 15 | 42 | 51.0 | 46.3 |
| 16 | 90 | 58.8 | 76.9 |
| 17 | 66 | 60.2 | 69.3 |

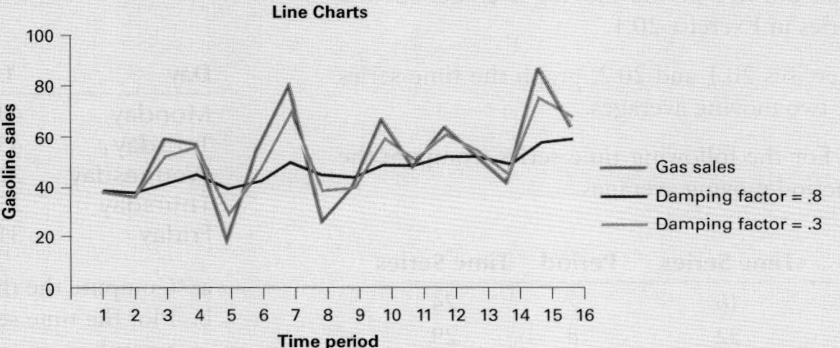


### *INSTRUCTIONS*

1. Type or import the data into one column (Open Xm20-01.)
2. Click **Data, Data Analysis,** and **Exponential Smoothing**.
3. Specify the **Input Range** (A1:A17). Type the **Damping factor**, which is $1 - w$ (.8). Specify the **Output Range** (B1). To calculate the second exponentially smoothed time series specify $1 - w$ (.3) **Output Range** (C1).

To modify the table so that the smoothed values appear the way we calculated, manually click the cell containing the last smoothed value displayed here (58.8) and drag it to the cell below to reveal the final smoothed value (60.2 and 69.3).

## INTERPRET

Figure 20.7 depicts the graph of the original time series and the exponentially smoothed series. As you can see, $w = .7$ results in very little smoothing, whereas $w = .2$ results in perhaps too much smoothing. In both smoothed time series, it is difficult to discern the seasonal pattern that we detected by using moving averages. A different value of $w$ (perhaps $w = .5$) would be likely to produce more satisfactory results.

Moving averages and exponential smoothing are relatively crude methods of removing the random variation to discover the existence of other components. In the next section, we attempt to measure these components more precisely.

# EXERCISES

**20.1** Xr20-01 For the following time series, compute the three-period moving averages.

| Period | Time Series | Period | Time Series |
|---|---|---|---|
| 1 | 48 | 7 | 43 |
| 2 | 41 | 8 | 52 |
| 3 | 37 | 9 | 60 |
| 4 | 32 | 10 | 48 |
| 5 | 36 | 11 | 41 |
| 6 | 31 | 12 | 30 |

**20.2** Compute the five-period moving averages for the time series in Exercise 20.1.

**20.3** For Exercises 20.1 and 20.2, graph the time series and the two moving averages.

**20.4** Xr20-04 For the following time series, compute the three-period moving averages.

| Period | Time Series | Period | Time Series |
|---|---|---|---|
| 1 | 16 | 7 | 24 |
| 2 | 22 | 8 | 29 |
| 3 | 19 | 9 | 21 |
| 4 | 24 | 10 | 23 |
| 5 | 30 | 11 | 19 |
| 6 | 26 | 12 | 15 |

**20.5** For Exercise 20.4, compute the five-period moving averages.

**20.6** For Exercises 20.4 and 20.5, graph the time series and the two moving averages.

**20.7** Xr20-07 Apply exponential smoothing with $w = .1$ to help detect the components of the following time series.

| Period | 1 | 2 | 3 | 4 | 5 |
|---|---|---|---|---|---|
| Time Series | 12 | 18 | 16 | 24 | 17 |
| **Period** | 6 | 7 | 8 | 9 | 10 |
| **Time Series** | 16 | 25 | 21 | 23 | 14 |

**20.8** Repeat Exercise 20.7 with $w = .8$.

**20.9** For Exercises 20.7 and 20.8, draw the time series and the two sets of exponentially smoothed values. Does there appear to be a trend component in the time series?

**20.10** Xr20-10 Apply exponential smoothing with $w = .1$ to help detect the components of the following time series.

| Period | 1 | 2 | 3 | 4 | 5 |
|---|---|---|---|---|---|
| Time Series | 38 | 43 | 42 | 45 | 46 |
| **Period** | 6 | 7 | 8 | 9 | 10 |
| **Time Series** | 48 | 50 | 49 | 46 | 45 |

**20.11** Repeat Exercise 20.10 with $w = .8$.

**20.12** For Exercises 20.10 and 20.11, draw the time series and the two sets of exponentially smoothed values. Does there appear to be a trend component in the time series?

**20.13** Xr20-13 The following daily sales figures have been recorded in a medium-size merchandising firm.

| | Week | | | |
|---|---|---|---|---|
| Day | 1 | 2 | 3 | 4 |
| Monday | 43 | 51 | 40 | 64 |
| Tuesday | 45 | 41 | 57 | 58 |
| Wednesday | 22 | 37 | 30 | 33 |
| Thursday | 25 | 22 | 33 | 38 |
| Friday | 31 | 25 | 37 | 25 |

a. Compute the three-day moving averages.
b. Plot the time series and the moving averages on a graph.
c. Does there appear to be a seasonal (weekly) pattern?

**20.14** For Exercise 20.13, compute the five-day moving averages, and superimpose these on the same graph. Does this help you answer part (c) of Exercise 20.13?

**20.15** Xr20-15 The following quarterly sales of a department store chain were recorded for the years 2013–2016.

| | Year | | | |
|---|---|---|---|---|
| Quarter | 2013 | 2014 | 2015 | 2016 |
| 1 | 18 | 33 | 25 | 41 |
| 2 | 22 | 20 | 36 | 33 |
| 3 | 27 | 38 | 44 | 52 |
| 4 | 31 | 26 | 29 | 45 |

a. Calculate the four-quarter centered moving averages.
b. Graph the time series and the moving averages.
c. What can you conclude from your time-series smoothing?

**20.16** Repeat Exercise 20.15, using exponential smoothing with $w = .4$.

**20.17** Repeat Exercise 20.15, using exponential smoothing with $w = .8$.

## 20-3 Trend and Seasonal Effects

In the previous section, we described how smoothing a time series can give us a clearer picture of which components are present. In order to forecast, however, we often need more precise measurements of the time-series components.

### 20-3a Trend Analysis

A trend can be linear or nonlinear and, indeed, can take on a whole host of functional forms. The easiest way of measuring the long-term trend is by regression analysis, where the independent variable is time. If we believe that the long-term trend is approximately linear, we will use the linear model introduced in Chapter 16:

$$y = \beta_0 + \beta_1 t + \varepsilon$$

If we believe that the trend is nonlinear, we can use one of the polynomial models described in Chapter 18. For example, the quadratic model is

$$y = \beta_0 + \beta_1 t + \beta_2 t^2 + \varepsilon$$

In most realistic applications, the linear model is used. We will demonstrate how the long-term trend is measured and applied later in this section.

### 20-3b Seasonal Analysis

Seasonal variation may occur within a year or within shorter intervals, such as a month, week, or day. To measure the seasonal effect, we compute seasonal indexes, which gauge the degree to which the seasons differ from one another. One requirement necessary to calculate seasonal indexes is a time series sufficiently long enough to allow us to observe the variable over several seasons. For example, if the seasons are defined as the quarters of a year, we need to observe the time series for at least 4 years. The **seasonal indexes** are computed in the following way.

### 20-3c Procedure for Computing Seasonal Indexes

1. Remove the effect of seasonal and random variation by regression analysis; that is, compute the sample regression line

$$\hat{y}_t = b_0 + b_1 t$$

2. For each time period compute the ratio

$$\frac{y_t}{\hat{y}_t}$$

This ratio removes most of the trend variation.

3. For each type of season, compute the average of the ratios in step 2. This procedure removes most (but seldom all) of the random variation, leaving a measure of seasonality.

4. Adjust the averages in step 3 so that the average of all the seasons is 1 (if necessary).

## EXAMPLE 20.3 Hotel Quarterly Occupancy Rates

DATA
Xm20-03

The tourist industry is subject to seasonal variation. In most resorts, the spring and summer seasons are considered the "high" seasons. Fall and winter (except for Christmas and New Year's) are "low" seasons. A hotel in Bermuda has recorded the occupancy rate for each quarter for the past 5 years. These data are shown here. Measure the seasonal variation by computing the seasonal indexes.

| Year | Quarter | Occupancy Rate |
|---|---|---|
| 2012 | 1 | .561 |
| | 2 | .702 |
| | 3 | .800 |
| | 4 | .568 |
| 2013 | 1 | .575 |
| | 2 | .738 |
| | 3 | .868 |
| | 4 | .605 |
| 2014 | 1 | .594 |
| | 2 | .738 |
| | 3 | .729 |
| | 4 | .600 |
| 2015 | 1 | .622 |
| | 2 | .708 |
| | 3 | .806 |
| | 4 | .632 |
| 2016 | 1 | .665 |
| | 2 | .835 |
| | 3 | .873 |
| | 4 | .670 |

SOLUTION:

COMPUTE

MANUALLY:

We performed a regression analysis with $y$ = occupancy rate and $t$ = time period 1, 2, . . . , 20. The regression equation is

$$\hat{y} = .639368 + .005246t$$

For each time period, we computed the ratio

$$\frac{y_t}{\hat{y}_t}$$

In the next step, we collected the ratios associated with each quarter and computed the average. We then computed the seasonal indexes by adjusting the average ratios so that they summed to 4.0, if necessary. In this example, it was not necessary.

| Year | Quarter | $t$ | $y_t$ | $\hat{y} = .639368 + .005246t$ | Ratio $\frac{y_t}{\hat{y}_t}$ |
|---|---|---|---|---|---|
| 2012 | 1 | 1 | .561 | .645 | .870 |
| | 2 | 2 | .702 | .650 | 1.080 |
| | 3 | 3 | .800 | .655 | 1.221 |
| | 4 | 4 | .568 | .660 | .860 |
| 2013 | 1 | 5 | .575 | .666 | .864 |
| | 2 | 6 | .738 | .671 | 1.100 |
| | 3 | 7 | .868 | .676 | 1.284 |
| | 4 | 8 | .605 | .681 | .888 |
| 2014 | 1 | 9 | .594 | .687 | .865 |
| | 2 | 10 | .738 | .692 | 1.067 |
| | 3 | 11 | .729 | .697 | 1.046 |
| | 4 | 12 | .600 | .702 | .854 |
| 2015 | 1 | 13 | .622 | .708 | .879 |
| | 2 | 14 | .708 | .713 | .993 |
| | 3 | 15 | .806 | .718 | 1.122 |
| | 4 | 16 | .632 | .723 | .874 |
| 2016 | 1 | 17 | .665 | .729 | .913 |
| | 2 | 18 | .835 | .734 | 1.138 |
| | 3 | 19 | .873 | .739 | 1.181 |
| | 4 | 20 | .670 | .744 | .900 |

| | Quarter | | | |
|---|---|---|---|---|
| Year | 1 | 2 | 3 | 4 |
| 2012 | .870 | 1.080 | 1.221 | .860 |
| 2013 | .864 | 1.100 | 1.284 | .888 |
| 2014 | .865 | 1.067 | 1.046 | .854 |
| 2015 | .879 | .993 | 1.122 | .874 |
| 2016 | .913 | 1.138 | 1.181 | .900 |
| Average | .878 | 1.076 | 1.171 | .875 |
| Index | .878 | 1.076 | 1.171 | .875 |

**INTERPRET**

The seasonal indexes tell us that, on average, the occupancy rates in the first and fourth quarters are below the annual average, and the occupancy rates in the second and third quarters are above the annual average. We expect the occupancy rate in the first quarter to be 12.2%(100% − 87.8%) below the annual rate. The second and third quarters' rates are expected to be 7.6% and 17.1%, respectively, above the annual rate. The fourth quarter's rate is 12.5% below the annual rate.

Figure 20.8 depicts the time series and the regression trend line.

FIGURE **20.8** **Time Series and Trend for Example 20.3**

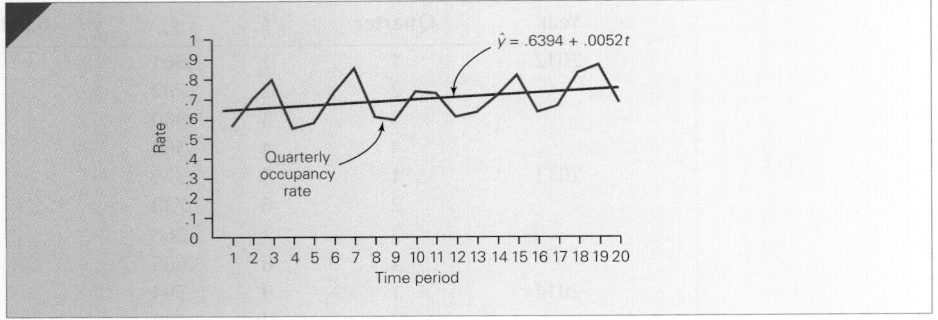


## 20-3d Deseasonalizing a Time Series

One application of seasonal indexes is to remove the seasonal variation in a time series. The process is called **deseasonalizing**, and the result is called a **seasonally adjusted time series.** Often this allows the statistics practitioner to more easily compare the time series across seasons. For example, the unemployment rate varies according to the season. During the winter months, unemployment usually rises; it falls in the spring and summer. The seasonally adjusted unemployment rate allows economists to determine whether unemployment has increased or decreased over the previous months. The process is easy: Simply divide the time series by the seasonal indexes. To illustrate, we have deseasonalized the occupancy rates in Example 20.3. The results are shown next.

| Year | Quarter | Occupancy Rate $y_t$ | Seasonal Index | Seasonally Adjusted Occupancy Rate |
|---|---|---|---|---|
| 2012 | 1 | .561 | .878 | .639 |
| | 2 | .702 | 1.076 | .652 |
| | 3 | .800 | 1.171 | .683 |
| | 4 | .568 | .875 | .649 |
| 2013 | 1 | .575 | .878 | .655 |
| | 2 | .738 | 1.076 | .686 |
| | 3 | .868 | 1.171 | .741 |
| | 4 | .605 | .875 | .691 |
| 2014 | 1 | .594 | .878 | .677 |
| | 2 | .738 | 1.076 | .686 |
| | 3 | .729 | 1.171 | .623 |
| | 4 | .600 | .875 | .686 |
| 2015 | 1 | .622 | .878 | .708 |
| | 2 | .708 | 1.076 | .658 |
| | 3 | .806 | 1.171 | .688 |
| | 4 | .632 | .875 | .722 |
| 2016 | 1 | .665 | .878 | .757 |
| | 2 | .835 | 1.076 | .776 |
| | 3 | .873 | 1.171 | .746 |
| | 4 | .670 | .875 | .766 |

By removing the seasonality, we can see when there has been a "real" increase or decrease in the occupancy rate. This enables the statistics practitioner to examine the factors that produced the rate change. We can more easily see that there has been an increase in the occupancy rate over the 5-year period.

In the next section, we show how to forecast with seasonal indexes.

## EXERCISES

**20.18** Xr20-18 Plot the following time series. Would the linear or quadratic model fit better?

| Period | 1 | 2 | 3 | 4 | 5 | 6 | 7 | 8 |
|---|---|---|---|---|---|---|---|---|
| Time Series | .5 | .6 | 1.3 | 2.7 | 4.1 | 6.9 | 10.8 | 19.2 |

**20.19** Xr20-19 Plot the following time series to determine which of the trend models appears to fit better.

| Period | 1 | 2 | 3 | 4 | 5 |
|---|---|---|---|---|---|
| Time Series | 55 | 57 | 53 | 49 | 47 |
| **Period** | 6 | 7 | 8 | 9 | 10 |
| **Time Series** | 39 | 41 | 33 | 28 | 20 |

**20.20** Refer to Exercise 20.18. Use regression analysis to calculate the linear and quadratic trends. Which line fits better?

**20.21** Refer to Exercise 20.19. Use regression analysis to calculate the linear and quadratic trends. Which line fits better?

**20.22** Xr20-22 For the following time series, compute the seasonal (daily) indexes.

The regression line is

$$\hat{y} = 16.8 + .366t \ \ (t = 1, 2, \ldots, 20)$$

| | Week | | | |
|---|---|---|---|---|
| **Day** | **1** | **2** | **3** | **4** |
| Monday | 12 | 11 | 14 | 17 |
| Tuesday | 18 | 17 | 16 | 21 |
| Wednesday | 16 | 19 | 16 | 20 |
| Thursday | 25 | 24 | 28 | 24 |
| Friday | 31 | 27 | 25 | 32 |

**20.23** Xr20-23 Given the following time series, compute the seasonal indexes.

The regression equation is

$$\hat{y} = 47.7 - 1.06t \ \ (t = 1, 2, \ldots, 20)$$

| | Year | | | | |
|---|---|---|---|---|---|
| **Quarter** | **1** | **2** | **3** | **4** | **5** |
| 1 | 55 | 41 | 43 | 36 | 50 |
| 2 | 44 | 38 | 39 | 32 | 25 |
| 3 | 46 | 37 | 39 | 30 | 24 |
| 4 | 39 | 30 | 35 | 25 | 22 |

**Applications**

**20.24** Xr20-24 The quarterly earnings (in $millions) of a large soft-drink manufacturer have been recorded for the years 2013–2016. These data are listed here. Compute the seasonal indexes given the regression line

$$\hat{y} = 61.75 + 1.18t \ \ (t = 1, 2, \ldots, 16)$$

| | Year | | | |
|---|---|---|---|---|
| **Quarter** | **2013** | **2014** | **2015** | **2016** |
| 1 | 52 | 57 | 60 | 66 |
| 2 | 67 | 75 | 77 | 82 |
| 3 | 85 | 90 | 94 | 98 |
| 4 | 54 | 61 | 63 | 67 |

*The following exercises require a computer and software.*

**20.25** Xr20-25 College and university enrollment increased sharply during the 1970s and 1980s. However, since then, the rate of growth has slowed. To help forecast future enrollments, an economist recorded the total U.S. college and university enrollment from 1993 to 2009. These data (in thousands) are listed here.

| Year | 1993 | 1994 | 1995 | 1996 | 1997 | 1998 | 1999 |
|---|---|---|---|---|---|---|---|
| Enrollment | 13,898 | 15,022 | 14,715 | 15,226 | 15,436 | 15,546 | 15,203 |
| **Year** | 2000 | 2001 | 2002 | 2003 | 2004 | 2005 | 2006 |
| **Enrollment** | 15,314 | 15,873 | 16,497 | 16,638 | 17,272 | 17,487 | 17,672 |
| **Year** | 2007 | 2008 | 2009 | | | | |
| **Enrollment** | 18,248 | 19,103 | 20,428 | | | | |

Source: *Statistical Abstract of the United States*, 2009, Table 279.

a. Plot the time series
b. Use regression analysis to determine the trend.

**20.26** Xr20-26 Foreign trade is important to the United States. No country exports and imports more. However, there has been a large trade imbalance in many sectors. To measure the extent of the problem, an economist recorded the difference between exports and imports of merchandise (excluding military) for the years 1980 to 2012.

a. Plot the trade balance.
b. Apply regression analysis to measure the trend.

Source: Federal Reserve St. Louis.

**20.27** Xr20-27 The number of cable television subscribers has increased over the past 5 years. The marketing manager for a cable company has recorded the numbers of subscribers for the past 24 quarters.

a. Plot the numbers.
b. Compute the seasonal (quarterly) indexes.

**20.28** Xr20-28 The owner of a pizzeria wants to forecast the number of pizzas she will sell each day. She recorded the numbers sold daily for the past 4 weeks. Calculate the seasonal (daily) indexes.

**20.29** Xr20-29 A manufacturer of ski equipment is in the process of reviewing his accounts receivable. He noticed that there appears to be a seasonal pattern with the accounts receivable increasing in the winter months and decreasing during the summer. The quarterly accounts receivable (in $millions) were recorded. Compute the seasonal (quarterly) indexes.

## 20-4 Introduction to Forecasting

Many different forecasting methods are available for the statistics practitioner. One factor to be considered in choosing among them is the type of component that makes up the time series. Even then, however, we have several different methods from which to choose. One way of deciding which method to apply is to select the technique that achieves the greatest forecast accuracy. The most commonly used measures of forecast accuracy are **mean absolute deviation (MAD)** and the **sum of squares for forecast errors (SSE)**.

**Mean Absolute Deviation**

$$\text{MAD} = \frac{\sum_{i=1}^{n} |y_t - F_t|}{n}$$

where

$y_t$ = Actual value of the time series at time period $t$

$F_t$ = Forecasted value of the time series at time period $t$

$n$ = Number of time periods

**Sum of Squares for Forecast Error**

$$\text{SSE} = \sum_{i=1}^{n} (y_t - F_t)^2$$

MAD averages the absolute differences between the actual and forecast values; SSE is the sum of the squared differences. Which measure to use in judging forecast accuracy depends on the circumstances. If avoiding large errors is important, SSE should be used because it penalizes large deviations more heavily than does MAD. Otherwise, use MAD.

It is probably best to use some of the observations of the time series to develop several competing forecasting models and then forecast for the remaining time periods. Afterward, compute MAD or SSE for the forecasts. For example, if we have 5 years of monthly observations, use the first 4 years to develop the forecasting models and then use them to forecast the fifth year. Because we know the actual values in the fifth year, we can choose the technique that results in the most accurate forecast using either MAD or SSE.

## EXAMPLE 20.4 Comparing Forecasting Models

Annual data from 1976 to 2012 were used to develop three different forecasting models. Each model was used to forecast the time series for 2013, 2014, 2015, and 2016. The forecasted and actual values for these years are shown here. Use MAD and SSE to determine which model performed best.

| Year | Actual Time Series | 1 | 2 | 3 |
|---|---|---|---|---|
| 2013 | 129 | 136 | 118 | 130 |
| 2014 | 142 | 148 | 141 | 146 |
| 2015 | 156 | 150 | 158 | 170 |
| 2016 | 183 | 175 | 163 | 180 |

SOLUTION:

For model 1, we have

$$\begin{aligned} \text{MAD} &= \frac{|129-136|+|142-148|+|156-150|+|183-175|}{4} \\ &= \frac{7+6+6+8}{4} = 6.75 \\ \text{SSE} &= (129-136)^2+(142-148)^2+(156-150)^2+(183-175)^2 \\ &= 49+36+36+64 = 185 \end{aligned}$$

For model 2, we compute

$$\begin{aligned} \text{MAD} &= \frac{|129-118|+|142-141|+|156-158|+|183-163|}{4} \\ &= \frac{11+1+2+20}{4} = 8.5 \\ \text{SSE} &= (129-118)^2+(142-141)^2+(156-158)^2+(183-163)^2 \\ &= 121+1+4+400 = 526 \end{aligned}$$

The measures of forecast accuracy for model 3 are

$$\begin{aligned} \text{MAD} &= \frac{|129-130|+|142-146|+|156-170|+|183-180|}{4} \\ &= \frac{1+4+14+3}{4} = 5.5 \\ \text{SSE} &= (129-130)^2+(142-146)^2+(156-170)^2+(183-180)^2 \\ &= 1+16+196+9 = 222 \end{aligned}$$

Model 2 is inferior to both models 1 and 3, no matter how we measure forecast accuracy. Using MAD, model 3 is best—but using SSE, model 1 is most accurate. The choice between model 1 and model 3 should be made on the basis of whether we prefer a model that consistently produces moderately accurate forecasts (model 1) or one whose forecasts come quite close to most actual values but miss badly in a small number of time periods (model 3).

## EXERCISES

**20.30** For the actual and forecast values of a time series shown here, calculate MAD and SSE.

| **Period** | 1 | 2 | 3 | 4 | 5 |
|---|---|---|---|---|---|
| **Forecast** | 173 | 186 | 192 | 211 | 223 |
| **Actual Value** | 166 | 179 | 195 | 214 | 220 |

**20.31** Two forecasting models were used to predict the future values of a time series. These are shown here together with the actual values. Compute MAD and SSE for each model to determine which was more accurate.

| **Period** | 1 | 2 | 3 | 4 |
|---|---|---|---|---|
| **Forecast (Model 1)** | 7.5 | 6.3 | 5.4 | 8.2 |
| **Forecast (Model 2)** | 6.3 | 6.7 | 7.1 | 7.5 |
| **Actual** | 6.0 | 6.6 | 7.3 | 9.4 |

**20.32** Calculate MAD and SSE for the forecasts that follow.

| **Period** | 1 | 2 | 3 | 4 | 5 |
|---|---|---|---|---|---|
| **Forecast** | 63 | 72 | 86 | 71 | 60 |
| **Actual** | 57 | 60 | 70 | 75 | 70 |

**20.33** Three forecasting techniques were used to predict the values of a time series. These values are given in the following table. Compute MAD and SSE for each technique to determine which was most accurate.

| **Period** | 1 | 2 | 3 | 4 | 5 |
|---|---|---|---|---|---|
| **Forecast (Model 1)** | 21 | 27 | 29 | 31 | 35 |
| **Forecast (Model 2)** | 22 | 24 | 26 | 28 | 30 |
| **Forecast (Model 3)** | 17 | 20 | 25 | 31 | 39 |
| **Actual** | 19 | 24 | 28 | 32 | 38 |

# 20-5 FORECASTING MODELS

There is a large number of different forecasting techniques available to statistics practitioners. However, many are beyond the level of this book. In this section, we present three models. Similar to the method of choosing the correct statistical inference technique in Chapters 12 to 19, the choice of model depends on the time-series components.

## 20-5a Forecasting with Exponential Smoothing

If the time series displays a gradual trend or no trend and no evidence of seasonal variation, exponential smoothing can be effective as a forecasting method. Suppose that $t$ represents the most recent time period and we've computed the exponentially smoothed value $S_t$. This value is then the forecasted value at time $t + 1$; that is,

$$F_{t+1} = S_t$$

If we wish, we can forecast two or three or any number of periods into the future:

$$F_{t+2} = S_t \qquad \text{or} \qquad F_{t+3} = S_t$$

It must be understood that the accuracy of the forecast decreases rapidly for predictions more than one time period into the future. However, as long as we're dealing with time series with no cyclical or seasonal variation, we can produce reasonably accurate predictions for the next time period.

## 20-5b Forecasting with Seasonal Indexes

If the time series is composed of seasonal variation and long-term trend, we can use seasonal indexes and the regression equation to forecast.

**Forecast of Trend and Seasonality**

The forecast for time period $t$ is

$$F_t = [b_0 + b_1 t] \times SI_t$$

where

$$F_t = \text{Forecast for period } t$$
$$b_0 + b_1 t = \text{Regression equation}$$
$$SI_t = \text{Seasonal index for period } t$$

EXAMPLE 20.5

## Forecasting Hotel Occupancy Rates

Forecast hotel occupancy rates for next year in Example 20.3.

SOLUTION:

In the process of computing the seasonal indexes, we computed the trend line. It is

$$\hat{y} = .639 + .00525t$$

For $t = 21, 22, 23$, and $24$, we calculate the forecasted trend values.

| Quarter | $t$ | $\hat{y} = .639 + .00525t$ |
|---|---|---|
| 1 | 21 | $.639 + .00525(21) = .749$ |
| 2 | 22 | $.639 + .00525(22) = .755$ |
| 3 | 23 | $.639 + .00525(23) = .760$ |
| 4 | 24 | $.639 + .00525(24) = .765$ |

We now multiply the forecasted trend values by the seasonal indexes calculated in Example 20.3. The seasonalized forecasts are as follows:

| Quarter | $t$ | Trend Value $\hat{y}_t$ | Seasonal Index | Forecast $F_t = \hat{y}_t \times SI_t$ |
|---|---|---|---|---|
| 1 | 21 | .749 | .878 | $.749 \times .878 = .658$ |
| 2 | 22 | .755 | 1.076 | $.755 \times 1.076 = .812$ |
| 3 | 23 | .760 | 1.171 | $.760 \times 1.171 = .890$ |
| 4 | 24 | .765 | .875 | $.765 \times .875 = .670$ |

INTERPRET

We forecast that the quarterly occupancy rates during the next year will be .658, .812, .890, and .670.

### 20-5c Autoregressive Model

In Chapter 17, we discussed autocorrelation wherein the errors are not independent of one another. The existence of strong autocorrelation indicates that the model has been misspecified, which usually means that until we improve the regression model, it will not provide an adequate fit. However, autocorrelation also provides us with an opportunity to develop another forecasting technique. If there is no obvious trend or seasonality and we believe that there is a correlation between consecutive residuals, the **autoregressive model** may be most effective.

**Autoregressive Forecasting Model**

$$y_t = \beta_0 + \beta_1 y_{t-1} + \varepsilon$$

The model specifies that consecutive values of the time series are correlated. We estimate the coefficient in the usual way. The estimated regression line is defined as

$$\hat{y}_t = b_0 + b_1 y_{t-1}$$

EXAMPLE 20.6

## Forecasting Changes to the Consumer Price Index

DATA Xm20-06

The consumer price index (CPI) is used as a general measure of inflation. It is an important measure because a high rate of inflation often influences governments to take corrective measures. The table below lists the consumer price index from 1980 to 2015 and the annual percentage increases in the CPI. Forecast next year's change in the CPI.

| Year | CPI | % Change | Year | CPI | % Change |
|---|---|---|---|---|---|
| 1980 | 82.4 | | 1998 | 163.0 | 1.55% |
| 1981 | 90.9 | 10.38% | 1999 | 166.6 | 2.19% |
| 1982 | 96.5 | 6.16% | 2000 | 172.2 | 3.37% |
| 1983 | 99.6 | 3.16% | 2001 | 177.0 | 2.82% |
| 1984 | 103.9 | 4.37% | 2002 | 179.9 | 1.60% |
| 1985 | 107.6 | 3.53% | 2003 | 184.0 | 2.30% |
| 1986 | 109.7 | 1.94% | 2004 | 188.9 | 2.67% |
| 1987 | 113.6 | 3.58% | 2005 | 195.3 | 3.37% |
| 1988 | 118.3 | 4.10% | 2006 | 201.6 | 3.22% |
| 1989 | 123.9 | 4.79% | 2007 | 207.3 | 2.87% |
| 1990 | 130.7 | 5.42% | 2008 | 215.3 | 3.81% |
| 1991 | 136.2 | 4.22% | 2009 | 214.6 | -0.32% |
| 1992 | 140.3 | 3.04% | 2010 | 218.1 | 1.64% |
| 1993 | 144.5 | 2.97% | 2011 | 224.9 | 3.14% |
| 1994 | 148.2 | 2.60% | 2012 | 229.6 | 2.08% |
| 1995 | 152.4 | 2.81% | 2013 | 233.0 | 1.47% |
| 1996 | 156.9 | 2.94% | 2014 | 236.7 | 1.61% |
| 1997 | 160.5 | 2.34% | 2015 | 237.0 | 0.12% |

*Source*: U.S. Bureau of Labor Statistics.

SOLUTION:

Notice that we included the CPI for 1980 because we wanted to determine the percentage change for 1981. We will use the percentage changes for 1981 to 2014 as the independent variable and the percentage change from 1982 to 2015 as the dependent variable. File Xm20-06 stores the data in the format necessary to determine the autoregressive model.

**EXCEL Data Analysis**

| | A | B | C | D | E |
|---|---|---|---|---|---|
| 1 | | *Coefficients* | *Standard Error* | *t Stat* | *P-value* |
| 2 | Intercept | 0.0145 | 0.0038 | 3.78 | 0.0007 |
| 3 | % Change | 0.4481 | 0.1058 | 4.23 | 0.0002 |

**INTERPRET**

The regression line is

$$\hat{y}_t = .0145 + .4481 y_{t-1}$$

Because the last CPI change is .12%, our forecast for 2016 is

$$\hat{y}_{2016} = .0145 + .4481 y_{2015}$$

$$= .0145 + .4481(.12\%) = .07\%$$

The autoregressive model forecasts a .07% increase in the CPI for the year 2016.

## Housing Starts: Solution

iStockphoto.com/stocknroll

A preliminary examination of the data reveals that there is a very small upward trend over the 5-year period. Moreover, the number of housing starts varies by month. The presence of these components suggests that we determine the linear trend and seasonal (monthly) indexes.

With housing starts as the dependent variable and the month as the independent variable, Excel yielded the following regression line:

$$\hat{y} = 11.46 + .0808t \qquad t = 1, 2, \ldots, 60$$

The seasonal indexes were computed as follows.

| Season | Index |
|---|---|
| 1 | .5974 |
| 2 | .6548 |
| 3 | .9800 |
| 4 | 1.0697 |
| 5 | 1.1110 |
| 6 | 1.1917 |
| 7 | 1.2050 |
| 8 | 1.2276 |
| 9 | 1.0960 |
| 10 | 1.0226 |
| 11 | .9960 |
| 12 | .8483 |

*(Continued)*

The regression equation was used again to predict the number of housing starts based on the linear trend:

$\hat{y} = 11.46 + .0808t \quad t = 61, 62, \ldots, 72$

These figures were multiplied by the seasonal indexes, which resulted in the following forecasts.

| Period | Month | $\hat{y} = 11.46 + .0808t$ | Seasonal Index | Forecasts |
|---|---|---|---|---|
| 61 | January | 16.39 | .5974 | 9.79 |
| 62 | February | 16.47 | .6548 | 10.79 |
| 63 | March | 16.55 | .9800 | 16.22 |
| 64 | April | 16.63 | 1.0697 | 17.79 |
| 65 | May | 16.71 | 1.1110 | 18.57 |
| 66 | June | 16.79 | 1.1917 | 20.01 |
| 67 | July | 16.87 | 1.2050 | 20.33 |
| 68 | August | 16.95 | 1.2276 | 20.81 |
| 69 | September | 17.04 | 1.0960 | 18.67 |
| 70 | October | 17.12 | 1.0226 | 17.50 |
| 71 | November | 17.20 | .9960 | 17.13 |
| 72 | December | 17.28 | .8483 | 14.66 |

This table displays the actual and forecasted housing starts for 2006. Figure 20.9 depicts the time series, trend line, and forecasts.

| Period | Month | Forecasts | Actual |
|---|---|---|---|
| 61 | January | 9.79 | 13.3 |
| 62 | February | 10.79 | 10.1 |
| 63 | March | 16.22 | 12.9 |
| 64 | April | 17.79 | 16.0 |
| 65 | May | 18.57 | 18.8 |
| 66 | June | 20.01 | 16.1 |
| 67 | July | 20.33 | 13.7 |
| 68 | August | 20.81 | 15.6 |
| 69 | September | 18.67 | 12.3 |
| 70 | October | 17.50 | 13.3 |
| 71 | November | 17.13 | 12.2 |
| 72 | December | 14.66 | 12.9 |

The size of the error was measured by MAD and SSE. They are

MAD = 42.55

SSE = 199.13

**FIGURE 20.9 Time Series, Trend, and Forecasts of Housing Starts**

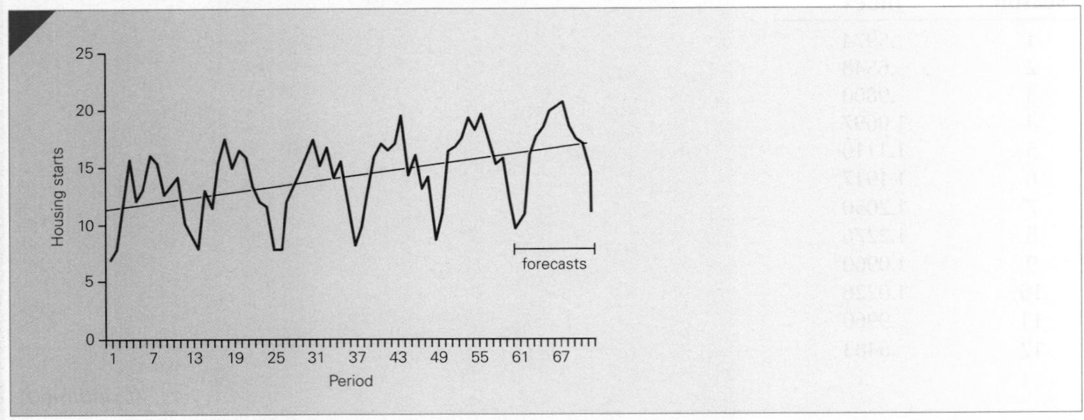

## EXERCISES

**20.34** The following trend line and seasonal indexes were computed from 10 years of quarterly observations. Forecast the next year's time series.

$\hat{y} = 150 + 3t \quad t = 1, 2, \ldots, 40$

| Quarter | Seasonal Index |
|---|---|
| 1 | .7 |
| 2 | 1.2 |
| 3 | 1.5 |
| 4 | .6 |

**20.35** The following trend line and seasonal indexes were computed from 4 weeks of daily observations. Forecast the 7 values for next week.

$\hat{y} = 120 + 2.3t \quad t = 1, 2, \ldots, 28$

| Day | Seasonal Index |
|---|---|
| Sunday | 1.5 |
| Monday | .4 |
| Tuesday | .5 |
| Wednesday | .6 |
| Thursday | .7 |
| Friday | 1.4 |
| Saturday | 1.9 |

**20.36** Use the following autoregressive equation to forecast the next value of the time series if the last observed value is 65.

$\hat{y} = 625 - 1.3y_{t-1}$

**20.37** The following autoregressive equation was developed. Forecast the next value if the last observed value was 11.

$\hat{y} = 155 + 21y_{t-1}$

**20.38** Apply exponential smoothing with $w = .4$ to forecast the next four quarters in Exercise 20.15.

**20.39** Use the seasonal indexes and trend line to forecast the time series for the next 5 days in Exercise 20.22.

**20.40** Refer to Exercise 20.23. Use the seasonal indexes and the trend line to forecast the time series for the next four quarters.

### Applications

**20.41** Use the seasonal indexes and trend line to forecast the quarterly earnings for the years 2014 and 2015 in Exercise 20.24.

**20.42** Refer to Exercise 20.25. Forecast next year's enrollment using the following methods.
a. Autoregressive forecasting model.
b. Exponential smoothing method with $w = .5$.

**20.43** Refer to Exercise 20.26. Forecast next year's merchandise trade balance using the following methods.
a. Autoregressive forecasting model.
b. Exponential smoothing method with $w = .7$.

**20.44** Use the seasonal indexes and trend line from Exercise 20.27 to forecast the number of cable subscribers for the next four quarters.

**20.45** Refer to Exercise 20.28. Use the seasonal indexes and trend line to forecast the number of pizzas to be sold for each of the next 7 days.

**20.46** Apply the trend line and seasonal indexes from Exercise 20.29 to forecast accounts receivable for the next four quarters.

*Exercises 20.47–20.51 are based on the following problem.*

Xr20-47 The revenues (in $millions) of a chain of ice cream stores are listed for each quarter during the previous 5 years.

| | Year | | | | |
|---|---|---|---|---|---|
| Quarter | 2012 | 2013 | 2014 | 2015 | 2016 |
| 1 | 16 | 14 | 17 | 18 | 21 |
| 2 | 25 | 27 | 31 | 29 | 30 |
| 3 | 31 | 32 | 40 | 45 | 52 |
| 4 | 24 | 23 | 27 | 24 | 32 |

**20.47** Plot the time series.

**20.48** Discuss why exponential smoothing is not recommended as a forecasting tool in this problem.

**20.49** Use regression analysis to determine the trend line.

**20.50** Determine the seasonal indexes.

**20.51** Using the seasonal indexes and trend line, forecast revenues for the next four quarters.

**20.52** Xr20-52 The number of housing starts (in 1,000s) in the northeast United States for the years 2004 to 2009 were recorded.
a. Use the 2004–2008 data to calculate the seasonal indexes.
b. Use the indexes and regression analysis to forecast the number of housing starts in 2009.
c. Calculate SSE and MAD to measure how well (or poorly) the forecasts fared.

# Chapter Summary

In this chapter, we discussed the classical time series and its decomposition into trend, seasonal, and random variation. Moving averages and exponential smoothing were used to remove some of the random variation, making it easier to detect trend and seasonality. The long-term trend was measured by regression analysis. Seasonal variation was measured by computing the seasonal indexes. Three forecasting techniques were described in this chapter: exponential smoothing, forecasting with seasonal indexes, and the autoregressive model.

## IMPORTANT TERMS:

Time series 832
Forecasting 832
Trend 833
Secular trend 833
Cyclical variation 834
Seasonal variation 834
Random variation 834
Moving average 834
Exponential smoothing 839
Seasonal indexes 843
Deseasonalizing 846
Seasonally adjusted time series 846
Mean absolute deviation (MAD) 848
Sum of squares for forecast error (SSE) 848
Autoregressive model 852

## SYMBOLS:

| Symbol | Represents |
|---|---|
| $y_y$ | Time series |
| $S_t$ | Exponentially smoothed time series |
| $w$ | Smoothing constant |
| $F_t$ | Forecasted time series |

## FORMULAS:

Exponential smoothing

$$S_t = wy_t + (1 - w)S_{t-1}$$

Mean absolute deviation

$$\text{MAD} = \frac{\sum_{i=1}^{n} |y_t - F_t|}{n}$$

Sum of squares for error

$$SSE = \sum_{i=1}^{n} (y_t - F_t)^2$$

Forecast of trend and seasonality

$$F_t = [b_0 + b_1 t] \times SI_t$$

Autoregressive model

$$y_t = \beta_0 + \beta_1 y_{t-1} + \varepsilon$$

## COMPUTER INSTRUCTIONS:

| Technique | Excel |
|---|---|
| Moving averages | 837 |
| Exponential smoothing | 841 |

Konstantin Chagin/Shutterstock.com

# 21 STATISTICAL PROCESS CONTROL

## CHAPTER OUTLINE



## Detecting the Source of Defective Discs

Data Xm21-00

A company that produces compact discs (CDs) has been receiving complaints from its customers about the large number of discs that will not store data properly. Company management has decided to institute statistical process control to remedy the problem. Every hour, a random sample of 200 discs is taken, and each disc is tested to determine whether it is defective. The number of defective discs in the samples of size 200 for the first 40 hours is shown here (in chronological order). Using these data, draw a *p* chart to monitor the production process. Was the process out of control when the sample results were generated?

| | | | | | | | | | | | | | | | | | | | |
|---|---|---|---|---|---|---|---|---|---|---|---|---|---|---|---|---|---|---|---|
| 19 | 5 | 16 | 20 | 6 | 12 | 18 | 6 | 13 | 15 | 10 | 6 | 7 | 10 | 18 | 20 | 13 | 6 | 8 | 3 |
| 8 | 7 | 4 | 19 | 3 | 19 | 9 | 10 | 10 | 18 | 15 | 16 | 5 | 14 | 3 | 10 | 19 | 13 | 19 | 9 |

Comstock Images/Royalty-free/Getty Images

See solution on page 880.

## Introduction

Operations managers are responsible for developing and maintaining the production processes that deliver quality products and services. In Section 14-6, we demonstrated an important application of the analysis of variance that is used to investigate sources of variation and determine ways to reduce that variation. The goal is to select the methods, materials, machines, and personnel (workers) that combine to yield the production process that features the smallest amount of variation at a reasonable cost. Once the production process is operating, it is necessary to constantly monitor the process to ensure that it functions the way it was designed. The statistical methods we are about to introduce are the most common applications of statistics. At any point in time, there are literally thousands of firms applying these methods. This chapter deals with the subject of **statistical process control or SPC** (formerly called **quality control**).

There are two general approaches to the management of quality. The first approach is to produce the product and, at the completion of the production process, inspect the unit to determine whether it conforms to specifications; if it doesn't, the unit is either discarded or repaired. This approach has several drawbacks. Foremost among them is producing substandard products that are later discarded or fixed is costly. In recent years, this approach has been employed by a decreasing number of companies. Instead, many firms have adopted the **prevention approach**. Using the concepts of hypothesis testing, statistics practitioners concentrate on the production process. Rather than inspect the product, they inspect the process to determine when the process starts producing units that do not conform to specifications. This allows them to correct the production process before it creates a large number of defective products.

In Section 21-1, we discuss the problem of process variation and why it is often the key to the management of quality. In Section 21-2, we also introduce the concept and logic of control charts and show why they work. In the rest of the chapter, we introduce three specific control charts. Neither Excel nor XLSTAT feature control charts. We will use Data Analysis Plus to perform the necessary calculations and draw the charts.

## 21-1 Process Variation

All production processes result in variation; that is, no product is exactly the same as another. You can see for yourself that this is true by weighing, for example, two boxes of breakfast cereal that are supposed to weigh 16 ounces each. They not only will not weigh exactly 16 ounces but also will not even have equal weights. All products exhibit some degree of variation. There are two sources of variation: *chance* and *assignable variation*. **Chance or common variation** is caused by a number of randomly occurring events that are part of the production process and, in general, cannot be eliminated without changing the process. In effect, chance variation was built into the product when the production process was first set up, perhaps as a result of a statistical analysis that attempted to minimize but not necessarily eliminate such variation. In Section 14-6, we discuss statistical techniques that allow firms to experiment to search for sources of variation and, in so doing, reduce the variation.

**Assignable or special variation** is caused by specific events or factors that are frequently temporary and that can usually be identified and eliminated. To illustrate, consider a paint company that produces and sells paint in 1-gallon cans. The cans are filled by an automatic valve that regulates the amount of paint in each can. The designers of the valve acknowledge that there will be some variation in the amount of paint even when the valve is working as it was designed to work. This is chance variation.

Occasionally the valve will malfunction, causing the variation in the amount delivered to each can to increase. This increase is the assignable variation.

Perhaps the best way to understand what is happening is to consider the volume of paint in each can as a random variable. If the only sources of variation are caused by chance, then each can's volume is drawn from identical distributions; that is, each distribution has the same shape, mean, and standard deviation. Under such circumstances, the production process is said to be **under control**. In recognition of the fact that variation in output will occur even when the process is under control and operating properly, most processes are designed so that their products will fall within designated **specification limits** or "specs." For example, the process that fills the paint cans may be designed so that the cans contain between .99 and 1.01 gallons. Inevitably, some event or combination of factors in a production process will cause the process distribution to change. When it does, the process is said to be **out of control**. There are several possible ways for the process to go out of control. Here is a list of the most commonly occurring possibilities and their likely assignable causes.

1. **Level shift**. This is a change in the mean of the process distribution. Assignable causes include machine breakdown, new machine or operator, or a change in the environment. In the paint-can illustration, a temperature or humidity change may affect the density of the paint, resulting in less paint in each can.

2. **Instability**. This is the name we apply to the process when the standard deviation increases. (As we discuss later, a decrease in the standard deviation is desirable.) This may be caused by a machine in need of repair, defective materials, worn tools, or a poorly trained operator. Suppose, for example, that a part in the valve that controls the amount of paint wears down, causing greater variation than normal.

3. **Trend**. When there is a slow steady shift (either up or down) in the process distribution mean, the result is a trend. This is frequently the result of less-than-regular maintenance, operator fatigue, residue or dirt buildup, or gradual loss of lubricant. If the paint-control valve becomes increasingly clogged, we would expect to see a steady decrease in the amount of paint delivered.

4. **Cycle**. This is a repeated series of small observations followed by large observations. Likely assignable causes include environmental changes, worn parts, or operator fatigue. If there are changes in the voltage in the electricity that runs the machines in the paint-can example, we might see series of overfilled cans and series of underfilled cans.

The key to quality is to detect when the process goes out of control so that we can correct the malfunction and restore control. The control chart is the statistical method that we use to detect problems.

## EXERCISES

**21.1** What is meant by *chance variation*?

**21.2** Provide two examples of production processes and their associated chance variation.

**21.3** What is meant by *special variation*?

**21.4** Your education as a statistics practitioner can be considered a production process overseen by the course instructor. The variable we measure is the grade achieved by each student.

a. Discuss chance variation—that is, describe the sources of variation that the instructor has no control over.

b. Discuss special variation.

## 21-2 Control Charts

A **control chart** is a plot of statistics over time. For example, an **$\bar{x}$ chart** plots a series of sample means taken over a period of time. Each control chart contains a **centerline** and *control limits*. The control limit above the centerline is called the **upper control limit** and that below the centerline is called the **lower control limit**. If, when the sample statistics are plotted, all points are randomly distributed between the control limits, we conclude that the process is under control. If the points are not randomly distributed between the control limits, we conclude that the process is out of control.

To illustrate the logic of control charts, let us suppose that in the paint-can example described previously we want to determine whether the central location of the distribution has changed from one period to another. We will draw our conclusion from an $\bar{x}$ chart. For the moment, let us assume that we know the mean $\mu$ and standard deviation $\sigma$ of the process when it is under control. We can construct the $\bar{x}$ chart as shown in Figure 21.1. The chart is drawn so that the vertical axis plots the values of $\bar{x}$ that will be calculated and the horizontal axis tracks the samples in the order in which they are drawn. The centerline is the value of $\mu$. The control limits are set at three standard errors from the centerline. Recall that the standard error of $\bar{x}$ is $\sigma/\sqrt{n}$. Hence, we define the control limits as follows:

$$\text{Lower control limit} = \mu - 3\frac{\sigma}{\sqrt{n}}$$

$$\text{Upper control limit} = \mu + 3\frac{\sigma}{\sqrt{n}}$$

FIGURE **21.1** **$\bar{x}$ Chart: $\mu$ and $\sigma$ Known**

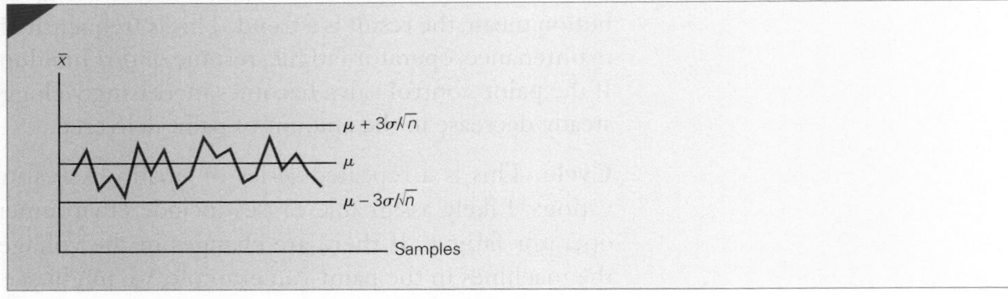


After we've constructed the chart by drawing the centerline and control limits, we use it to plot the sample means, which are joined to make it easier to interpret. The principles underlying control charts are identical to the principles of hypothesis testing. The null and alternative hypotheses are

$H_0$: The process is under control.

$H_1$: The process is out of control.

For an $\bar{x}$ chart, the test statistic is the sample mean $\bar{x}$. However, because we're dealing with a dynamic process rather than a fixed population, we test a series of sample means: We compute the mean for each of a continuing series of samples taken over time. For each series of samples, we want to determine whether there is sufficient evidence to infer that the process mean has changed. We reject the null hypothesis if at any time the sample mean falls outside the control limits. It is logical to ask why we use 3 standard errors and not 2 or 1.96 or 1.645 as we did when we tested hypotheses about a population mean in Chapter 11. The answer lies in the way in which all tests are conducted. Because test conclusions are based on sample data, there are two possible errors. In statistical process control, a Type I error occurs if we conclude that the process is out of control when, in fact, it is not. This error can be quite expensive because the production process must be stopped and the causes of the variation found and repaired. Consequently, we want the probability of a Type I error to be small. With control limits set at 3 standard errors from the mean, the probability of a Type I error for each sample is

$$\alpha = P(|z| > 3) = .0026$$

Recall that a small value of $\alpha$ results in a relatively large value of the probability of a Type II error. A Type II error occurs when at any sample we do not reject a false null hypothesis. This means that, for each sample, we are less likely to recognize when the process goes out of control. However, because we will be performing a series of tests (one for each sample), we will eventually discover that the process is out of control and take steps to rectify the problem.

Suppose that in order to test the production process that fills 1-gallon paint cans, we choose to take a sample of size 4 every hour. Let us also assume that we know the mean and standard deviation of the process distribution of the amount of paint when the process is under control, say, $\mu = 1.001$ and $\sigma = .006$. (This means that when the valve is working the way it was designed, the amount of paint put into each can is a random variable whose mean is 1.001 gallons and whose standard deviation is .006 gallon.) Thus,

$$\text{Centerline} = \mu = 1.001$$

$$\text{Lower control limit} = \mu - 3\frac{\sigma}{\sqrt{n}} = 1.001 - 3\frac{.006}{\sqrt{4}} = 1.001 - .009 = .992$$

$$\text{Upper control limit} = \mu + 3\frac{\sigma}{\sqrt{n}} = 1.001 + 3\frac{.006}{\sqrt{4}} = 1.001 + .009 = 1.010$$

Figure 21.2 depicts a situation in which the first 15 samples were taken when the process was under control. However, after the 15th sample was drawn, the process went out of control and produced sample means outside the control limits. We conclude that the process distribution has changed because the data display variability beyond that predicted for a process with the specified mean and standard deviation. This means that the variation is assignable and that the cause must be identified and corrected.

FIGURE **21.2** $\bar{x}$ **Chart: Process Out of Control**

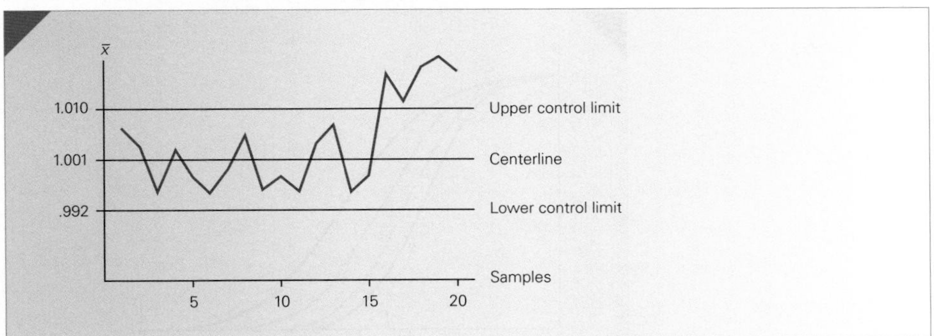

As we stated previously, SPC is a slightly different form of hypothesis testing. The concept is the same, but there are differences that you should be aware of. The most important difference is that when we tested means and proportions in Chapters 11 and 12, we were dealing with fixed but unknown parameters of populations. For instance, in Example 11.1 the population we dealt with was the account balances of the department store customers. The population mean balance was a constant value that we simply did not know. The purpose of the test was to determine whether there was enough statistical evidence to allow us to infer that the mean balance was greater than $170. So we took one sample and based the decision on the sample mean. When dealing with a production process, it's important to realize that the process distribution itself is variable; that is, at any time, the process distribution of the amount of paint fill may change if the valve malfunctions. Consequently, we do not simply take one sample and make the decision. Instead, we plot a number of statistics over time in the control chart. Simply put, in Chapters 11 through 18, we assumed static population distributions with fixed but unknown parameters, whereas in this chapter we assume a dynamic process distribution with parameters subject to possible shifts.

## 21-2a Sample Size and Sampling Frequency

In designing a control chart, the statistics practitioner must select a sample size and a sampling frequency. These decisions are based on several factors, including the costs of making Type I and Type II errors, the length of the production run, and the typical change in the process distribution when the process goes out of control. A useful aid in making the decision is the operating characteristic (OC) curve.

**Operating Characteristic Curve** Recall that in Chapter 11 we drew the **operating characteristic (OC) curve** that plotted the probabilities of Type II errors and population means. Here is how the OC curve for the $\bar{x}$ chart is drawn.

Suppose that when the production process is under control the mean and standard deviation of the process variable are $\mu_0$ and $\sigma$, respectively. For specific values of $\alpha$ and $n$, we can compute the probability of a Type II error when the process mean changes to $\mu_1 = \mu_0 + k\sigma$. A Type II error occurs when a sample mean falls between the control limits when the process is out of control. In other words, the probability of a Type II error is the probability that the $\bar{x}$ chart will be unable to detect a shift of $k\sigma$ in the process mean on the first sample after the shift has occurred. Figure 21.3 depicts the OC curve

FIGURE **21.3** **Operating Characteristic Curve for $n$ = 2, 3, 4, and 5**

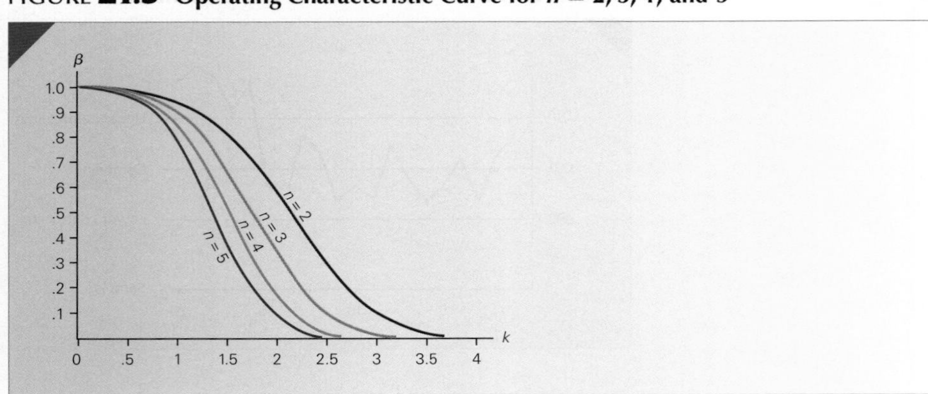

FIGURE **21.4** **Operating Characteristic Curve for $n = 10, 15, 20$, and 25**

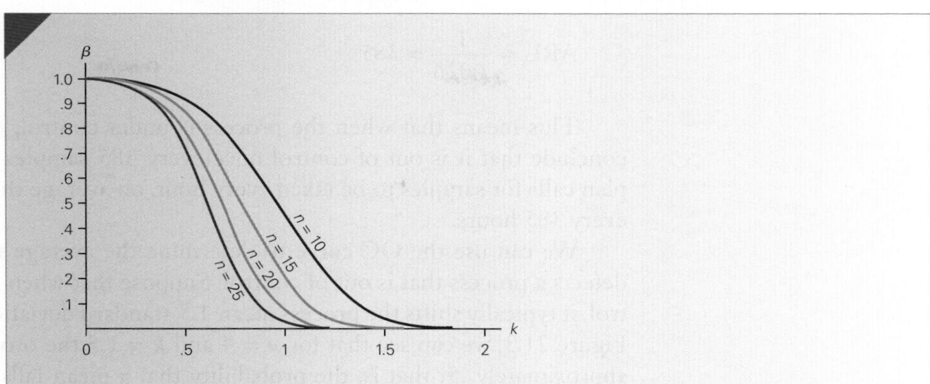


for $n = 2, 3, 4$, and 5. Figure 21.4 is the OC curve for $n = 10, 15, 20$, and 25. (We drew two sets of curves because one alone would not provide the precision we need.) We can use the OC curves to help determine the sample size we should use.

Figure 21.3 tells us that for small shifts in the mean of 1 standard deviation or less, samples of size 2 to 5 produce probabilities of not detecting shifts that range between .8 and .95 (approximately). To appreciate the effect of large probabilities of Type II errors, consider the paint-can illustration. Suppose that when the process goes out of control it shifts the mean by about 1 standard deviation. The probability that the first sample after the shift will not detect this shift is approximately .85. The probability that it will not detect the shift for the first $m$ samples after the shift is $.85^m$. Thus, for $m = 5$ the probability of not detecting the shift for the first five samples after the shift is .44. If the process fills 1,000 cans per hour, a large proportion of the 5,000 cans filled will be overfilled or underfilled (depending on the direction of the shift). Figure 21.4 suggests that when the shift moves the process mean by 1 standard deviation, samples of size 15 or 20 are recommended. For $n = 15$, the probability that a shift of 1 standard deviation will not be detected by the first sample is approximately .2.

If the typical shift is 2 or more standard deviations, samples of size 4 or 5 will likely suffice. For $n = 5$, the probability of a Type II error is about .07.

## 21-2b Average Run Length

The **average run length (ARL)** is the expected number of samples that must be taken before the chart indicates that the process has gone out of control. The ARL is determined by

$$\text{ARL} = \frac{1}{P}$$

where $P$ is the probability that a sample mean falls outside the control limits. Assuming that the control limits are defined as 3 standard errors above and below the centerline, the probability that a sample mean falls outside the control limits when the process is under control is

$$P = P(|z| > 3) = .0026$$

Thus,

$$\text{ARL} = \frac{1}{.0026} = 385$$

This means that when the process is under control, the $\bar{x}$ chart will erroneously conclude that it is out of control once every 385 samples on average. If the sampling plan calls for samples to be taken every hour, on average there will be a *false alarm* once every 385 hours.

We can use the OC curve to determine the average run length until the $\bar{x}$ chart detects a process that is out of control. Suppose that when the process goes out of control, it typically shifts the process mean 1.5 standard deviations to the right or left. From Figure 21.3, we can see that for $n = 4$ and $k = 1.5$ the probability of a Type II error is approximately .5; that is, the probability that a mean falls between the control limits, which indicates that the process is under control when there has been a shift of 1.5 standard deviations, is .5. The probability that the sample mean falls outside the control limits is $P = 1 - .5 = .5$. Thus, the average run length is

$$\text{ARL} = \frac{1}{.5} = 2$$

This means that the control chart will require two samples on average to detect a shift of 1.5 standard deviations. Suppose that a shift of this magnitude results in an unacceptably high number of nonconforming cans. We can reduce that number in two ways: by sampling more frequently or increasing the sample size. For example, if we take samples of size 4 every half hour, then on average it will take 1 hour to detect the shift and make repairs. If we take samples of size 10 every hour, Figure 21.4 indicates that the probability of a Type II error when the shift is 1.5 standard deviations is about .05. Thus, $P = 1 - .05 = .95$ and

$$\text{ARL} = \frac{1}{.95} = 1.05$$

This tells us that a sample size of 10 will allow the statistics practitioner to detect a shift of 1.5 standard deviations about twice as quickly as a sample of size 4.

## 21-2c Changing the Control Limits

Another way to decrease the probability of a Type II error is to increase the probability of making a Type I error. Thus, we may define the control limits so that they are two standard errors above and below the centerline. To judge whether this is advisable, it is necessary to draw the OC curve for this plan.

In our demonstration of the logic of control charts, we resorted to traditional methods of presenting inferential methods; we assumed that the process parameters were known. When the parameters are unknown, we estimate their values from the sample data. In the next two sections, we discuss how to construct and use control charts in more realistic situations. In Section 21-3, we present control charts when the data are interval. In the context of statistical process control, we call these

**control charts for variables**. Section 21-4 demonstrates the use of control charts that record whether a unit is defective or nondefective. These are called **control charts for attributes**.

## EXERCISES

**21.5** If the control limits of an $\bar{x}$ chart are set at 2.5 standard errors from the centerline, what is the probability that on any sample the control chart will indicate that the process is out of control when it is under control?

**21.6** Refer to Exercise 21.5. What is the average run length until the $\bar{x}$ chart signals that the process is out of control when it is under control?

**21.7** The control limits of an $\bar{x}$ chart are set at two standard errors from the centerline. Calculate the probability that on any sample the control chart will indicate that the process is out of control when it is under control.

**21.8** Refer to Exercise 21.7. Determine the ARL until the $\bar{x}$ chart signals that the process is out of control when it is under control.

*Exercises 21.9 to 21.15 are based on the following scenario.*

A production facility produces 100 units per hour and uses an $\bar{x}$ chart to monitor its quality. The control limits are set at 3 standard errors from the mean. When the process goes out of control, it usually shifts the mean by 1.5 standard deviations. Sampling is conducted once per hour with a sample size of 3.

**21.9** On average, how many units will be produced until the control chart signals that the process is out of control when it is under control?

**21.10** Refer to Exercise 21.9.

a. Find the probability that the $\bar{x}$ chart does not detect a shift of 1.5 standard deviations on the first sample after the shift occurs.

b. Compute the probability that the $\bar{x}$ chart will not detect the shift for the first eight samples after the shift.

**21.11** Refer to Exercise 21.10. Find the average run length to detect the shift.

**21.12** The operations manager is unsatisfied with the current sampling plan. He changes it to samples of size 2 every half hour. What is the average number of units produced until the chart indicates that the process is out of control when it is not?

**21.13** Refer to Exercise 21.12.

a. Find the probability that the $\bar{x}$ chart does not detect a shift of 1.5 standard deviations on the first sample after the shift occurs.

b. Compute the probability that the $\bar{x}$ chart will not detect the shift for the first eight samples after the shift.

**21.14** Refer to Exercise 21.13. What is the average run length to detect the shift?

**21.15** Write a brief report comparing the sampling plans described in Exercises 21.9 and 21.12. Discuss the relative costs of the two plans and the frequency of Type I and Type II errors.

*Exercises 21.16 to 21.22 are based on the following scenario.*

A firm that manufactures notebook computers uses statistical process control to monitor all its production processes. For one component, the company draws samples of size 10 every 30 minutes. The company makes 4,000 of these components per hour. The control limits of the $\bar{x}$ chart are set at 3 standard errors from the mean. When the process goes out of control, it usually shifts the mean by .75 standard deviation.

**21.16** On average how many units will be produced until the control chart signals that the process is out of control when it is under control?

**21.17** Refer to Exercise 21.16.

a. Find the probability that the $\bar{x}$ chart does not detect a shift of .75 standard deviation on the first sample after the shift occurs.

b. Compute the probability that the $\bar{x}$ chart will not detect the shift for the first four samples after the shift.

**21.18** Refer to Exercise 21.17. Find the average run length to detect the shift.

**21.19** The company is considering changing the sampling plan so that 20 components are sampled every hour. What is the average number of units produced until the chart indicates that the process is out of control when it is not?

**21.20** Refer to Exercise 21.19.
a. Find the probability that the $\bar{x}$ chart does not detect a shift of .75 standard deviation on the first sample after the shift occurs.
b. Compute the probability that the $\bar{x}$ chart will not detect the shift for the first four samples after the shift.

**21.21** Refer to Exercise 21.20. What is the average run length to detect the shift?

**21.22** Write a brief report comparing the sampling plans described in Exercises 21.16 and 21.19. Discuss the relative costs of the two plans and the frequency of Type I and Type II errors.

# 21-3 Control Charts for Variables: $\overline{X}$ and $S$ Charts

There are several ways to judge whether a change in the process distribution has occurred when the data are interval. To determine whether the distribution means have changed, we employ the $\bar{x}$ chart. To determine whether the process distribution standard deviation has changed, we can use the $S$ (which stands for *standard deviation*) chart or the $R$ (which stands for *range*) chart.

Throughout this textbook, we have used the sample standard deviation to estimate the population standard deviation. However, for a variety of reasons, SPC frequently employs the range instead of the standard deviation. This is primarily because computing the range is simpler than computing the standard deviation. Because many practitioners conducting SPC perform calculations by hand (with the assistance of a calculator), they select the computationally simple range as the method to estimate the process standard deviation. In this section, we will introduce control charts that feature the sample standard deviation. In the online appendix Control Charts for Variables: $\overline{X}$ and R, we employ the sample range to construct our charts.

## 21-3a $\bar{x}$ Chart

In Section 21-2, we determined the centerline and control limits of an $\bar{x}$ chart using the mean and standard deviation of the process distribution. However, it is unrealistic to believe that the mean and standard deviation of the process distribution are known. Thus, to construct the $\bar{x}$ chart, we need to estimate the relevant parameters from the data.

We begin by drawing samples when we have determined that the process is under control. The sample size must lie between 2 and 25. We discuss later how to determine that the process is under control. For each sample, we compute the mean and the standard deviation. The estimator of the mean of the distribution is the mean of the sample means (denoted $\bar{\bar{x}}$):

$$\bar{\bar{x}} = \frac{\sum_{j=1}^{k} \bar{x}_j}{k}$$

where $\bar{x}_j$ is the mean of the $j$th sample and there are $k$ samples. (Note that $\bar{\bar{x}}$ is simply the average of all $nk$ observations.)

To estimate the standard deviation of the process distribution, we calculate the sample variance $s_j^2$ for each sample. We then compute the pooled standard deviation,* which we denote $S$ and define as

$$S = \sqrt{\frac{\sum_{j=1}^{k} s_j^2}{k}}$$

In the previous section, where we assumed that the process distribution mean and variance were known, the centerline and control limits were defined as

$$\text{Centerline} = \mu$$

$$\text{Lower control limit} = \mu - 3\frac{\sigma}{\sqrt{n}}$$

$$\text{Upper control limit} = \mu + 3\frac{\sigma}{\sqrt{n}}$$

Because the values of $\mu$ and $\sigma$ are unknown, we must use the sample data to estimate them. The estimator of $\mu$ is $\bar{x}$, and the estimator of $\mu$ is $S$. Therefore, the centerline and control limits are as shown in the box.

**Centerline and Control Limits for $\bar{x}$ Chart**

$$\text{Centerline} = \bar{\bar{x}}$$

$$\text{Lower control limit} = \bar{\bar{x}} - 3\frac{S}{\sqrt{n}}$$

$$\text{Upper control limit} = \bar{\bar{x}} + 3\frac{S}{\sqrt{n}}$$

EXAMPLE 21.1

Data Xm21-01

## Statistical Process Control at Lear Seating, Part 1

Lear Seating of Kitchener, Ontario, manufactures seats for Chrysler, Ford, and General Motors cars. Several years ago, Lear instituted statistical process control, which has resulted in improved quality and lower costs. One of the components of a front-seat cushion is a wire spring produced from 4-mm (millimeter) steel wire. A machine is used to bend the wire so that the spring's length is 500 mm. If the springs are longer than 500 mm, they will loosen and eventually fall out. If they are too short, they won't easily fit into position. (In fact, in the past, when there were a relatively large number of short springs, workers incurred arm and hand injuries when attempting to install the springs.) To determine whether the process is under control, random samples of four springs are taken every hour. The last 25 samples are shown here. Construct an $\bar{x}$ chart from these data.

*This formula requires that the sample size be the same for all samples, a condition that is imposed throughout this chapter.

| SAMPLE | | | | |
|---|---|---|---|---|
| 1 | 501.02 | 501.65 | 504.34 | 501.10 |
| 2 | 499.80 | 498.89 | 499.47 | 497.90 |
| 3 | 497.12 | 498.35 | 500.34 | 499.33 |
| 4 | 500.68 | 501.39 | 499.74 | 500.41 |
| 5 | 495.87 | 500.92 | 498.00 | 499.44 |
| 6 | 497.89 | 499.22 | 502.10 | 500.03 |
| 7 | 497.24 | 501.04 | 498.74 | 503.51 |
| 8 | 501.22 | 504.53 | 499.06 | 505.37 |
| 9 | 499.15 | 501.11 | 497.96 | 502.39 |
| 10 | 498.90 | 505.99 | 500.05 | 499.33 |
| 11 | 497.38 | 497.80 | 497.57 | 500.72 |
| 12 | 499.70 | 500.99 | 501.35 | 496.48 |
| 13 | 501.44 | 500.46 | 502.07 | 500.50 |
| 14 | 498.26 | 495.54 | 495.21 | 501.27 |
| 15 | 497.57 | 497.00 | 500.32 | 501.22 |
| 16 | 500.95 | 502.07 | 500.60 | 500.44 |
| 17 | 499.70 | 500.56 | 501.18 | 502.36 |
| 18 | 501.57 | 502.09 | 501.18 | 504.98 |
| 19 | 504.20 | 500.92 | 500.02 | 501.71 |
| 20 | 498.61 | 499.63 | 498.68 | 501.84 |
| 21 | 499.05 | 501.82 | 500.67 | 497.36 |
| 22 | 497.85 | 494.08 | 501.79 | 501.95 |
| 23 | 501.08 | 503.12 | 503.06 | 503.56 |
| 24 | 500.75 | 501.18 | 501.09 | 502.88 |
| 25 | 502.03 | 501.44 | 498.76 | 499.39 |

SOLUTION:

COMPUTE

MANUALLY:

The means and standard deviations for each sample were computed and are listed in Table 21.1. We then calculated the mean of the means (which is also the mean of all 100 numbers) and the pooled standard deviation:

$$\bar{\bar{x}} = 500.296$$

$$S = 1.971$$

Thus, the centerline and control limits are

$$\text{Centerline} = \bar{\bar{x}} = 500.296$$

$$\text{Lower control limit} = \bar{\bar{x}} - 3\frac{S}{\sqrt{n}} = 500.296 - 3\frac{1.971}{\sqrt{4}} = 497.340$$

$$\text{Upper control limit} = \bar{\bar{x}} + 3\frac{S}{\sqrt{n}} = 500.296 + 3\frac{1.971}{\sqrt{4}} = 503.253$$

The centerline and control limits are drawn and the sample means plotted in the order in which they occurred. The manually drawn chart is identical to the Data Analysis Plus version shown here.

TABLE **21.1** **Means and Standard Deviations of Samples in Example 21.1**

| SAMPLE | | | | | $\bar{x}_j$ | $s_j$ |
|---|---|---|---|---|---|---|
| 1 | 501.02 | 501.65 | 504.34 | 501.10 | 502.03 | 1.567 |
| 2 | 499.80 | 498.89 | 499.47 | 497.90 | 499.02 | 0.833 |
| 3 | 497.12 | 498.35 | 500.34 | 499.33 | 498.79 | 1.376 |
| 4 | 500.68 | 501.39 | 499.74 | 500.41 | 500.56 | 0.683 |
| 5 | 495.87 | 500.92 | 498.00 | 499.44 | 498.56 | 2.152 |
| 6 | 497.89 | 499.22 | 502.10 | 500.03 | 499.81 | 1.763 |
| 7 | 497.24 | 501.04 | 498.74 | 503.51 | 500.13 | 2.741 |
| 8 | 501.22 | 504.53 | 499.06 | 505.37 | 502.55 | 2.934 |
| 9 | 499.15 | 501.11 | 497.96 | 502.39 | 500.15 | 1.978 |
| 10 | 498.90 | 505.99 | 500.05 | 499.33 | 501.07 | 3.316 |
| 11 | 497.38 | 497.80 | 497.57 | 500.72 | 498.37 | 1.578 |
| 12 | 499.70 | 500.99 | 501.35 | 496.48 | 499.63 | 2.216 |
| 13 | 501.44 | 500.46 | 502.07 | 500.50 | 501.12 | 0.780 |
| 14 | 498.26 | 495.54 | 495.21 | 501.27 | 497.57 | 2.820 |
| 15 | 497.57 | 497.00 | 500.32 | 501.22 | 499.03 | 2.059 |
| 16 | 500.95 | 502.07 | 500.60 | 500.44 | 501.02 | 0.735 |
| 17 | 499.70 | 500.56 | 501.18 | 502.36 | 500.95 | 1.119 |
| 18 | 501.57 | 502.09 | 501.18 | 504.98 | 502.46 | 1.724 |
| 19 | 504.20 | 500.92 | 500.02 | 501.71 | 501.71 | 1.796 |
| 20 | 498.61 | 499.63 | 498.68 | 501.84 | 499.69 | 1.507 |
| 21 | 499.05 | 501.82 | 500.67 | 497.36 | 499.73 | 1.943 |
| 22 | 497.85 | 494.08 | 501.79 | 501.95 | 498.92 | 3.741 |
| 23 | 501.08 | 503.12 | 503.06 | 503.56 | 502.71 | 1.106 |
| 24 | 500.75 | 501.18 | 501.09 | 502.88 | 501.48 | 0.955 |
| 25 | 502.03 | 501.44 | 498.76 | 499.39 | 500.41 | 1.576 |

## DATA Analysis Plus

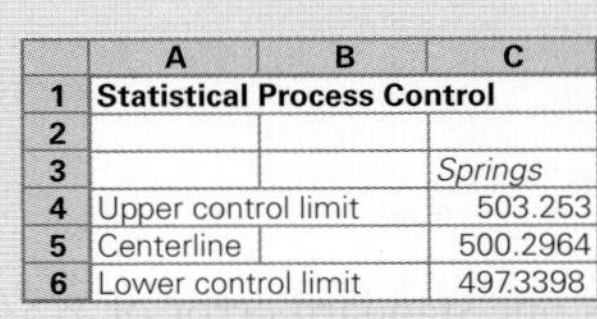

| | A | B | C |
|---|---|---|---|
| 1 | Statistical Process Control | | |
| 2 | | | |
| 3 | | | *Springs* |
| 4 | Upper control limit | | 503.253 |
| 5 | Centerline | | 500.2964 |
| 6 | Lower control limit | | 497.3398 |

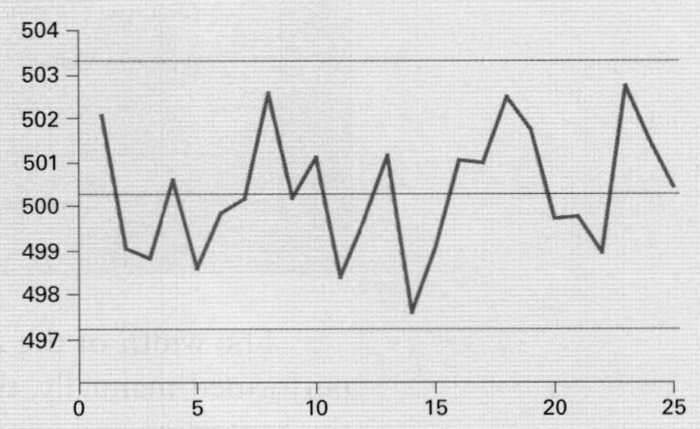


*INSTRUCTIONS*

1. Type or import the data into one column. (Open Xm21-01.)
2. Click **Add-Ins, Data Analysis Plus**, and **Statistical Process Control**.
3. Specify the **Input Range** (A1:101) and the **Sample Size** (4). Click **XBAR (Using S)**.

**INTERPRET**

As you can see, no point lies outside the control limits. We conclude that the variation in the lengths of the springs is caused by chance—that is, there is not enough evidence to infer that the process is out of control. No remedial action by the operator is called for.

We stress that statistical process control allows us to detect assignable variation only. In Example 21.1, we determined that the process is under control, which means that there are no detectable sources of assignable variation. However, this does not mean that the process is a good one. It may well be that the production process yields a large proportion of defective units because the amount of chance variation is large. Recall that in Section 14-6 we noted that chance variation decreases product quality and increases costs. If the costs of producing defective units are high because of large chance variation, we can improve quality and reduce costs only by changing the process itself, which is management's responsibility.

## 21-3b Pattern Tests to Determine When the Process Is Out of Control

When we tested hypotheses in the other parts of this book, we used only one sample statistic to make a decision. However, in statistical process control, the decision is made from a series of sample statistics. In the $\bar{x}$ chart, we make the decision after plotting at least 25 sample means. As a result, we can develop tests that are based on the pattern the sample means make when plotted. To describe them, we need to divide the $\bar{x}$ chart between the control limits into six zones, as shown in Figure 21.5. The C zones represent the area within one standard error of the centerline. The B zones are the regions between one and two standard errors from the centerline. The spaces between two and three standard errors from the centerline are defined as A zones.

FIGURE **21.5** **Zones of $\bar{x}$ Chart**

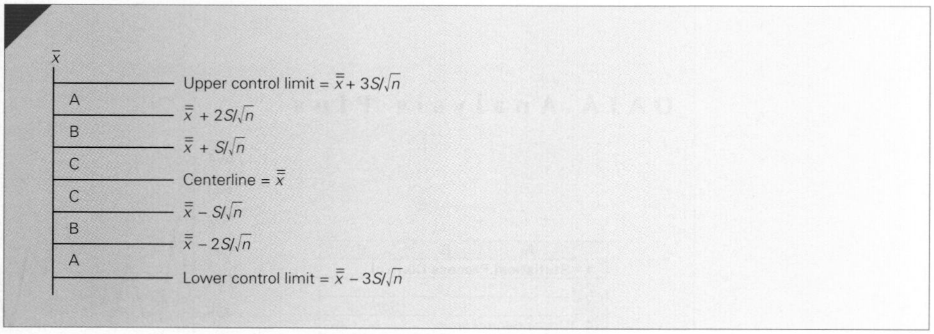

The width of the zones is one standard error of $\bar{x}(S/\sqrt{n})$. If the calculations were performed manually, the value of $S$ will be known. However, if a computer was used, the centerline and control limits are the only statistics printed. We can calculate $S/\sqrt{n}$ by finding the difference between the upper and lower control limits and dividing the difference by 6; that is,

$$S/\sqrt{n} = \frac{(\bar{\bar{x}} + 3S/\sqrt{n}) - (\bar{\bar{x}} - 3S/\sqrt{n})}{6} = \frac{503.253 - 497.340}{6} = .9855$$

Figure 21.6 describes the centerline, control limits, and zones for Example 21.1.

FIGURE **21.6** **Zones of $\bar{x}$ Chart: Example 21.1**

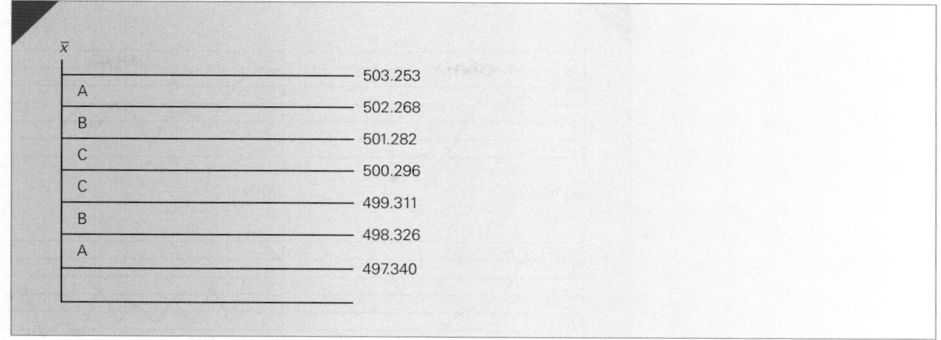


Several pattern tests can be applied. We list eight tests that are conducted by Data Analysis Plus.

*Test 1*: One point beyond zone A. This is the method discussed previously, where we conclude that the process is out of control if any point is outside the control limits.

*Test 2:* Nine points in a row in zone C or beyond (on the same side of the centerline).

*Test 3:* Six increasing or six decreasing points in a row.

*Test 4:* Fourteen points in a row alternating up and down.

*Test 5:* Two out of three points in a row in zone A or beyond (on the same side of the centerline).

*Test 6:* Four out of five points in a row in zone B or beyond (on the same side of the centerline).

*Test 7:* Fifteen points in a row in zone C (on both sides of the centerline).

*Test 8:* Eight points in a row beyond zone C (on both sides of the centerline).

In the examples shown in Figure 21.7, each of the eight tests indicates a process out of control.

All eight tests are based on the same concepts used to test hypotheses throughout this book. In other words, each pattern is a rare event that is unlikely to occur when a process is under control. Thus, when any one of these patterns is recognized, the statistics practitioner has reason to believe that the process is out of control. In fact, it is often possible to identify the cause of the problem from the pattern in the control chart.

Figure 21.8 depicts the zones and the means for Example 21.1. After checking each of the eight pattern tests, we conclude that the process is under control.

## 21-3c Pattern Tests in Practice

There appears to be a great deal of disagreement among statisticians with regard to pattern tests. Some authors and statistical software packages apply eight tests, whereas others employ a different number. In addition, some statisticians apply pattern tests to $\bar{x}$ charts, but not to other charts. Rather than joining the debate with our own opinions, we will follow Minitab's rules. There are eight pattern tests for $\bar{x}$ charts, no pattern tests for $S$ and $R$ charts, and four pattern tests for the chart presented in Section 21-4 ($p$ charts). The same rules apply to Data Analysis Plus.

FIGURE **21.7** **Examples of Patterns Indicating Process Out of Control**

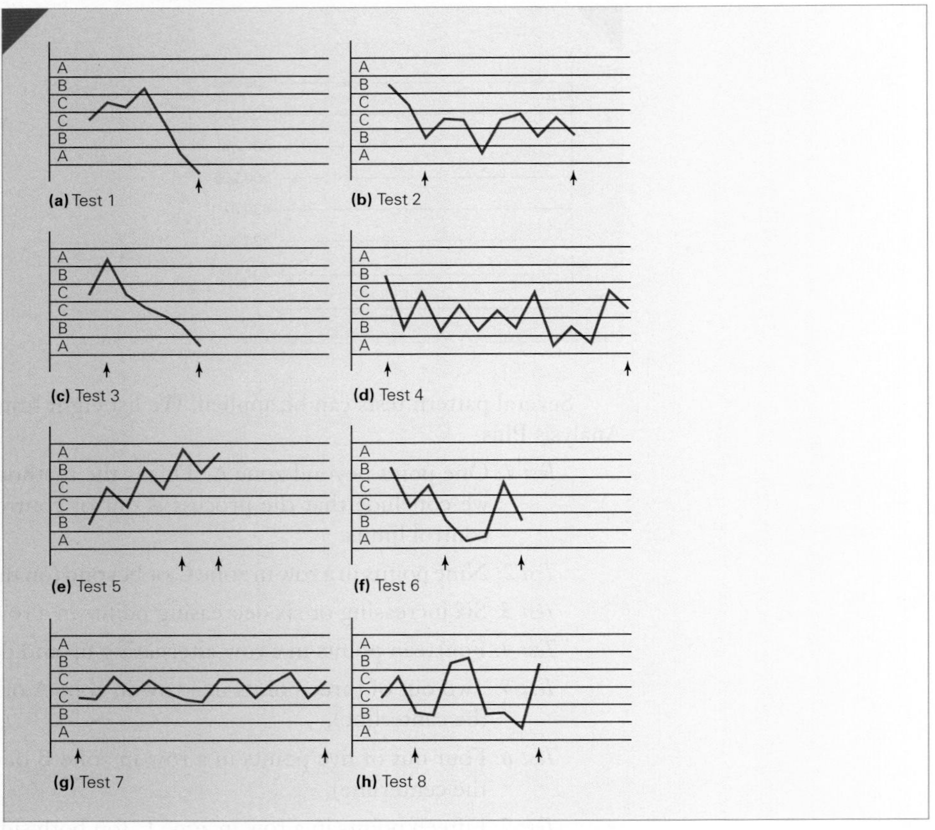


FIGURE **21.8** **$\bar{x}$ Chart with Zones: Example 21.1**

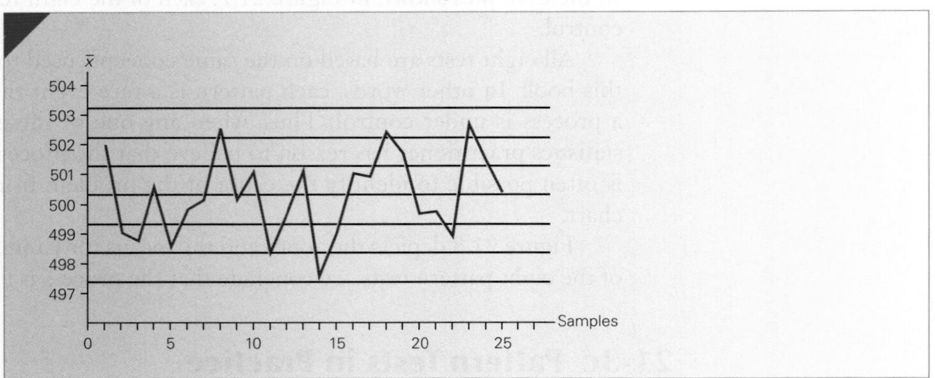


## DATA Analysis Plus

Data Analysis Plus automatically performs all eight tests. Any that fail will be reported on the spreadsheet.

## 21-3d *S* Charts

The ***S* chart** graphs sample standard deviations to determine whether the process distribution standard deviation has changed. The format is similar to that of the $\bar{x}$ chart: The *S* chart will display a centerline and control limits. However, the formulas for the centerline and control limits are more complicated than those for the $\bar{x}$ chart. Consequently, we will not display the formulas; instead we will let the computer do all the work.

EXAMPLE 21.2

## Statistical Process Control at Lear Seating, Part 2

Using the data provided in Example 21.1, determine whether there is evidence to indicate that the process distribution standard deviation has changed over the period when the samples were taken.

SOLUTION:

COMPUTE

DATA Analysis Plus

| | A | B | C |
|---|---|---|---|
| 1 | Statistical Process Control | | |
| 2 | | | |
| 3 | | | *Springs* |
| 4 | Upper control limit | | 4.1288 |
| 5 | Centerline | | 1.822 |
| 6 | Lower control limit | | 0 |

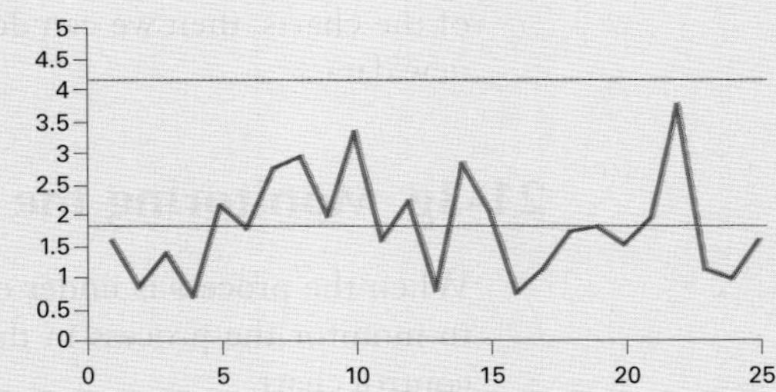


*INSTRUCTIONS*

1. Type or import the data into one column. (Open Xm21-01.)
2. Click **Add-Ins, Data Analysis Plus**, and **Statistical Process Control**.
3. Specify the **Input Range** (A1:101) and the **Sample Size** (4). Click **S**.

INTERPRET

There are no points outside the control limits. Because we do not apply any of the pattern tests, we conclude that there is no evidence to believe that the standard deviation has changed over this period.

## 21-3e Good News and Bad News About *S* Charts

In analyzing *S* charts, we would conclude that the process distribution has changed if we observe points outside the control limits. Obviously, points above the upper control limit indicate that the process standard deviation has increased—an undesirable situation. Points below the lower control limit also indicate that the process standard deviation has changed. However, cases in which the standard deviation has decreased are welcome occurrences because reducing the variation generally leads to improvements in quality. The operations manager should investigate cases where the sample standard deviations or ranges are small to determine the factors that produced such results. The objective is to determine whether permanent improvements in the production process can be made. Care must be exercised in cases in which the $S$ chart reveals a decrease in the standard deviation because this is often caused by improper sampling.

### 21-3f Using the $\bar{x}$ and $S$ Charts

In this section, we have introduced $\bar{x}$ and $S$ charts as separate procedures. In actual practice, however, the two charts must be drawn and assessed together. The reason for this is that the $\bar{x}$ chart uses $S$ to calculate the control limits and zone boundaries. Consequently, if the $S$ chart indicates that the process is out of control, the value of $S$ will not lead to an accurate estimate of the standard deviation of the process distribution. The usual procedure is to draw the $S$ chart first. If it indicates that the process is under control, we then draw the $\bar{x}$ chart. If the $\bar{x}$ chart also indicates that the process is under control, we are then in a position to use both charts to maintain control. If either chart shows that the process was out of control at some time during the creation of the charts, then we can detect and fix the problem and then redraw the charts with new data.

### 21-3g Monitoring the Production Process

When the process is under control, we can use the control chart limits and centerline to monitor the process in the future. We do so by plotting all future statistics on the control chart.

EXAMPLE 21.3

### Statistical Process Control at Lear Seating, Part 3

After determining that the process is under control, the company in Example 21.1 began using the statistics generated in the creation of the $\bar{x}$ and $S$ charts to monitor the production process. The sampling plan calls for samples of size 4 every hour. The following table lists the lengths of the springs taken during the first 6 hours.

| **Sample** | | | | |
|---|---|---|---|---|
| 1 | 502.653 | 498.354 | 502.209 | 500.080 |
| 2 | 501.212 | 494.454 | 500.918 | 501.855 |
| 3 | 500.086 | 500.826 | 496.426 | 503.591 |
| 4 | 502.994 | 500.481 | 502.996 | 503.113 |
| 5 | 500.549 | 498.780 | 502.480 | 499.836 |
| 6 | 500.441 | 502.666 | 502.569 | 503.248 |

SOLUTION:

After each sample is taken, the mean and standard deviation are computed. The standard deviations are plotted on the $S$ chart using the previously determined control limits when the process variation was deemed to be in control. The sample means are plotted on the $\bar{x}$ chart, again using the zone limits determined when the process was deemed to be in control, and the pattern tests are checked after each point is plotted. The first six samples are shown in Figure 21.9. After the standard deviation and mean of the sixth sample are plotted, the technician would stop the production process. Although the process variation still appears to be in control, the fourth and sixth means on the $\bar{x}$ chart combine to indicate that test 5 has failed; there are two out of three points in a row that are in zone A or beyond. Thus, it appears that the process mean has shifted upward. Technicians need to find the source of the problem and make repairs. After repairs are completed, production resumes and new control charts and their centerlines and control limits are recalculated.

FIGURE **21.9** ***S* and $\bar{x}$ Charts for Example 21.3**

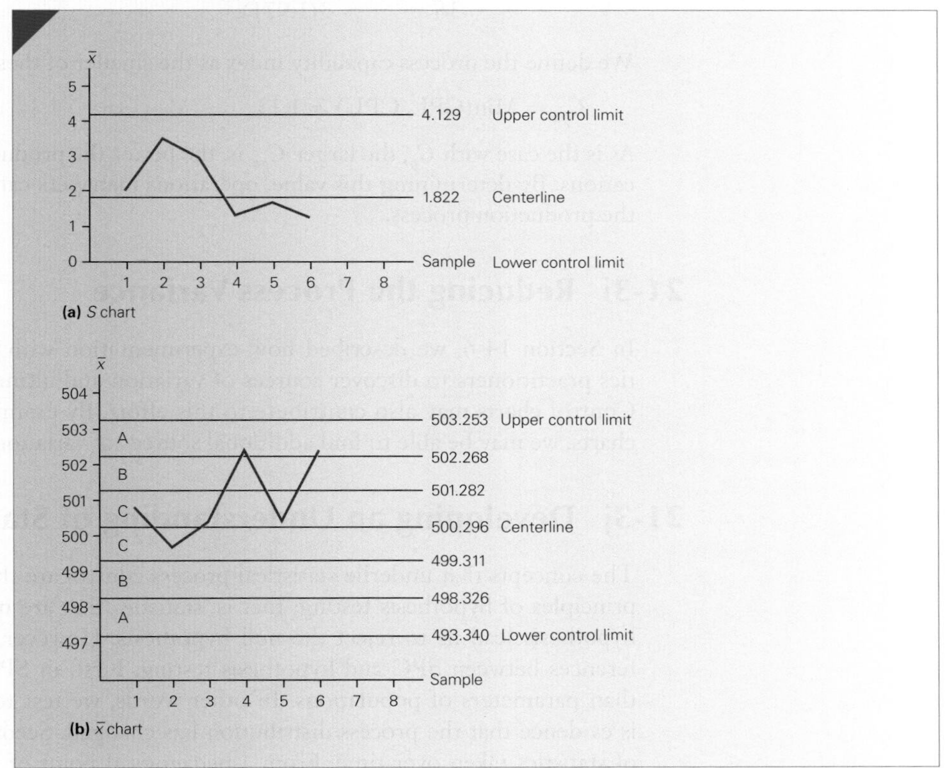


## 21-3h Process Capability Index

In Section 14-6, we discussed the **process capability index**, which measures the capability of the process to produce units whose dimensions fall within the specifications. We defined the index as

$$C_p = \frac{\text{USL} - \text{LSL}}{6\sigma}$$

where USL and LSL are the upper and lower specification limits, respectively. To compute the process capability index, we need to know these limits and the process standard deviation. The standard deviation is a population parameter that is generally unknown. Thus, $C_p$ measures the theoretical or potential process capability. To produce a measure of the process's actual capability, we must use statistics computed in the construction of the control chart. Suppose that in Example 21.1 the operations manager determined that the springs will fit, provided that their lengths fall between the lower specification limit LSL = 493 and the upper specification limit USL = 507. In Example 21.1, we found $\bar{\bar{x}} = 500.296$ and $S = 1.971$.

We define the following:

$$\text{CPL} = \frac{\bar{\bar{x}} - \text{LSL}}{3S} = \frac{500.296 - 493}{3(1.971)} = 1.23$$

$$\text{CPU} = \frac{\text{USL} - \bar{\bar{x}}}{3S} = \frac{507 - 500.296}{3(1.971)} = 1.13$$

We define the process capability index as the smaller of these two indexes; that is,

$$C_{pk} = \text{Min}(\text{CPL}, \text{CPU}) = 1.13$$

As is the case with $C_p$, the larger $C_{pk}$ is, the better the production process meets specifications. By determining this value, operations managers can measure improvements in the production process.

## 21-3i Reducing the Process Variance

In Section 14-6, we described how experimentation with the four M's allows statistics practitioners to discover sources of variation and ultimately reduce that variation. Control charts may also contribute to this effort. By examining the results of control charts, we may be able to find additional sources of variation.

## 21-3j Developing an Understanding of Statistical Concepts

The concepts that underlie statistical process control are the same as the fundamental principles of hypothesis testing; that is, statistics that are not consistent with the null hypothesis lead us to reject the null hypothesis. However, there are two critical differences between SPC and hypothesis testing. First, in SPC we test processes rather than parameters of populations. In other words, we test to determine whether there is evidence that the process distribution has changed. Second, in SPC we test a series of statistics taken over time. From a pedagogical point of view, there is another fundamental difference. Many students of statistics have difficulty identifying the correct hypothesis-testing procedure to employ. However, SPC applications tend to be rather uncomplicated. We use control charts for variables to determine whether the process is under control when the product produced must be measured quantitatively. Identifying the correct technique is seldom difficult and thus does not require the technique-identification skills developed throughout this book.

## EXERCISES

**21.23** Given the following statistics drawn from 30 samples of size 4, calculate the centerline and control limits for the $\bar{x}$ chart.

$\bar{\bar{x}} = 453.6 \qquad S = 12.5$

**21.24** The mean of the sample means and the pooled standard deviation of 40 samples of size 9 taken from a production process under control are shown here. Compute the centerline, control limits, and zone boundaries for the $\bar{x}$ chart.

$\bar{\bar{x}} = 181.1 \qquad S = 11.0$

**21.25** Twenty-five samples of size 4 were taken from a production process. The sample means are listed in chronological order below. The mean of the sample means and the pooled standard deviation are $\bar{\bar{x}} = 13.3$ and $S = 3.8$, respectively.

| | | | | | | |
|---|---|---|---|---|---|---|
| 14.5 | 10.3 | 17.0 | 9.4 | 13.2 | 9.3 | 17.1 |
| 5.5 | 5.3 | 16.3 | 10.5 | 11.5 | 8.8 | 12.6 |
| 10.5 | 16.3 | 8.7 | 9.4 | 11.4 | 17.6 | 20.5 |
| 21.1 | 16.3 | 18.5 | 20.9 | | | |

a. Find the centerline and control limits for the $\bar{x}$ chart.
b. Plot the sample means on the $\bar{x}$ chart.
c. Is the process under control? Explain.

*The following exercises require a computer and statistical software.*

**21.26** Xr21-26 Thirty samples of size 4 were drawn from a production process.
a. Construct an $S$ chart.
b. Construct an $\bar{x}$ chart.
c. Do the charts allow you to conclude that the process is under control?
d. If the process went out of control, which of the following is the likely cause: level shift, instability, trend, or cycle?

**21.27** Xr21-27 The fence of a saw is set so that it automatically cuts 2-by-4 boards into 96-inch lengths needed to produce prefabricated homes. To ensure that the lumber is cut properly, three pieces of wood are measured after each 100 cuts are made. The measurements in inches for the last 40 samples were recorded.
a. Do these data indicate that the process is out of control?
b. If so, when did it go out of control? What is the likely cause: level shift, instability, trend, or cycle?
c. Speculate on how the problem could be corrected.

**21.28** Xr21-28 An arc extinguishing unit (AEU) is used in the high-voltage electrical industry to eliminate the occurrence of electrical flash from one live 25,000-volt switch contact to another. A small but important component of an AEU is a nonconductive sliding bearing called a (ST-90811) pin guide. The dimensional accuracy of this pin guide is critical to the overall operation of the AEU. If any one of its dimensions is "out of spec" (specification), the part will bind within the AEU, causing failure. This would cause the complete destruction of both the AEU and the 25,000 volt-switch contacts, resulting in a power blackout. A pin guide has a square shape with a circular hole in the center, as shown below with its specified dimensions. The specification limits are LSL = .4335 and USL = .4435.

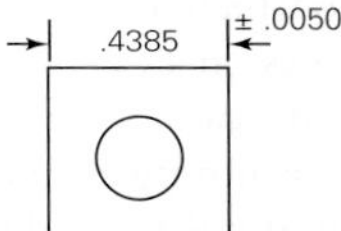


Because of the critical nature of the dimensions of the pin guide, statistical process control is used during long production runs to check that the production process is under control. Suppose that samples of five pin guides are drawn every hour. The results of the last 25 samples were recorded. Do these data allow the technician to conclude that the process is out of control?

**21.29** Refer to Exercise 21.28. Find the process capability index $C_{pk}$.

**21.30** Xr21-30 KW Paints is a company that manufactures various kinds of paints and sells them in 1- and 4-liter cans. The cans are filled on an assembly line with an automatic valve regulating the amount of paint. If the cans are overfilled, paint and money will be wasted. If the cans are underfilled, customers will complain. To ensure that the proper amount of paint goes into each can, statistical process control is used. Every hour, five cans are opened, and the volume of paint is measured. The results from the last 30 hours from the 1-liter production line were recorded. To avoid rounding errors, we recorded the volumes in cubic centimeters (cc) after subtracting 1,000. Thus, the file contains the amounts of overfill and underfill. Draw the $\bar{x}$ and $S$ charts to determine whether the process is under control.

**21.31** Refer to Exercise 21.30. If the lower and upper specification limits are 995 cc and 1005 cc, respectively, what is $C_{pk}$?

**21.32** Xr21-32 Lear Seating of Kitchener, Ontario, produces seats for Cadillacs and other GM cars and trucks. The Cadillac seat includes a part called the EK headrest. The frame of the headrest is made from steel rods. A machine is used to bend the rod into a U-shape described as shown. The width is critical; if it is too wide or too narrow, it will not fit into the holes drilled into the seat frame. The process is checked by drawing samples of size 3 every 2 hours. The last 20 samples were recorded.

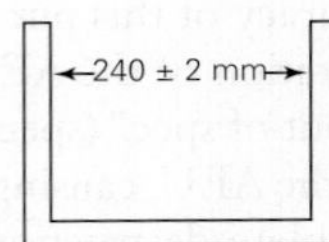


a. What do these data tell you about the process?
b. If it went out of control, at what sample did this occur?
c. What is the likely assignable cause?

**21.33** Xr21-33 The degree to which nuts and bolts are tightened in numerous places on a car is often important. For example, in Toyota cars, a nut holds the rear signal light. If the nut is not tightened sufficiently, it will loosen and fall off; if it is too tight, the light may break. The nut is tightened with a torque wrench with a set clutch. The target torque is 8 kgf/cm (kilogram-force per centimeter) with specification limits LSL = 7kgf/cm and USL = 9 kgf/cm. Statistical process control is employed to constantly check the process. Random samples of size 4 are drawn after every 200 nuts are tightened. The data from the last 25 samples were recorded.

a. Determine whether the process is under control.
b. If it is out of control, identify when this occurred and the likely cause.

**21.34** Xr21-34 The seats for the *F*-150 series Ford trucks are manufactured by Lear Seating. The frames must be 1,496 mm wide with specification limits LSL = 1,486 mm and USL = 1,506 mm. Frames that are wider than 1,506 mm or narrower than 1,486 mm result in assembly problems because seat cushions and/or other parts won't fit. The process is tested by drawing random samples of five frames every 2 hours. The last 25 samples were recorded. What can we conclude from these data?

**21.35** Xr21-35 Long Manufacturing produces heat exchangers, primarily for the automotive industry. One such product, a transmission oil cooler, is used in the cooling of bus transmissions. It is composed of a series of copper tubes that are soldered into a header. The header must have a diameter of 4.984 inches with specification limits LSL = 4.978 inches and USL = 4.990 inches. Oversized headers result in fluid mixing and possible failure of the device. For every 100 headers produced, the operations manager draws a sample of size 4. The data from the last 25 samples were recorded. What can we conclude from these data?

**21.36** Find the process capability index for Exercise 21.35.

**21.37** Xr21-37 Refer to Exercise 21.35. Nuts and bolts are used in the assembly of the transmission oil coolers. They are supposed to be tightened by a torque wrench to 7 foot-pounds with specification limits LSL = 6 foot-pounds and USL = 8 foot-pounds. To test the process, three nuts are tested every 3 hours. The results for the last 75 hours were recorded. Does it appear that the process is under control?

**21.38** Xr21-38 Motor oil is packaged and sold in plastic bottles. The bottles are often handled quite roughly in delivery to the stores (bottles are packed in boxes, which are stacked to conserve truck space), in the stores themselves, and by consumers. The bottles must be hardy enough to withstand this treatment without leaking. Before leaving the plant, the bottles undergo statistical process control procedures. Five out of every 10,000 bottles are sampled. The burst strength (the pressure required to burst the bottle) is measured in pounds per square inch (psi). The process is designed to produce bottles that can withstand as much as 800 psi. The burst strengths of the last 30 samples were recorded.

a. Draw the appropriate control chart(s).
b. Does it appear that the process went out of control? If so, when did this happen, and what are the likely causes and remedies?

**21.39** Xr21-39 Almost all computer hardware and software producers offer a toll-free telephone number to solve problems associated with their products. The ability to work quickly to resolve difficulties is critical. One software maker's policy is that all calls must be answered by a software consultant within 120 seconds. (All calls are initially answered by computer and the caller is put on hold until a consultant attends to the caller.) To help maintain the quality of the service, four calls per day are monitored. The amount of time before the consultant responds to the calls was recorded for the last 30 days.

a. Draw the appropriate control chart(s).
b. Does it appear that the process went out of control? If so, when did this happen, and what are the likely causes and remedies?

**21.40** Xr21-40 Plastic pipe is used for plumbing in almost all new homes. If the pipes are too narrow or too wide, they will not connect properly with other parts of the plumbing system. A manufacturer of 3-inch-diameter pipes uses statistical process control to maintain the quality of its products. The sampling plan is to draw samples of three 10-foot-long pipes every hour and measure the diameters. Twenty hours ago, the production process was shut down for repairs. The results of the first 20 samples taken since were recorded. Does it appear that the production process is under control?

**21.41** If the specification limits for the plastic pipes in Exercise 21.40 are LSL = 2.9 inches and USL = 3.1 inches, determine the process capability index $C_{pk}$.

**21.42** Calculate the process capability index for Exercise 21.34. Does the value of this index indicate that the production process is poor? Explain.

## 21-4 Control Charts for Attributes: *P* Chart

In this section, we introduce a control chart that is used to monitor a process whose results are categorized as either defective or nondefective. We construct a ***p* chart** to track the proportion of defective units in a series of samples.

### 21-4a *p* Chart

We draw the $p$ chart in a way similar to the construction of the $\bar{x}$ chart. We draw samples of size $n$ from the process at a minimum of 25 time periods. For each sample, we calculate the sample proportion of defective units, which we label $\hat{p}_j$. We then compute the mean of the sample proportions, which is labeled $\bar{p}$; that is,

$$\bar{p} = \frac{\sum_{j=1}^{k} \hat{p}_j}{k}$$

The centerline and control limits are as follows.

**Centerline and Control Limits for the *p* Chart**

$$\text{Centerline} = \bar{p}$$

$$\text{Lower control limit} = \bar{p} - 3\sqrt{\frac{\bar{p}(1-\bar{p})}{n}}$$

$$\text{Upper control limit} = \bar{p} + 3\sqrt{\frac{\bar{p}(1-\bar{p})}{n}}$$

If the lower limit is negative, set it equal to 0.

### 21-4b Pattern Tests

Here are the tests that Data Analysis Plus performs:

*Test 1:* One point beyond zone A.

*Test 2:* Nine points in a row in zone C or beyond (on the same side of the centerline).

*Test 3:* Six increasing or six decreasing points in a row.

*Test 4:* Fourteen points in a row alternating up and down.

We'll demonstrate this technique using the chapter-opening example.

## Detecting the Source of Defective Discs: Solution

Comstock Images/Royalty-free/Getty Images

For each sample, we compute the proportion of defective discs and calculate the mean sample proportion, which is $\bar{p} = .05762$. Thus,

$$\text{Centerline} = \bar{p} = .05762$$

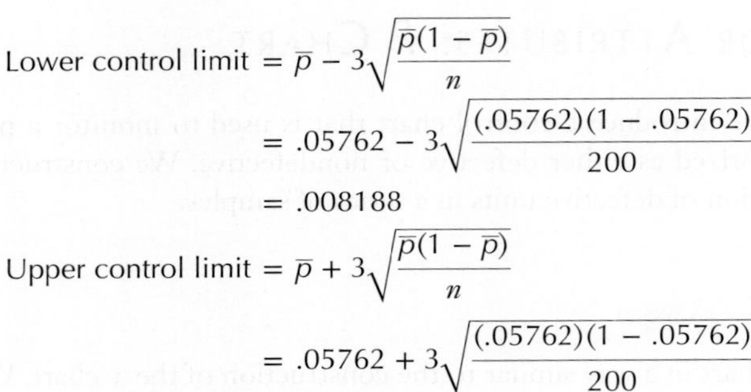

$$\text{Lower control limit} = \bar{p} - 3\sqrt{\frac{\bar{p}(1-\bar{p})}{n}}$$

$$= .05762 - 3\sqrt{\frac{(.05762)(1-.05762)}{200}}$$

$$= .008188$$

$$\text{Upper control limit} = \bar{p} + 3\sqrt{\frac{\bar{p}(1-\bar{p})}{n}}$$

$$= .05762 + 3\sqrt{\frac{(.05762)(1-.05762)}{200}}$$

$$= .1071$$

Because

$$\sqrt{\frac{\bar{p}(1-\bar{p})}{n}} = \sqrt{\frac{(.05762)(1-.05762)}{200}} = .01648$$

The boundaries of the zones are as follows:

Zone C: $.05762 \pm .01648 = (.04114, .0741)$
Zone B: $.05762 \pm 2(.01648) = (.02467, .09057)$
Zone A: $.05762 \pm 3(.01648) = (.008188, .1071)$

The following output exhibits this $p$ chart.

**DATA Analysis Plus**

| | A | B | C |
|---|---|---|---|
| 1 | **Statistical Process Control** | | |
| 2 | | | |
| 3 | | | *Disks* |
| 4 | Upper control limit | | 0.1071 |
| 5 | Centerline | | 0.0576 |
| 6 | Lower control limit | | 0.0082 |

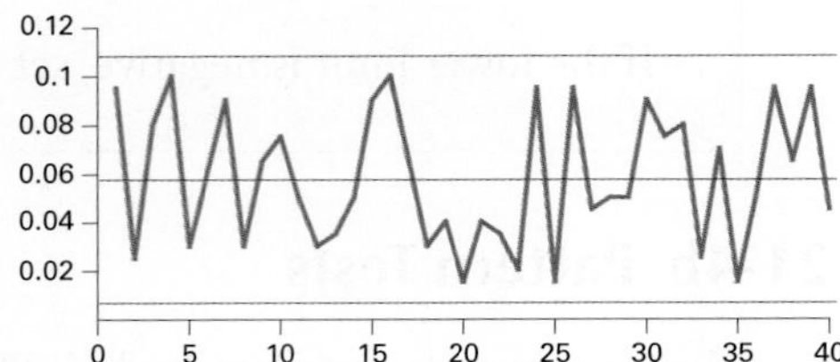


*INSTRUCTIONS*

1. Type or import the data into one column. (Open Xm21-00.)
2. Click **Add-Ins, Data Analysis Plus**, and **Statistical Process Control**.
3. Specify the **Input Range** (A1:41) and the **Sample Size** (200). Click **P**.

## INTERPRET

None of the points lies outside the control limits (test 1), and the other test results are negative. There is no evidence to infer that the process is out of control. However, this does not mean that 5.76% is an acceptable proportion of defects. Management should continually improve the process to reduce the defective rate and improve the process.

The comment we made about $S$ charts is also valid for $p$ charts: Sample proportions that are less than the lower control limit indicate a change in the process that we would like to make permanent. We need to investigate the reasons for such a change just as vigorously as we investigate the causes of large proportions of defects.

## EXERCISES

**21.43** To ensure that a manufacturing process is under control, 40 samples of size 1,000 were drawn, and the number of defectives in each sample was counted. The mean sample proportion was .035. Compute the centerline and control limits for the $p$ chart.

**21.44** Xr21-44 Random samples of 200 copier machines were taken on an assembly line every hour for the past 25 hours. The number of defective machines is shown here. Are there any points beyond the control limits? If so, what do they tell you about the production process?

3 5 3 2 2 11 12 6 7 5 0 7 8
2 10 6 4 2 10 5 4 11 10 13 14

**21.45** Xr21-45 Raytheon of Canada Limited produces printed circuit boards (PCBs), which involve a number of soldering operations. At the end of the process, the PCBs are tested to determine whether they work properly. There are several causes of PCB failure, including bad flux, improper heating, and impurities. A reject rate of less than .80% is considered acceptable. Statistical process control is used by Raytheon to constantly check quality. Every hour, 500 PCBs are tested. The number of defective PCBs for the past 25 hours is shown here. Draw a $p$ chart and apply the pattern tests to determine whether the process is under control.

3 1 2 2 1 2 3 3 3 2 3 0 0
0 2 0 0 2 4 1 1 1 4 1 3

**21.46** Xr21-46 A plant produces 1,000 cordless telephones daily. A random sample of 100 telephones is inspected each day. After 30 days, the following number of defectives were found. Construct a $p$ chart to determine whether the process is out of control.

5 0 4 3 0 3 1 1 5 0 2 1 6 0 3
0 5 5 8 5 0 1 9 6 11 6 6 4 5 10

**21.47** Xr21-47 The Woodsworth Publishing Company produces millions of books containing hundreds of millions of pages each year. To ensure the quality of the printed page, Woodsworth uses statistical process control. In each production run, 1,000 pages are randomly inspected. The examiners look for print clarity and whether the material is centered on the page properly. The numbers of defective pages in the last 40 production runs are listed here. Draw the $p$ chart. Using the pattern tests, can we conclude that the production process is under control?

11 9 17 19 15 15 18 21 18 6 27 14 7 18
18 19 17 15 7 16 17 22 12 12 12 16 12
9 21 17 20 17 17 18 23 29 24 27 23 21

*The following exercises require the use of a computer and statistical software.*

**21.48** Xr21-48 A company that manufactures batteries employs statistical process control to ensure that its product functions properly. The sampling plan for the D-cell batteries calls for samples of 500 batteries to be taken and tested. The numbers of defective batteries in the last 30 samples were recorded. Determine whether the process is under control.

**21.49** Xr21-49 A courier delivery company advertises that it guarantees delivery by noon the following day. The statistical process control plan calls for sampling 2,000 deliveries each day to ensure that the advertisement is reasonable. The number of late deliveries for the last 30 days were recorded. What can we conclude from these data?

**21.50** Xr21-50 Optical scanners are used in all supermarkets to speed the checkout process. Whenever the scanner fails to read the bar code on the product, the cashier is required to manually punch the code into the register. Obviously, unreadable bar codes slow the checkout process. Statistical process control is used to determine whether the scanner is working properly. Once a day at each checkout counter, a sample of 500 scans is taken, and the number of times the scanner is unable to read the bar code is determined. (The sampling process is performed automatically by the cash register.) The results for one checkout counter for the past 25 days were recorded.

a. Draw the appropriate control chart(s).
b. Does it appear that the process went out of control? If so, identify when this happened and suggest several possible explanations for the cause.

## CHAPTER SUMMARY

In this chapter, we introduced **statistical process control** and explained how it contributes to the maintenance of quality. We discussed how **control charts** detect changes in the process distribution and introduced the **$\bar{x}$ chart**, **$S$ chart**, and **$p$ chart**.

### IMPORTANT TERMS:

Statistical process control (SPC) 858
Quality control 858
Prevention approach 858
Chance or common variation 858
Assignable or special variation 858
Under control 859
Specification limits 859
Out of control 859
Control chart 860
$\bar{x}$ chart 860
Centerline 860
Upper control limit 860
Lower control limit 860
Operating characteristic (OC) curve 862
Average run length (ARL) 863
Control charts for variables 865
Control charts for attributes 865
$S$ chart 873
Process capability index 875
$p$ chart 879

### SYMBOLS:

| Symbol | Pronounced | Represents |
|---|---|---|
| $S$ | | Pooled standard deviation |
| $s_j$ | *s*-sub-*j* | Standard deviation of the *j*th sample |
| $\hat{p}_j$ | *p*-hat-sub-*j* | Proportion of defectives in *j*th sample |
| $\bar{p}$ | *p*-bar | Mean proportion of defectives |

## FORMULAS:

Centerline and control limits for $\bar{x}$ chart using $S$

Centerline $= \bar{\bar{x}}$

$$\text{Lower control limit} = \bar{\bar{x}} - 3\frac{S}{\sqrt{n}}$$

$$\text{Upper control limit} = \bar{\bar{x}} + 3\frac{S}{\sqrt{n}}$$

Centerline and control limits for the $p$ chart

Centerline $= \bar{p}$

$$\text{Lower control limit} = \bar{p} - 3\sqrt{\frac{\bar{p}(1-\bar{p})}{n}}$$

$$\text{Upper control limit} = \bar{p} + 3\sqrt{\frac{\bar{p}(1-\bar{p})}{n}}$$

## COMPUTER OUTPUT AND INSTRUCTIONS:

| Technique | Data Analysis Plus |
|---|---|
| $\bar{x}$ chart using $S$ | 869 |
| $S$ chart | 873 |
| $p$ chart | 880 |

22

Rubberball/Mike Kemp/Getty Images

# DECISION ANALYSIS

**CHAPTER OUTLINE**



## Acceptance Sampling

A factory produces a small but important component used in computers. The factory manufactures the component in 1,000-unit lots. Because of the relatively advanced technology, the manufacturing process results in a large proportion of defective units. In fact, the operations manager has observed that the percentage of defective units per lot has been either 15% or 35%. In the past year, 60% of the lots have had 15% defectives, and 40% have had 35% defectives. The current policy of the company is to send the lot to the customer, replace all defectives, and pay any additional costs. The total cost of replacing a defective unit that has been sent to the customer is $10/unit. Because of the high costs, the company management is considering inspecting all

Image Source/Getty Images

**On page 897 we provide answers to our questions.**

units and replacing the defective units before shipment. The sampling cost is \$2/unit, and the replacement cost is \$.50/unit. Each unit sells for \$5.

a. Based on the history of the past year, should the company adopt the 100% inspection plan?
b. Is it worthwhile to take a sample of size 2 from the lot before deciding whether to inspect 100%?

## INTRODUCTION

In previous chapters, we dealt with techniques for summarizing data in order to make decisions about population parameters and population characteristics. Our focus in this chapter is also on decision making, but the types of problems we deal with here differ in several ways. First, the technique for hypothesis testing concludes with either rejecting or not rejecting some hypothesis concerning a dimension of a population. In decision analysis, we deal with the problem of selecting one alternative from a list of several possible decisions. Second, in hypothesis testing, the decision is based on the statistical evidence available. In decision analysis, there may be no statistical data, or if there are data, the decision may depend only partly on them. Third, costs (and profits) are only indirectly considered (in the selection of a significance level or in interpreting the *p*-value) in the formulation of a hypothesis test. Decision analysis directly involves profits and losses. Because of these major differences, the only topics covered previously in the text that are required for an understanding of decision analysis are probability (including Bayes's Law) and expected value.

## 22-1 DECISION PROBLEM

You would think that, by this point in the text, we would already have introduced all the necessary concepts and terminology. Unfortunately, because decision analysis is so radically different from statistical inference, several more terms must be defined. They will be introduced in the following example.

EXAMPLE 22.1

### An Investment Decision

A man wants to invest \$1 million for 1 year. After analyzing and eliminating numerous possibilities, he has narrowed his choice to one of three alternatives. These alternatives are referred to as **acts** and are denoted $a_i$.

$a_1$: Invest in a guaranteed income certificate paying 3%.
$a_2$: Invest in a bond with a coupon value of 2%.
$a_3$: Invest in a well-diversified portfolio of stocks.

He believes that the payoffs associated with the last two acts depend on a number of factors, foremost among which is interest rates. He concludes that there are three possible **states of nature**, denoted $s_j$.

$s_1$: Interest rates increase.
$s_2$: Interest rates stay the same.
$s_3$: Interest rates decrease.

After further analysis, he determines the amount of profit he will make for each possible combination of an act and a state of nature. Of course, the payoff for the guaranteed income certificate will be \$30,000 no matter which state of nature occurs. The profits from each alternative investment are summarized in Table 22.1, in what is called a **payoff table**. Notice that for example, when the decision is $a_2$ and the state of nature is $s_1$, the investor would suffer a \$15,000 loss, which is represented by a –\$15,000 payoff.

TABLE **22.1** **Payoff Table for Example 22.1**

| STATES OF NATURE | $a_1$ (GIC) | $a_2$ (BOND) | $a_3$ (STOCKS) |
|---|---|---|---|
| $s_1$ (interest rates increase) | \$30,000 | –\$15,000 | \$40,000 |
| $s_2$ (interest rates stay the same) | 30,000 | 20,000 | 27,500 |
| $s_3$ (interest rates decrease) | 30,000 | 60,000 | 15,000 |

Another way of expressing the consequence of an act involves measuring the opportunity loss associated with each combination of an act and a state of nature. An **opportunity loss** is the difference between what the decision maker's profit for an act is and what the profit could have been had the best decision been made. For example, consider the first row of Table 22.1. If $s_1$ is the state of nature that occurs and the investor chooses act $a_1$, he makes a profit of \$30,000. However, had he chosen act $a_3$, he would have made a profit of \$40,000. The difference between what he could have made (\$40,000) and what he actually made (\$30,000) is the opportunity loss. Thus, given that $s_1$ is the state of nature, the opportunity loss of act $a_1$, is \$10,000. The opportunity loss of act $a_2$ is \$55,000, which is the difference between \$40,000 and –\$15,000. The opportunity loss of act $a_3$ is 0, because there is no opportunity loss when the best alternative is chosen. In a similar manner, we can compute the remaining opportunity losses for this example (see Table 22.2). Notice that we can never experience a negative opportunity loss.

TABLE **22.2** **Opportunity Loss Table for Example 22.1**

| STATES OF NATURE | $a_1$ (GIC) | $a_2$ (BOND) | $a_3$ (STOCKS) |
|---|---|---|---|
| $s_1$ (interest rates increase) | \$10,000 | \$55,000 | 0 |
| $s_2$ (interest rates stay the same) | 0 | 10,000 | 2,500 |
| $s_3$ (interest rates decrease) | 30,000 | 0 | 45,000 |

## Decision Trees

Most problems involving a simple choice of alternatives can readily be resolved by using the payoff table (or the opportunity loss table). In other situations, however, the decision maker must choose between sequences of acts. In Section 22-2, we introduce one form of such situations. In these cases, a payoff table will not suffice to determine the best alternative; instead, we require a **decision tree**.

In Chapter 6, we suggested the probability tree as a useful device for computing probabilities. In this type of tree, all the branches represent stages of events. In a decision tree, however, the branches represent both acts and events (states of nature). We

FIGURE **22.1** **Decision Tree for Example 22.1**

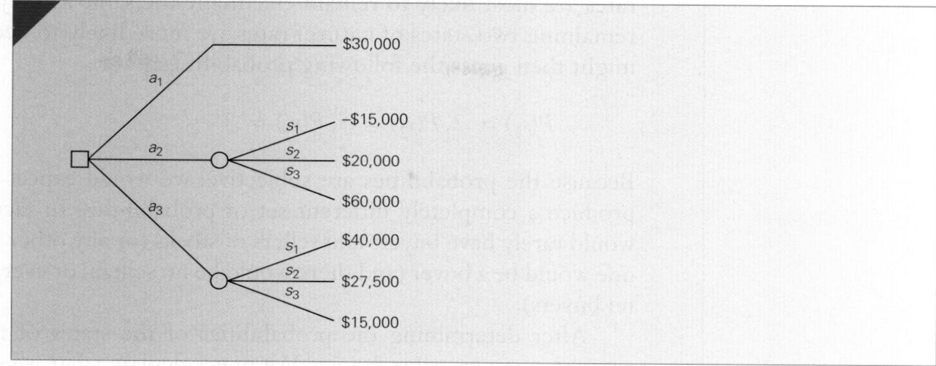


distinguish between them in the following way: A square node represents a point where a decision is to be made; a point where a state of nature occurs is represented by a round node. Figure 22.1 depicts the decision tree for Example 22.1.

The tree begins with a square node; that is, we begin by making a choice among $a_1, a_2$, and $a_3$. The branches emanating from the square node represent these alternatives. At the ends of branches $a_2$ and $a_3$, we reach round nodes representing the occurrence of some state of nature. These are depicted as branches representing $s_1, s_2$, and $s_3$. At the end of branch $a_1$, we don't really have a state of nature, because the payoff is fixed at $30,000 no matter what happens to interest rates.

At the ends of the branches, the payoffs are shown (alternatively, we could have worked with opportunity losses instead of with payoffs). These are, of course, the same values that appear in Table 22.1.

Up to this point, all we have done is set up the problem; we have not made any attempt to determine the decision. It should be noted that in many real-life problems, determining the payoff table or decision tree can be a formidable task in itself. Many managers, however, have observed that this task is often extremely helpful in decision making.

## Expected Monetary Value Decision

In many decision problems, it is possible to assign probabilities to the states of nature. For example, if the decision involves trying to decide whether to draw to an inside straight in the game of poker, the probability of succeeding can easily be determined by the use of simple rules of probability. If we must decide whether to replace a machine that has broken down frequently in the past, we can assign probabilities on the basis of the relative frequency of the breakdowns. In many other instances, however, formal rules and techniques of probability cannot be applied. In Example 22.1, the historical relative frequencies of the ups and downs of interest rates will supply scant useful information to help the investor assign probabilities to the behavior of interest rates during the coming year. In such cases, probabilities must be assigned subjectively. In other words, the determination of the probabilities must be based on the experience, knowledge, and (perhaps) guesswork of the decision maker.

If, in Example 22.1, the investor has some knowledge about a number of economic variables, he might have a reasonable guess about what will happen to interest rates in the next year. Suppose, for example, that our investor believes that future interest rates are most likely to remain essentially the same as they are today and that (of the remaining two states of nature) rates are more likely to decrease than to increase. He might then guess the following probabilities:

$$P(s_1) = .2, P(s_2) = .5, P(s_3) = .3$$

Because the probabilities are subjective, we would expect another decision maker to produce a completely different set of probabilities. In fact, if this were not true, we would rarely have buyers and sellers of stocks (or any other investment), because everyone would be a buyer (and there would be no sellers) or everyone would be a seller (with no buyers).

After determining the probabilities of the states of nature, we can address the *expected monetary value decision*. We now calculate what we expect will happen for each decision. Because we generally measure the consequences of each decision in monetary terms, we compute the **expected monetary value (EMV)** of each act. Recall from Section 7-1 that we calculate expected values by multiplying the values of the random variables by their respective probabilities and then summing the products. Thus, in our example, the expected monetary value of alternative $a_1$ is:

$$\text{EMV}(a_1) = .2(30{,}000) + .5(30{,}000) + .3(30{,}000) = \$30{,}000$$

The expected values of the other decisions are found in the same way:

$$\text{EMV}(a_2) = .2(-15{,}000) + .5(20{,}000) + .3(60.000) = \$25{,}000$$
$$\text{EMV}(a_3) = .2(40{,}000) + .5(27{,}500) + .3(15{,}000) = \$26{,}250$$

We choose the decision with the largest expected monetary value, which is $a_1$, and label its expected value EMV*. Hence, EMV* = \$30,000.

In general, the expected monetary values do not represent possible payoffs. For example, the expected monetary value of act $a_2$ is \$25,000, yet the payoff table indicates that the only possible payoffs from choosing $a_2$ are −\$15,000, \$20,000, and \$60,000. Of course, the expected monetary value of act $a_1$(\$30,000) is possible, because that is the only payoff of the act.

What, then, does the expected monetary value represent? If the investment is made a large number of times, with exactly the same payoffs and probabilities, the expected monetary value is the average payoff per investment. That is, if the investment is repeated an infinite number of times with act $a_2$, 20% of the investments will result in a \$15,000 loss, 50% will result in a \$20,000 profit, and 30% will result in a \$60,000 profit. The average of all these investments is the expected monetary value, \$25,000. If act $a_3$ is chosen, the average payoff in the long run will be \$26,250.

An important point is raised by the question of how many investments are going to be made. The answer is one. Even if the investor intends to make the same type of investment annually, the payoffs and the probabilities of the states of nature will undoubtedly change from year to year. Hence, we are faced with having determined the expected monetary value decision on the basis of an infinite number of investments, when there will be only one investment. We can rationalize this apparent contradiction in two ways. First, the expected value decision is the only method that allows us to combine the two most important factors in the decision process—the payoffs and their probabilities. It seems inconceivable that, where both factors are known, the investor would want to ignore either one. (There are processes that make decisions on the basis of the payoffs alone; however, these processes assume no knowledge of the probabilities, which is not the case with our example.) Second, typical decision makers make a large number of decisions over their lifetimes. By using the expected value decision, the decision maker should perform at least as well as anyone else. Thus, despite the problem of interpretation, we advocate the expected monetary value decision.

## Expected Opportunity Loss Decision

We can also calculate the **expected opportunity loss (EOL)** of each act. From the opportunity loss table (Table 22.2), we get the following values:

$$\text{EOL}(a_1) = .2(10{,}000) + .5(0) + .3(30{,}000) = \$11{,}000$$
$$\text{EOL}(a_2) = .2(55{,}000) + .5(10{,}000) + .3(0) = \$16{,}000$$
$$\text{EOL}(a_3) = .2(0) + .5(2{,}500) + .3(45{,}000) = \$14{,}750$$

Because we want to minimize losses, we choose the act that produces the smallest expected opportunity loss, which is $a_1$. We label its expected value EOL*. Observe that the EMV decision is the same as the EOL decision. This is not a coincidence—the opportunity loss table was produced directly from the payoff table.

## Rollback Technique for Decision Trees

Figure 22.2 presents the decision tree for Example 22.1, with the probabilities of the states of nature included. The process of determining the EMV decision is called the **rollback technique**; it operates as follows. Beginning at the end of the tree (right-hand side), we calculate the expected monetary value at each round node. The numbers above the round nodes in Figure 22.2 specify these expected monetary values.

At each square node, we make a decision by choosing the branch with the largest EMV. In our example, there is only one square node. Our optimal decision is, of course, $a_1$.

FIGURE **22.2** **Rollback Technique for Example 22.1**

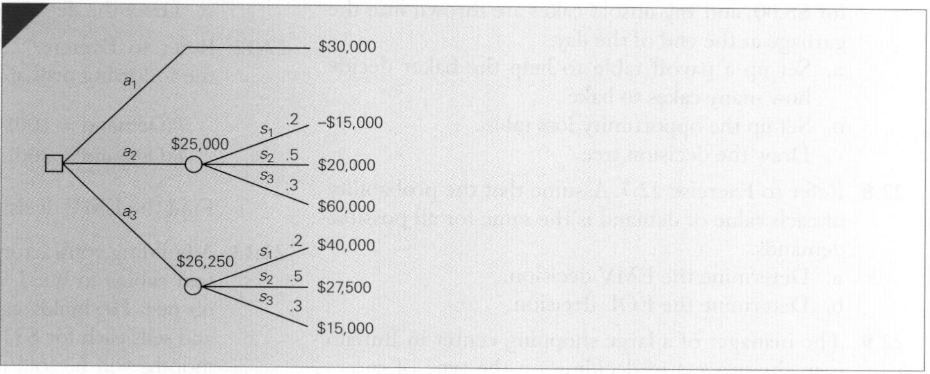

## EXERCISES

**22.1** Set up the opportunity loss table from the following payoff table:

| | $a_1$ | $a_2$ |
|---|---|---|
| $s_1$ | 55 | 26 |
| $s_2$ | 43 | 38 |
| $s_3$ | 29 | 43 |
| $s_4$ | 15 | 51 |

**22.2** Draw the decision tree for Exercise 22.1.

**22.3** If we assign the following probabilities to the states of nature in Exercise 22.1, determine the EMV decision:

$P(s_1) = .4 \quad P(s_2) = .1 \quad P(s_3) = .3 \quad P(s_4) = .2$

**22.4** Given the following payoff table, draw the decision tree:

| | $a_1$ | $a_2$ | $a_3$ |
|---|---|---|---|
| $s_1$ | 20 | 5 | −1 |
| $s_2$ | 8 | 5 | 4 |
| $s_3$ | −10 | 5 | 10 |

**22.5** Refer to Exercise 22.4. Set up the opportunity loss table.

**22.6** If we assign the following probabilities to the states of nature in Exercise 22.5, determine the EOL decision:

$P(s_1) = .2 \quad P(s_2) = .6 \quad P(s_3) = .2$

### Applications

**22.7** A baker must decide how many specialty cakes to bake each morning. From past experience, she knows that the daily demand for cakes ranges from 0 to 3. Each cake costs $3.00 to produce and sells for $8.00, and any unsold cakes are thrown into the garbage at the end of the day.

a. Set up a payoff table to help the baker decide how many cakes to bake.
b. Set up the opportunity loss table.
c. Draw the decision tree.

**22.8** Refer to Exercise 22.7. Assume that the probability of each value of demand is the same for all possible demands.

a. Determine the EMV decision.
b. Determine the EOL decision.

**22.9** The manager of a large shopping center in Buffalo is in the process of deciding on the type of snow-clearing service to hire for his parking lot. Two services are available. The White Christmas Company will clear all snowfalls for a flat fee of $40,000 for the entire winter season. The Weplowem Company charges $18,000 for each snowfall it clears. Set up the payoff table to help the manager decide, assuming that the number of snowfalls per winter season ranges from 0 to 4.

**22.10** Refer to Exercise 22.9. Using subjective assessments the manager has assigned the following probabilities to the number of snowfalls. Determine the optimal decision.

$P(0) = .05 \quad P(1) = .15 \quad P(2) = .30 \quad P(3) = .40$
$P(4) = .10$

**22.11** The owner of a clothing store must decide how many men's shirts to order for the new season. For a particular type of shirt, she must order in quantities of 100 shirts. If she orders 100 shirts, her cost is $10 per shirt; if she orders 200 shirts, her cost is $9 per shirt; and if she orders 300 or more shirts, her cost is $8.50 per shirt. Her selling price for the shirt is $12, but any shirts that remain unsold at the end of the season are sold at her famous "half-price, end-of-season sale." For the sake of simplicity, she is willing to assume that the demand for this type of shirt will be 100, 150, 200, or 250 shirts. Of course, she cannot sell more shirts than she stocks. She is also willing to assume that she will suffer no loss of goodwill among her customers if she understocks and the customers cannot buy all the shirts they want. Furthermore, she must place her order today for the entire season; she cannot wait to see how the demand is running for this type of shirt.

a. Construct the payoff table to help the owner decide how many shirts to order.
b. Set up the opportunity loss table.
c. Draw the decision tree.

**22.12** Refer to Exercise 22.11. The owner has assigned the following probabilities:

$P(\text{Demand} = 100) = .2, \quad P(\text{Demand} = 150) = .25,$
$P(\text{Demand} = 200) = .40, \quad P(\text{Demand} = 250) = .15$

Find the EMV decision.

**22.13** A building contractor must decide how many mountain cabins to build in the ski resort area of Chick-oh-pee. He builds each cabin at a cost of $26,000 and sells each for $33,000. All cabins unsold after 10 months will be sold to a local investor for $20,000. The contractor believes that the demand for cabins follows a Poisson distribution, with a mean of .5. He assumes that any probability less than .01 can be treated as 0. Construct the payoff table and the opportunity loss table for this decision problem.

**22.14** The electric company is in the process of building a new power plant. There is some uncertainty regarding the size of the plant to be built. If the community that the plant will service attracts a large number of industries, the demand for electricity will be high. If commercial establishments (offices and retail stores) are attracted, demand will be moderate. If neither industries nor commercial stores locate in the community, the electricity demand will be low. The company can build a small, medium, or large plant, but if the plant is too small, the company will incur extra costs. The total costs (in $millions) of all options are shown in the accompanying table.

| | Size of Plant | | |
|---|---|---|---|
| **Electricity Demand** | **Small** | **Medium** | **Large** |
| Low | 220 | 300 | 350 |
| Moderate | 330 | 320 | 350 |
| High | 440 | 390 | 350 |

The following probabilities are assigned to the electricity demand:

| Demand | *P*(Demand) |
|---|---|
| Low | .15 |
| Moderate | .55 |
| High | .30 |

a. Determine the act with the largest expected monetary value. (*Caution*: All the values in the table are costs.)
b. Draw up an opportunity loss table.
c. Calculate the expected opportunity loss for each decision, and determine the optimal decision.

**22.15** A retailer buys bushels of mushrooms for $2 each and sells them for $5 each. The quality of the mushrooms begins to decline after the first day they are offered for sale; therefore, to sell the mushrooms for $5/bushel, he must sell them on the first day. Bushels not sold on the first day can be sold to a wholesaler who buys day-old mushrooms at the following rates.

| **Amount purchased (bushels)** | 1 | 2 | 3 | 4 or more |
|---|---|---|---|---|
| **Price per bushel** | $2.00 | $1.75 | $1.50 | $1.25 |

A 90-day observation of past demand yields the following information:

| **Daily demand (bushels)** | 10 | 11 | 12 | 13 |
|---|---|---|---|---|
| **Number of days** | 9 | 18 | 36 | 27 |

a. Set up a payoff table that could be used by the retailer to decide how many bushels to buy.
b. Find the optimal number of bushels the retailer should buy to maximize profit.

**22.16** An international manufacturer of electronic products is contemplating introducing a new type of compact disk player. After some analysis of the market, the president of the company concludes that, within 2 years, the new product will have a market share of 5%, 10%, or 15%. She assesses the probabilities of these events as .15, .45, and .40, respectively. The vice-president of finance informs her that, if the product captures only a 5% market share, the company will lose $28 million. A 10% market share will produce a $2 million profit, and a 15% market share will produce an $8 million profit. If the company decides not to begin production of the new compact disk player, there will be no profit or loss. Based on the expected value decision, what should the company do?

## 22-2 Acquiring, Using, and Evaluating Additional Information

In this section, we discuss methods of introducing and incorporating additional information into the decision process. Such information generally has value, but it also has attendant costs; that is, we can acquire useful information from consultants, surveys, or other experiments, but we usually must pay for this information. We can calculate the maximum price that a decision maker should be willing to pay for any information by determining the value of perfect information. We begin by calculating the **expected payoff with perfect information** (EPPI).

If we knew in advance which state of nature would occur, we would certainly make our decisions accordingly. For instance, if the investor in Example 22.1 knew before investing his money what interest rates would do, he would choose the best act to suit that case. Referring to Table 22.1, if he knew that $s_1$ was going to occur, he would choose act $a_3$;

if $s_2$ were certain to occur, he'd choose $a_1$, and if $s_3$ were certain, he'd choose $a_2$. Thus, in the long run, his expected payoff from perfect information would be:

$$\text{EPPI} = .2(40{,}000) + .5(30{,}000) + .3(60{,}000) = \$41{,}000$$

Notice that we compute EPPI by multiplying the probability of each state of nature by the largest payoff associated with that state of nature and then summing the products.

This figure, however, does not represent the maximum amount he'd be willing to pay for perfect information. Because the investor could make an expected profit of EMV* = $30,000 without perfect information, we subtract EMV* from EPPI to determine the **expected value of perfect information (EVPI)**. That is:

$$\text{EVPI} = \text{EPPI} - \text{EMV}^* = \$41{,}000 - \$30{,}000 = \$11{,}000$$

This means that, if perfect information were available, the investor should be willing to pay up to $311,000 to acquire it.

You may have noticed that the expected value of perfect information (EVPI) equals the smallest expected opportunity loss (EOL*). Again, this is not a coincidence—it will always be the case. In future questions, if the opportunity loss table has been determined, you need only calculate EOL* in order to know EVPI.

## 22-2a Decision Making with Additional Information

Suppose the investor in our continuing example wants to improve his decision-making capabilities. He learns about Investment Management Consultants (IMC), who, for a fee of $5,000, will analyze the economic conditions and forecast the behavior of interest rates over the next 12 months. The investor, who is quite shrewd (after all, he does have $l million to invest), asks for some measure of IMC's past successes. IMC has been forecasting interest rates for many years and so provides him with various conditional probabilities (referred to as **likelihood probabilities**), as shown in Table 22.3. Table 22.3 uses the following notation:

$I_1$: IMC predicts that interest rates will increase.
$I_2$: IMC predicts that interest rates will stay the same.
$I_3$: IMC predicts that interest rates will decrease.

TABLE **22.3** **Likelihood Probabilities $P(I_i \mid s_j)$**

| | $I_1$(PREDICT $s_1$) | $I_2$(PREDICT $s_2$) | $I_3$(PREDICT $s_3$) |
|---|---|---|---|
| $s_1$ | $P(I_1 \mid s_1) = .60$ | $P(I_2 \mid s_1) = .30$ | $P(I_3 \mid s_1) = .10$ |
| $s_2$ | $P(I_1 \mid s_2) = .10$ | $P(I_2 \mid s_2) = .80$ | $P(I_3 \mid s_2) = .10$ |
| $s_3$ | $P(I_1 \mid s_3) = .10$ | $P(I_2 \mid s_3) = .20$ | $P(I_3 \mid s_3) = .70$ |

The $I_i$ terms are referred to as **experimental outcomes**, and the process by which we gather additional information is called the **experiment**.

Examine the first line of Table 22.3. When $s_1$ actually did occur in the past, IMC correctly predicted $s_1$ 60% of the time; 30% of the time, it predicted $s_2$; and 10% of the time, it predicted $s_3$. The second row gives the conditional probabilities of $I_1$, $I_2$, and $I_3$ when $s_2$ actually occurred. The third row shows the conditional probabilities of $I_1$, $I_2$, and $I_3$ when $s_3$ actually occurred.

The following question now arises: How is the investor going to use the forecast that IMC produces? One approach is simply to assume that whatever IMC forecasts will actually take place and to choose the act accordingly. There are several drawbacks to this approach. Foremost among them is that it puts the investor in the position of ignoring whatever knowledge (in the form of subjective probabilities) he had concerning the issue. Instead the decision maker should use this information to modify his initial assessment of the probabilities of the states of nature. To incorporate the investor's subjective probabilities with the consultant's forecast requires the use of Bayes's Law, which we introduced in Section 6-4. We'll review Bayes's Law in the context of our example.

Suppose that the investor pays IMC the \$5,000 fee and IMC forecasts that $s_1$ will occur. We want to revise our estimates for the probabilities of the states of nature, given that $I_1$ is the outcome of the experiment. That is, we want $P(s_1|I_1)$, $P(s_2|I_1)$, and $P(s_3|I_1)$. Before proceeding, let's develop some terminology.

Recall from Section 6-4 that the original probabilities, $P(s_1)$, $P(s_2)$, and $P(s_3)$, are called **prior probabilities**, because they were determined prior to the acquisition of any additional information. In this example, they were based on the investor's experience. The set of probabilities we want to compute—$P(s_1|I_1)$, $P(s_2|I_1)$, and $P(s_3|I_1)$—are called **posterior or revised probabilities**.

Now we will calculate the posterior probabilities, first by using a probability tree and then by applying a less time-consuming method. Figure 22.3 depicts the probability tree. We begin with the branches of the prior probabilities, which are followed by the likelihood probabilities.

FIGURE **22.3** **Probability Tree to Compute Posterior Probabilities**

$s_1$ .2 — $I_1|s_1$ .60 — $P(s_1 \text{ and } I_1) = .12$

$s_2$ .5 — $I_1|s_2$ .10 — $P(s_2 \text{ and } I_1) = .05$

$s_3$ .3 — $I_1|s_3$ .10 — $P(s_3 \text{ and } I_1) = .03$

$P(I_1) = .20$

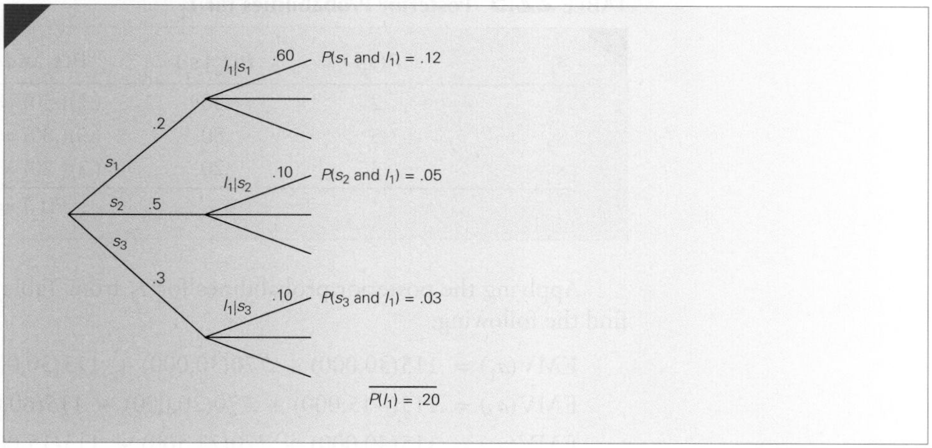

Notice that we label only $P(I_1|s_1)$, $P(I_1|s_2)$, and $P(I_1|s_3)$ because (at this point) we are assuming that $I_1$ is the experimental outcome. Now recall that conditional probability is defined as:

$$P(A|B) = \frac{P(A \text{ and } B)}{P(B)}$$

At the end of each branch, we have the joint probability $P(s_j \text{ and } I_1)$. By summing the joint probabilities $P(s_j \text{ and } I_1)$ for $j = 1, 2,$ and $3$, we calculate $P(I_1)$. Finally:

$$P(s_j|I_1) = \frac{P(s_j \text{ and } I_1)}{P(I_1)}$$

Table 22.4 performs exactly the same calculations as the probability tree except without the tree. So, for example, our revised probability for $s_3$, which was initially .3, is now .15.

TABLE **22.4** **Posterior Probabilities for $I_1$**

| $s_j$ | $P(s_j)$ | $P(I_1 \mid s_j)$ | $P(s_j \text{ and } I_1)$ | $P(s_j \mid I_1)$ |
|---|---|---|---|---|
| $s_1$ | .2 | .60 | (.2)(.60) = .12 | .12/.20 = .60 |
| $s_2$ | .5 | .10 | (.5)(.10) = .05 | .05/.20 = .25 |
| $s_3$ | .3 | .10 | (.3)(.10) = .03 | .03/.20 = .15 |
| | | | $P(I_1) = .20$ | |

After the probabilities have been revised, we can use them in exactly the same way we used the prior probabilities. That is, we can calculate the expected monetary value of each act:

$$\text{EMV}(a_1) = .60(30{,}000) + .25(30{,}000) + .15(30{,}000) = \$30{,}000$$
$$\text{EMV}(a_2) = .60(-15{,}000) + .25(20{,}000) + .15(60{,}000) = \$5{,}000$$
$$\text{EMV}(a_3) = .60(40{,}000) + .25(27{,}500) + .15(15{,}000) = \$33{,}125$$

Thus, if IMC forecasts $s_1$, the optimal act is $a_3$, and the expected monetary value of the decision is $33,125.

As a further illustration, we now repeat the process for $I_2$ and $I_3$ in Tables 22.5 and 22.6, respectively.

TABLE **22.5** **Posterior Probabilities for $I_2$**

| $s_j$ | $P(s_j)$ | $P(I_2 \mid s_j)$ | $P(s_j \text{ and } I_2)$ | $P(s_j \mid I_2)$ |
|---|---|---|---|---|
| $s_1$ | .2 | .30 | (.2)(.30) = .06 | .06/.52 = .115 |
| $s_2$ | .5 | .80 | (.5)(.80) = .40 | .40/.52 = .770 |
| $s_3$ | .3 | .20 | (.3)(.20) = .06 | .06/.52 = .115 |
| | | | $P(I_2) = .52$ | |

Applying the posterior probabilities for $I_2$ from Table 22.5 to the payoff table, we find the following:

$$\text{EMV}(a_1) = .115(30{,}000) + .770(30{,}000) + .115(30{,}000) = \$30{,}000$$
$$\text{EMV}(a_2) = .115(-15{,}000) + .770(20{,}000) + .115(60{,}000) = \$20{,}575$$
$$\text{EMV}(a_3) = .115(40{,}000) + .770(27{,}500) + .115(15{,}000) = \$27{,}500$$

As you can see, if IMC predicts that $s_2$ will occur, the optimal act is $a_1$, with an expected monetary value of $30,000.

TABLE **22.6** **Posterior Probabilities for $I_3$**

| $s_j$ | $P(s_j)$ | $P(I_3 \mid s_j)$ | $P(s_j \text{ and } I_3)$ | $P(s_j \mid I_3)$ |
|---|---|---|---|---|
| $s_1$ | .2 | .10 | (.2)(.10) = .02 | .02/.28 = .071 |
| $s_2$ | .5 | .10 | (.5)(.10) = .05 | .05/.28 = .179 |
| $s_3$ | .3 | .70 | (.3)(.70) = .21 | .21/.28 = .750 |
| | | | $P(I_3) = .28$ | |

With the set of posterior probabilities for $I_3$ from Table 22.6, the expected monetary values are as follows:

$$EMV(a_1) = .071(30{,}000) + .179(30{,}000) + .750(30{,}000) = \$30{,}000$$
$$EMV(a_2) = .071(-15{,}000) + .179(20{,}000) + .750(60{,}000) = \$47{,}515$$
$$EMV(a_3) = .071(40{,}000) + .179(27{,}500) + .750(15{,}000) = \$19{,}013$$

If IMC predicts that $s_3$ will occur, the optimal act is $a_2$, with an expected monetary value of \$47,515.

At this point, we know the following:

If IMC predicts $s_1$, then the optimal act is $a_3$.
If IMC predicts $s_2$, then the optimal act is $a_1$.
If IMC predicts $s_3$, then the optimal act is $a_2$.

Thus, even before IMC makes its forecast, the investor knows which act is optimal for each of the three possible IMC forecasts. Of course, all these calculations can be performed before paying IMC its \$5,000 fee. This leads to an extremely important calculation. By performing the computations just described, the investor can determine *whether* he should hire IMC, that is, he can determine whether the value of IMC's forecast exceeds the cost of its information. Such a determination is called a **preposterior analysis.**

## 22-2b Preposterior Analysis

The objective of a preposterior analysis is to determine whether the value of the prediction is greater or less than the cost of the information. *Posterior* refers to the revision of the probabilities, and the *pre* indicates that this calculation is performed before paying the fee.

We begin by finding the expected monetary value of using the additional information. This value is denoted EMV′, which for our example is determined on the basis of the following analysis:

If IMC predicts $s_1$, then the optimal act is $a_3$, and the expected payoff is \$33,125.
If IMC predicts $s_2$, then the optimal act is $a_1$, and the expected payoff is \$30,000.
If IMC predicts $s_3$, then the optimal act is $a_2$, and the expected payoff is \$47,515.

A useful by-product of calculating the posterior probabilities is the set of probabilities of $I_1$, $I_2$, and $I_3$:

$$P(I_1) = .20, \qquad P(I_2) = .52, \qquad P(I_3) = .28$$

(Notice that these probabilities sum to 1.) Now imagine that the investor seeks the advice of IMC an infinite number of times. (This is the basis for the expected value decision.) The set of probabilities of $I_1$, $I_2$, and $I_3$ indicates the following outcome distribution: 20% of the time, IMC will predict $s_1$ and the expected monetary value will be \$33,125; 52% of the time, IMC will predict $s_2$ and the expected monetary value will be \$30,000; and 28% of the time, IMC will predict $s_3$ and the expected monetary value will be \$47,515.

The expected monetary value with additional information is the weighted average of the expected monetary values, where the weights are $P(I_1)$, $P(I_2)$, and $P(I_3)$. Hence:

$$EMV' = .20(33{,}125) + .52(30{,}000) + .28(47{,}515) = \$35{,}529$$

The value of IMC's forecast is the difference between the expected monetary value with additional information (EMV′) and the expected monetary value without additional information (EMV*). This difference is called the **expected value of sample information** and is denoted EVSI. Thus:

$$\text{EVSI} = \text{EMV}' - \text{EMV}^* = \$35{,}529 - \$30{,}000 = \$5{,}529$$

By using IMC's forecast, the investor can make an average additional profit of $5,529 in the long run. Because the cost of the forecast is only $5,000, the investor is advised to hire IMC.

If you review this problem, you'll see that the investor had to make two decisions. The first (chronologically) was whether to hire IMC, and the second was which type of investment to make. A decision tree is quite helpful in describing the acts and states of nature in this question. Figure 22.4 provides the complete tree diagram.

**FIGURE 22.4 Complete Decision Tree for Example 22.1**

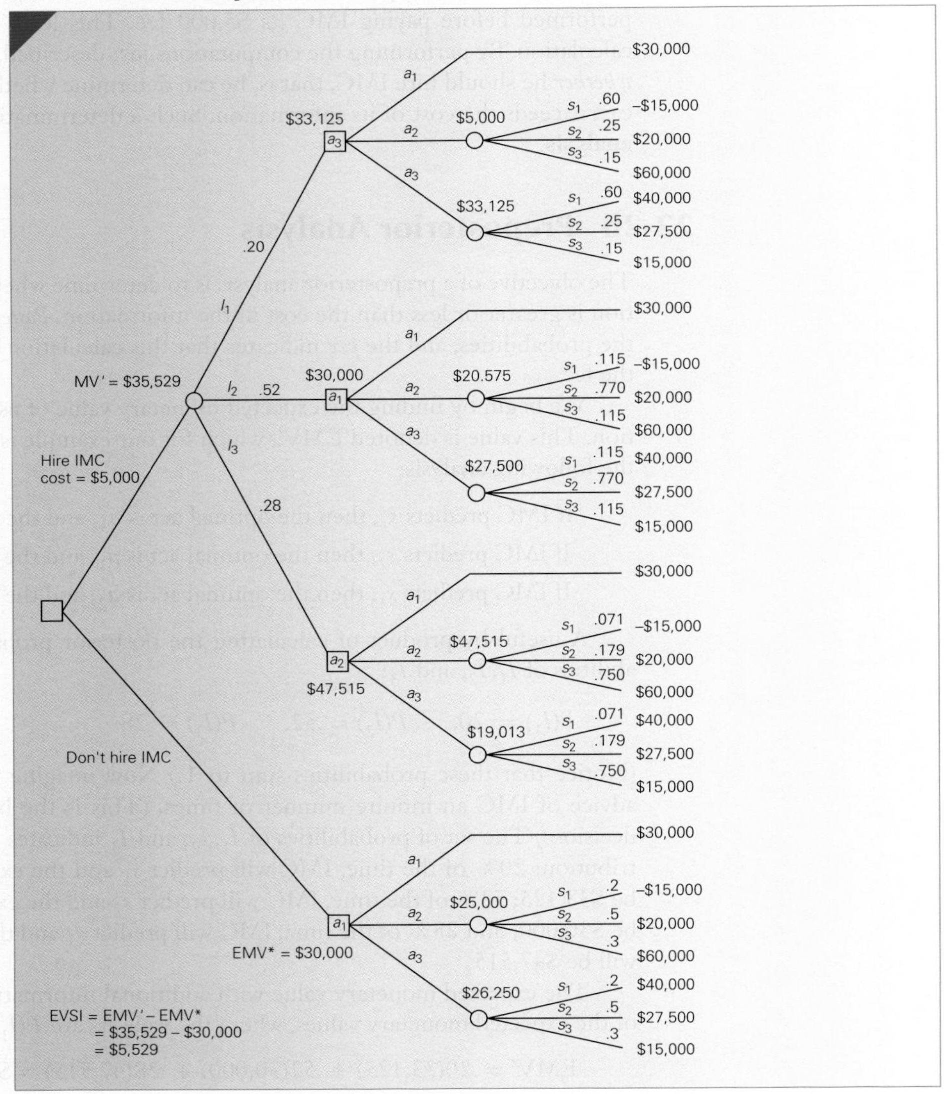

## Acceptance Sampling: Solution

Image Source/Getty Images

a. The two alternatives are

$a_1$: No inspection (the current policy)

$a_2$: 100% inspection

The two states of nature are

$s_1$: The lot contains 15% defectives

$s_2$: The lot contains 35% defectives

Based on the past year's historical record,

$P(s_1) = .60$ and $P(s_2) = .40$

The payoff table is constructed as shown in Table 22.7.

TABLE **22.7** **Payoff Table**

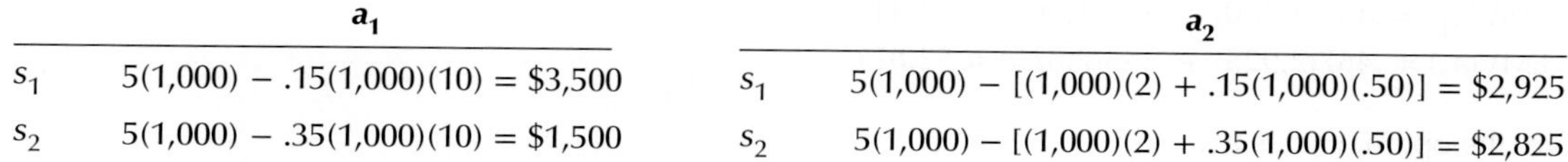

| | $a_1$ | | $a_2$ |
|---|---|---|---|
| $s_1$ | $5(1{,}000) - .15(1{,}000)(10) = \$3{,}500$ | $s_1$ | $5(1{,}000) - [(1{,}000)(2) + .15(1{,}000)(.50)] = \$2{,}925$ |
| $s_2$ | $5(1{,}000) - .35(1{,}000)(10) = \$1{,}500$ | $s_2$ | $5(1{,}000) - [(1{,}000)(2) + .35(1{,}000)(.50)] = \$2{,}825$ |

The expected monetary values are

$$\text{EMV}(a_1) = .60(3{,}500) + .40(1{,}500) = \$2{,}700$$
$$\text{EMV}(a_2) = .60(2{,}925) + .40(2{,}825) = \$2{,}885$$

The optimal act is $a_2$ with $\text{EMV}^* = \$2{,}885$.

b. The cost of the proposed sampling is \$4. (The cost of inspecting a single unit is \$2.) To determine whether we should sample, we need to calculate the expected value of sample information—that is, we need to perform a preposterior analysis.

The first step of the preposterior analysis is to calculate the likelihood probabilities. There are three possible sample outcomes:

$I_0$: No defectives in the sample

$I_1$: One defective in the sample

$I_2$: Two defectives in the sample

Because the sampling process is a binomial experiment, the likelihood probabilities are calculated by using the binomial probability distribution as summarized in Table 22.8.

TABLE **22.8** **Likelihood Probability Table**

| | $P(I_0 \mid s_j)$ | $P(I_1 \mid s_j)$ | $P(I_2 \mid s_j)$ |
|---|---|---|---|
| $s_1(p = .15)$ | $P(I_0 \mid s_1) = (.85)^2 = .7225$ | $P(I_1 \mid s_1) = 2(.15)(.85) = .2550$ | $P(I_2 \mid s_1) = (.15)^2 = .0225$ |
| $s_2(p = .35)$ | $P(I_0 \mid s_2) = (.65)^2 = .4225$ | $P(I_1 \mid s_2) = 2(.35)(.65) = .4550$ | $P(I_2 \mid s_2) = (.35)^2 = .1225$ |

If $I_0$ is the sample outcome, the posterior probabilities are calculated as shown in Table 22.9.

TABLE **22.9** **Posterior Probabilities for $I_0$**

| $s_j$ | $P(s_j)$ | $P(I_0 \mid s_j)$ | $P(s_j \text{ and } I_0)$ | $P(s_j \mid I_0)$ |
|---|---|---|---|---|
| $s_1$ | .60 | .7225 | $(.60)(.7225) = .4335$ | $.4335/.6025 = .720$ |
| $s_2$ | .40 | .4225 | $(.40)(.4225) = .1690$ | $.1690/.6025 = .280$ |
| | | | $P(I_0) = .6025$ | |

*(Continued)*

The expected monetary values if the sample outcome is $I_0$ are

$$\text{EMV}(a_1) = .720(3{,}500) + .280(1{,}500) = \$2{,}940$$
$$\text{EMV}(a_2) = .720(2{,}925) + .280(2{,}825) = \$2{,}897$$

Therefore, the optimal act is $a_1$.

If $I_1$ is the sample outcome, the posterior probabilities are calculated as shown in Table 22.10.

TABLE **22.10** **Posterior Probabilities for $I_1$**

| $s_j$ | $P(s_j)$ | $P(I_1 \mid s_j)$ | $P(s_j \text{ and } I_1)$ | $P(s_j \mid I_1)$ |
|---|---|---|---|---|
| $s_1$ | .60 | .2550 | (.60)(.2550) = .1530 | .1530/.3350 = .457 |
| $s_2$ | .40 | .4550 | (.40)(.4550) = .1820 | .1820/.3350 = .543 |
| | | | $P(I_1)$ = .3350 | |

The expected monetary values if the sample outcome is $I_1$ are

$$\text{EMV}(a_1) = .457(3{,}500) + .543(1{,}500) = \$2{,}414$$
$$\text{EMV}(a_2) = .457(2{,}925) + .543(2{,}825) = \$2{,}871$$

Therefore, the optimal act is $a_2$.

If $I_2$ is the sample outcome, the posterior probabilities are calculated as shown in Table 22.11.

TABLE **22.11** **Posterior Probabilities for $I_2$**

| $s_j$ | $P(s_j)$ | $P(I_2 \mid s_j)$ | $P(s_j \text{ and } I_2)$ | $P(s_j \mid I_2)$ |
|---|---|---|---|---|
| $s_1$ | .60 | .0225 | (.60)(.0225) = .0135 | .0135/.0625 = .216 |
| $s_2$ | .40 | .1225 | (.40)(.1225) = .0490 | .0490/.0625 = .784 |
| | | | $P(I_2)$ = .0625 | |

The expected monetary values if the sample outcome is $I_2$ are

$$\text{EMV}(a_1) = .216(3{,}500) + .784(1{,}500) = \$1{,}932$$
$$\text{EMV}(a_2) = .216(2{,}925) + .784(2{,}825) = \$2{,}847$$

Therefore, the optimal act is $a_2$.

We can now summarize these results, as shown in Table 22.12.

TABLE **22.12** **Summary of Optimal Acts**

| Sample Outcome | Probability | Optimal Act | Expected Monetary Value ($) |
|---|---|---|---|
| $I_0$ | .6025 | $a_1$ | 2,940 |
| $I_1$ | .3350 | $a_2$ | 2,871 |
| $I_2$ | .0625 | $a_2$ | 2,847 |

The expected monetary value with additional information is

$$\text{EMV}' = .6025(2{,}940) + .3350(2{,}871) + .0625(2{,}847) = \$2{,}911$$

The expected value of sample information is

$$\text{EVSI} = \text{EMV}' - \text{EMV}^* = 2{,}911 - 2{,}885 = \$26$$

Because the expected value of sample information is $26 and the sampling cost is $4, the company should take a sample of 2 units before deciding whether to inspect 100%. The optimal sequence is as follows:

1. Take a sample of 2 units.
2. If there are no defective units in the sample, continue the current policy of no inspection. If either one or two of the sample units are defective, perform a complete inspection of the lot.

## 22-2c Bayesian Statistics

In Chapters 10–18, we dealt with inference about unknown parameters. In Chapter 10, we pointed out that when interpreting the confidence interval estimate, we cannot make probability statements about parameters because they are not variables. However, Bayesian statistics specifies that parameters are variables, and we can assume various probability distributions. The acceptance sampling example illustrates this concept. The parameter was the proportion $p$ of defective units in the 1,000-unit batch. The example was unrealistic because we allowed the parameter to assume one of only two values, 15% and 35%. We assigned prior probabilities using the relative frequency approach; that is, based on historic records we had

$$P(p = 15\%) = .60 \quad \text{and} \quad P(p = 35\%) = .40$$

To make the problem more realistic, we let $p$ be a continuous random variable rather than a discrete one. In other words, $p$ can take on any value between 0 and 100%. We assign a density function also based on historical records. We can express the payoffs as a linear function of $p$. Then, using calculus, we can determine the optimum decision. We can also revise the prior probabilities based on the outcome of the sampling of two units. The technique requires some calculus, but the concept is the same as the one developed in this chapter. It should be noted that there is a parallel universe of Bayesian statistics that more or less matches the material in the inference part of this book. Interested readers can learn more about Bayesian statistics from additional courses dedicated to the subject.

## EXERCISES

**22.17** Find EPPI, EMV*, and EVPI for the accompanying payoff table and probabilities.

| | $a_1$ | $a_2$ | $a_3$ |
|---|---|---|---|
| $s_1$ | 60 | 110 | 75 |
| $s_2$ | 40 | 110 | 150 |
| $s_3$ | 220 | 120 | 85 |
| $s_4$ | 250 | 120 | 130 |

$P(s_1) = .10 \quad P(s_2) = .25 \quad P(s_3) = .50 \quad P(s_4) = .15$

**22.18** For Exercise 22.17, determine the opportunity loss table and compute EOL*. Confirm that EOL* = EVPI.

**22.19** Given the following payoff table and probabilities, determine EVPI.

| | $a_1$ | $a_2$ | $a_3$ | $a_4$ |
|---|---|---|---|---|
| $s_1$ | 65 | 20 | 45 | 30 |
| $s_2$ | 70 | 110 | 80 | 95 |

$P(s_1) = .5 \quad P(s_2) = .5$

**22.20** Redo Exercise 22.19, changing the probabilities to the following values.

a. $P(s_1) = .75 \quad P(s_2) = .25$
b. $P(s_1) = .95 \quad P(s_2) = .05$

**22.21** What conclusion can you draw about the effect of the probabilities on EVPI from Exercises 22.19 and 22.20?

**22.22** Determine the posterior probabilities, given the following prior and likelihood probabilities.

**Prior probabilities**

$P(s_1) = .25 \quad P(s_2) = .40 \quad P(s_3) = .35$

**Likelihood Probabilities**

| | $I_1$ | $I_2$ | $I_3$ | $I_4$ |
|---|---|---|---|---|
| $s_1$ | .40 | .30 | .20 | .10 |
| $s_2$ | .25 | .25 | .25 | .25 |
| $s_3$ | 0 | .30 | .40 | .30 |

**22.23** Calculate the posterior probabilities from the prior and likelihood probabilities that follow.

**Prior Probabilities**

$P(s_1) = .5 \quad P(s_2) = .5$

**Likelihood Probabilities**

| | $I_1$ | $I_2$ |
|---|---|---|
| $s_1$ | .98 | .02 |
| $s_2$ | .05 | .95 |

**22.24** With the accompanying payoff table and the prior and posterior probabilities computed in Exercise 22.23 calculate the following.

a. The optimal act for each experimental outcome
b. The expected value of sample information

**Payoff Table**

| | $a_1$ | $a_2$ | $a_3$ |
|---|---|---|---|
| $s_1$ | 10 | 18 | 23 |
| $s_2$ | 22 | 19 | 15 |

**22.25** Given the following payoff table, prior probabilities, and likelihood probabilities, find the expected value of sample information.

**Payoff Table**

| | $a_1$ | $a_2$ |
|---|---|---|
| $s_1$ | 60 | 90 |
| $s_2$ | 90 | 90 |
| $s_3$ | 150 | 90 |

**Prior probabilities**

$P(s_1) = \frac{1}{3} \quad P(s_2) = \frac{1}{3} \quad P(s_3) = \frac{1}{3}$

**Likelihood Probabilities**

| | $I_1$ | $I_2$ |
|---|---|---|
| $s_1$ | .7 | .3 |
| $s_2$ | .5 | .5 |
| $s_3$ | .2 | .8 |

**22.26** Repeat Exercise 22.25 with the following prior probabilities.

$P(s_1) = .5 \quad P(s_2) = .4 \quad P(s_3) = .1$

**22.27** Repeat Exercise 22.25 with the following prior probabilities.

$P(s_1) = .90 \quad P(s_2) = .05 \quad P(s_3) = .05$

**22.28** What conclusions can you draw about the effect of the prior probabilities on EVSI from Exercises 22.25–22.27?

## Applications

**22.29** A sporting-goods storeowner has the opportunity to purchase a lot of 50,000 footballs for $100,000. He believes that he can sell some or all by taking out mail-order advertisements in a magazine. Each football will be sold for $6. The advertising cost is $25,000, and the mailing cost per football is $1. He believes that the demand distribution is as follows.

| Demand | P(Demand) |
|---|---|
| 10,000 | .2 |
| 30,000 | .5 |
| 50,000 | .3 |

What is the maximum price the owner should pay for additional information about demand?

**22.30** What is the maximum price the electronics product manufacturer should be willing to pay for perfect information regarding the market share in Exercise 22.16?

**22.31** To improve her decision-making capability, the electronics products manufacturer in Exercise 22.16 performs a survey of potential buyers of compact disc players. She describes the product to 25 individuals, 3 of whom say they would buy it. Using this additional information together with the prior probabilities, determine whether the new product should be produced.

**22.32** A radio station that currently directs its programming toward middle-age listeners is contemplating switching to rock-and-roll music. After analyzing advertising revenues and operating costs, the owner concludes that, for each percentage point of market share, revenues increase by $100,000 per year. Fixed annual operating costs are $700,000. The owner believes that, with the change, the station will get a 5%, 10%, or 20% market share, with probabilities .4, .4, and .2, respectively. The current annual profit is $285,000.

a. Set up the payoff table.
b. Determine the optimal act.
c. What is the most the owner should be willing to pay to acquire additional information about the market share?

**22.33** There is a garbage crisis in North America—too much garbage and no place to put it. As a consequence, the idea of recycling has become quite popular. A waste-management company in a large city is willing to begin recycling newspapers, aluminum cans, and plastic containers. However, it is profitable to do so only if a sufficiently large proportion of households is willing to participate. In this city, 1 million households are potential recyclers. After some analysis, it was determined that, for every 1,000 households that participate in the program, the contribution to profit is \$500. It was also discovered that fixed costs are \$55,000 per year. It is believed that 50,000, 100,000, 200,000, or 300,000 households will participate, with probabilities .5, .3, .1, and .1, respectively. A preliminary survey was performed wherein 25 households were asked whether they would be willing to be part of this recycling program. Suppose only 3 of the 25 respond affirmatively, incorporate this information into the decision-making process to decide whether the waste-management company should proceed with the recycling venture.

**22.34** Repeat Exercise 22.33, given that 12 out of 100 households respond affirmatively.

**22.35** Suppose that in Exercise 22.14 a consultant offers to analyze the problem and predict the amount of electricity required by the new community. To induce the electric company to hire her, the consultant provides the set of likelihood probabilities given here. Perform a preposterior analysis to determine the expected value of the consultant's sample information.

| | $I_1$ (predict low demand) | $I_2$ (predict moderate demand) | $I_3$ (predict high demand) |
|---|---|---|---|
| $s_1$ | .5 | .3 | .2 |
| $s_2$ | .3 | .6 | .1 |
| $s_3$ | .2 | .2 | .6 |

**22.36** In Exercise 22.32, suppose that it is possible to survey radio listeners to determine whether they would tune in to the station if the format changed to rock and roll. What would a survey of size 2 be worth?

**22.37** Suppose that in Exercise 22.32 a random sample of 25 radio listeners revealed that 2 people would be regular listeners of the station. What is the optimal decision now?

**22.38** The president of an automobile battery company must decide which one of three new types of batteries to produce. The fixed and variable costs of each battery are shown in the accompanying table.

| Battery | Fixed Cost (\$) | Variable Cost (per Unit) (\$) |
|---|---|---|
| 1 | 900,000 | 20 |
| 2 | 1,150,000 | 17 |
| 3 | 1,400,000 | 15 |

The president believes that demand will be 50,000, 100,000, or 150,000 batteries, with probabilities .3, .3, and .4, respectively. The selling price of the battery will be \$40.

a. Determine the payoff table.
b. Determine the opportunity loss table.
c. Find the expected monetary value for each act, and select the optimal one.
d. What is the most the president should be willing to pay for additional information about demand?

**22.39** Credibility is often the most effective feature of an advertising campaign. Suppose that, for a particular advertisement, 32% of people surveyed currently believe what the ad claims. A marketing manager believes that for each 1-point increase in that percentage, annual sales will increase by \$1 million. For each 1-point decrease, annual sales will decrease by \$1 million. The manager believes that a change in the advertising approach can influence the ad's credibility. The probability distribution of the potential percentage changes is listed here.

| Percentage Change | Probability |
|---|---|
| −2 | .1 |
| −1 | .1 |
| 0 | .2 |
| +1 | .3 |
| +2 | .3 |

If for each dollar of sales the profit contribution is 10 cents and the overall cost of changing the ad is \$58,000, should the ad be changed?

**22.40** Suppose that in Exercise 22.39 it is possible to perform a survey to determine the percentage of people who believe the ad. What would a sample of size 1 be worth?

**22.41** Suppose that in Exercise 22.39 a sample of size 5 showed that only one person believes the new ad. In light of this additional information, what should the manager do?

**22.42** Max the Bookie is trying to decide how many telephones to install in his new bookmaking operation. Because of heavy police activity, he cannot increase or decrease the number of telephones once he sets up his operation. He has narrowed the possible choices to three. He can install 25, 50, or 100 telephones. His profit for 1 year (the usual length of time he can remain in business before the police close him down) depends on the average number of calls he receives. The number of calls is Poisson distributed. After some deliberation, he concludes that the average number of calls per minute can be

.5, 1.0, or 1.5, with probabilities of .50, .25, and .25, respectively. Max then produces the payoffs given in the accompanying table.

**Payoff Table**

| | 25 Telephones ($) | 50 Telephones ($) | 100 Telephones ($) |
|---|---|---|---|
| $s_1(\mu = .5)$ | 50,000 | 30,000 | 20,000 |
| $s_2(\mu = 1.0)$ | 50,000 | 60,000 | 40,000 |
| $s_3(\mu = 1.5)$ | 50,000 | 60,000 | 80,000 |

Max's assistant, Lefty (who attended a business school for 2 years), points out that Max may be able to get more information by observing a competitor's similar operation. However, he will be able to watch for only 10 minutes, and doing so will cost him $4,000. Max determines that if he counts fewer than 8 calls, that would be a low number; at least 8 but fewer than 17 would be a medium number; and at least 17 would be a large number of calls. Max also decides that, if the experiment is run, he will record only whether there is a small, medium, or large number of calls. Help Max by performing a preposterior analysis to determine whether the sample should be taken. Conclude by specifying clearly what the optimal strategy is.

**22.43** The Megabuck Computer Company is thinking of introducing two new products. The first, Model 101, is a small computer designed specifically for children between ages 8 and 16. The second, Model 202, is a medium-size computer suitable for managers. Because of limited production capacity, Megabuck has decided to produce only one of the products.

The profitability of each model depends on the proportion of the potential market that would actually buy the computer. For Model 101, the size of the market is estimated at 10 million, whereas for Model 202, the estimate is 3 million.

After careful analysis, the management of Megabuck has concluded that the percentage of buyers of Model 101 is 5%, 10%, or 15%. The respective profits are given here.

| Percent Who Buy Model 101 | Net Profits ($ Millions) |
|---|---|
| 5 | 20 |
| 10 | 100 |
| 15 | 210 |

An expert in probability from the local university estimated the probability of the percentages as $P(5\%) = .2$, $P(10\%) = .4$, and $P(15\%) = .4$.

A similar analysis for Model 202 produced the following table.

| Percent Who Buy Model 202 | Net Profits ($ Millions) |
|---|---|
| 30 | 70 |
| 40 | 100 |
| 50 | 150 |

For this model, the expert estimated the probabilities as $P(30\%) = .1$, $P(40\%) = .4$, and $P(50\%) = .5$.

a. Based on this information, and with the objective of maximizing expected profit, which model should Megabuck produce?

b. To make a better decision, Megabuck sampled 10 potential buyers of Model 101 and 20 potential buyers of Model 202. Only 1 of the 10 wished to purchase the Model 101, whereas 9 of the 20 indicated that they would buy Model 202. Given this information, revise the prior probabilities and determine which model should be produced.

**22.44** A major movie studio has just completed its latest epic, a musical comedy about the life of Attila the Hun. Because the movie is different (no sex or violence), the studio is uncertain about how to distribute it. The studio executives must decide whether to release the movie to North American audiences or to sell it to a European distributor and realize a profit of $12 million. If the movie is shown in North America, the studio profit depends on its level of success, which can be classified as excellent, good, or fair. The payoffs and the prior subjective probabilities of the success levels are shown in the accompanying table.

| Success Level | Payoff ($ Million) | Probability |
|---|---|---|
| Excellent | 33 | .5 |
| Good | 12 | .3 |
| Fair | −15 | .2 |

Another possibility is to have the movie shown to a random sample of North Americans and use their collective judgment to help the studio make a decision. These judgments are categorized as "rave review," "lukewarm response," and "poor response." The cost of the sample is $100,000. The sampling process has been used several times in the past. The likelihood probabilities describing the audience judgments and the movie's success level are shown next. Perform a preposterior analysis to determine what the studio executives should do.

| | Judgment | | |
|---|---|---|---|
| Success Level | Rave Review | Lukewarm Response | Poor Response |
| Excellent | .8 | .1 | .1 |
| Good | .5 | .3 | .2 |
| Fair | .4 | .3 | .3 |

## Chapter Summary

The objective of decision analysis is to select the optimal act from a list of alternative acts. We define as optimal the act with the largest expected monetary value or smallest expected opportunity loss. The expected values are calculated after assigning prior probabilities to the states of nature. The acts, states of nature, and their consequences may be presented in a payoff table, an opportunity loss table, or a decision tree. We also discussed a method by which additional information in the form of an experiment can be incorporated in the analysis. This method involves combining prior and likelihood probabilities to produce posterior probabilities. The preposterior analysis allows us to decide whether to pay for and acquire the experimental outcome. That decision is based on the expected value of sample information and on the sampling cost.

### IMPORTANT TERMS:

Acts 885
States of nature 885
Payoff table 886
Opportunity loss 886
Decision tree 886
Expected monetary value (EMV) 888
Expected opportunity loss (EOL) 889
Rollback technique 889
Expected payoff with perfect information (EPPI) 891
Expected value of perfect information (EVPI) 892
Likelihood probabilities 892
Experimental outcomes 892
Experiment 892
Prior probabilities 893
Posterior or revised probabilities 893
Preposterior analysis 895
Expected value of sample information 896

### SYMBOLS:

| Symbol | Represents |
|---|---|
| $a_i$ | Acts |
| $s_j$ | States of nature |
| $I_i$ | Experimental outcomes |
| $P(s_j)$ | Prior probability |
| $P(I_i \mid s_j)$ | Likelihood probability |
| $P(s_j \text{ and } I_i)$ | Joint probability |
| $P(s_j \mid I_i)$ | Posterior probability |

Cosma/Shutterstock.com

# CONCLUSION

We have come to the end of the journey that began with the words "Statistics is a way to get information from data." You will shortly write the final examination in your statistics course. (We assume that readers of this book are taking a statistics course and not just reading it for fun.) If you believe that this event will be the point where you and statistics part company, you could not be more wrong. In the world into which you are about to graduate, the potential applications of statistical techniques are virtually limitless.

However, if you are unable or unwilling to employ statistics, you cannot consider yourself to be competent. Can you imagine a marketing manager who does not fully understand marketing concepts and techniques? Can an accountant who knows little about accounting principles do his or her job? Similarly, you cannot be a competent decision maker without a comprehension of statistical concepts and techniques.

In our experience, we have come across far too many people who display an astonishing ignorance of probability and statistics. In some cases, this is displayed in the way they gamble. (Talk to people in a casino in Las Vegas or Atlantic City and discover how many understand probability; see how many of them lose money.) We have seen managers who regularly make decisions involving millions of dollars who don't understand the fundamental principles that should govern the way decisions are made. The worst may be the managers who have access to vast amounts of information no farther away than the nearest computer but don't know how to get it or even know it is there.

This raises the question, What statistical concepts and techniques will you need for your life after the final exam? We don't expect students to remember the formulas (or computer commands) that calculate the confidence interval estimates or test statistics. (Statistics reference books are available for that purpose.) However, you must know what you can and cannot do with statistical techniques. You must remember a number of important principles that were covered in this book. To assist you, we have selected the

12 most important concepts and list them here. They are drawn from the "Developing an Understanding of Statistical Concepts" subsections that are scattered throughout the book. We hope that they prove useful to you.

## 23-1 Twelve Statistical Concepts You Need for Life after the Statistics Final Exam

1. Statistical techniques are processes that convert data into information. Descriptive techniques describe and summarize; inferential techniques allow us to make estimates and draw conclusions about populations from samples.

2. We need a large number of techniques because there are numerous objectives and types of data. There are three types of data: interval (real numbers), nominal (categories), and ordinal (ratings). Each combination of data type and objective requires specific techniques.

3. We gather data by various sampling plans. However, the validity of any statistical outcome is dependent on the validity of the sampling. "Garbage in, garbage out" very much applies in statistics.

4. The sampling distribution is the source of statistical inference. The confidence interval estimator and the test statistic are derived directly from the sampling distribution. All inferences are actually probability statements based on the sampling distribution.

5. All tests of hypotheses are conducted similarly. We assume that the null hypothesis is true. We then compute the value of the test statistic. If the difference between what we have observed (and calculated) and what we expect to observe is too large, we reject the null hypothesis. The standard that decides what is "too large" is determined by the probability of a Type I error.

6. In any test of hypothesis (and in most decisions) there are two possible errors: Type I and Type II. The relationship between the probabilities of these errors helps us decide where to set the standard. If we set the standard so high that the probability of a Type I error is very small, we increase the probability of a Type II error. A procedure designed to decrease the probability of a Type II error must have a relatively large probability of a Type I error.

7. We can improve the exactitude of a confidence interval estimator or decrease the probability of a Type II error by increasing the sample size. More data mean more information, which results in narrower intervals or lower probabilities of making mistakes, which in turn leads to better decisions.

8. The sampling distributions that are used for interval data are the Student $t$ and the $F$. These distributions are related so that the various techniques for interval data are themselves related. We can use the analysis of variance in place of the $t$-test of two means. We can use regression analysis with indicator variables in place of the analysis of variance. We often build a model to represent relationships among interval variables, including indicator variables.

9. In analyzing interval data, we attempt to explain as much of the variation as possible. By doing so, we can learn a great deal about whether populations differ and what variables affect the response (dependent) variable.

10. The techniques used on nominal data require that we count the number of times each category occurs. The counts are then used to compute statistics. The sampling distributions we use for nominal data are the standard normal and the chi-squared. These distributions are related, as are the techniques.

11. The techniques used on ordinal data are based on a ranking procedure. We call these techniques *nonparametric*. Because the requirements for the use of nonparametric techniques are less stringent than those for a parametric procedure, we often use nonparametric techniques in place of parametric ones when the required conditions for the parametric test are not satisfied. To ensure the validity of a statistical technique, we must check the required conditions.

12. We can obtain data through experimentation or by observation. Observational data lend themselves to several conflicting interpretations. Data gathered by an experiment are more likely to lead to a definitive interpretation. In addition to designing experiments, statistics practitioners can also select particular sample sizes to produce the accuracy and confidence they desire.